BOOK OF THE
CRANBERRY
ISLANDS

*the text of this book is printed
on 100% recycled paper*

by Richard Grossinger

Solar Journal: Oecological Sections (1970)

Mars: A Science Fiction Vision (1971)

Spaces Wild and Tame (1971)

Book of the Earth & Sky, Books I & II (1971)

The Continents (1973)

Early Field Notes from the All-American Revival Church
(1973)

RICHARD GROSSINGER

BOOK OF THE CRANBERRY ISLANDS

HARPER COLOPHON BOOKS

HARPER & ROW, PUBLISHERS

NEW YORK, EVANSTON, SAN FRANCISCO, LONDON

A hardcover edition of this book is published by Black Sparrow Press.

BOOK OF THE CRANBERRY ISLANDS. Copyright © 1974 by Richard Grossinger. All rights reserved. Printed in the United States of America.
No part of this book may be used or reproduced in any manner without
written permission except in the case of brief quotations embodied in
critical articles and reviews. For information address Harper & Row,
Publishers, Inc., 10 East 53d Street, New York, N. Y. 10022. Published
simultaneously in Canada by Fitzhenry & Whiteside Limited, Toronto.

First HARPER COLOPHON edition published 1975.

STANDARD BOOK NUMBER: 06–131866–3

75 76 77 10 9 8 7 6 5 4 3 2 1

For Charles Olson

CONTENTS

Book of the Cranberry Islands is a statement of a level of being. That level comes into being as the book does, grows with it, changes gradually as its energies are transformed into other orders of energy, and ultimately passes thru itself into a totally other thing. The book itself is the discovery, the journey. The writing of life seeks to realize levels and changes so that they can be lived and felt more fully, by the writer, not the reader, from which the reader benefits more than any false altruism in his behalf. There are no facts to be communicated and no themes or events to be proven. Like the moods and pulses associated with them, levels of being disappear totally when they come totally into being. My own writing is not in the past, where events exist only to be exploited. If I don't learn the things myself at the moment I write them the writing has no honorable justification; it is ego and derivation rather than vision and truth. I provide here the only fact of any value: the original, not a secondhand text from which some unknown source must be reconstructed, but the source, from which other narratives derive.

Much of the seeking in this book is done against the weight and tension of circumstances of Mount Desert Island, where I did eight months of ethnographic fieldwork. The seeking itself is concerned with the simultaneity of a cosmic process and the pattern and path of my own individuation, and that originates at my own beginning, and grows into *Book of the Cranberry Islands* most directly from the books of mine that precede it, and out of it into the books that follow. In the sequence of my work, which takes stage and continuity seriously, *Book of the Cranberry Islands* is the bridge between *The Continents* and *The Provinces*. Certain of its elements appear in more and less developed forms in the books that precede and succeed it. The theme of "continents" and "New World" is grounded in a specific New World site before being transformed into the more remote spaces and infinities that provincial geography suggests. Elements are not minimized by their disappearance, nor are they discarded. Once they come into the fullness of their being there is no need to recount them, because their proof or reality is not the issue.

I would now like to take up this same question at a remove of several steps, almost as if I were not the author of my own book and could therefore talk about it as genre and literary history. Such luxurious objectivity, however, is hardly on the level of actual writing, and runs the risk of both reductionism and oversimplification. If the book is truly a record of itself happening, it is very difficult for me to claim that that fact is merely the consequence of other events and decisions. In any case:

Book of the Cranberry Islands, as a narrative of mixed prose forms, is difficult to categorize because it borrows from so many different genres without becoming fully any one of them. Depending on one's preference, the book is either a novel, an ethnography, a philosophical journal, or a long regional poem in the William Carlos Williams-Charles Olson tradition. I experience the form not as a hybrid but as my own, and I assume that radical art means simply that the artist always makes his own (as well as content) form.

Given my social experience with my own form, I would go to great lengths to insist it is not stream of consciousness, at least as I understand the meaning of that term. The journal element means only that the book was done consecutively, day after day adding to it; the accumulation is transformational, with a large number of rewritings and restructurings, hopefully not to alter the original form but to recover those events lost in certain monotonies of the writing. Thus I am not a purist in my own moral system of writing; that possibility is still contained in my own growth, and I suspect that I move toward it. At this point the density seems valid, and the recovery of it tries not to manipulate the text. Stream of consciousness implies a linearity that the book does not have; the levels are forced together by an act of will, under the necessity of a more remote god than psychologism or confession, and toward an identity and communication more interior than persona or personal stance. In fact, I have nothing to confess, and streams of energy are a little more engaging than stream of consciousness especially insofar as they find ways to allow in what is not conscious.

The list of genres above is neither facetious nor random. To one degree or another I have been involved with all of them and they are part of my experience. The first intense writing I did was during the last two years of high school; and it was a kind of narrative autobiographical prose. By the end of my first year of college I had produced three novels in that form, the latter two attempting the translation from personal recounting to fiction and secondarily constructed plot. The writing and its rhythms came directly out of both my childhood and teenage experience with psychoanalysis and my reading of novels, science fiction, and fantasy. The act of telling and then interpreting one's dreams in psychoanalysis seems to me, at this distance, to be the primary mystery my writing began upon, plus the visionary and ecstatic sense of "telling it all," as Creeley later wrote in a review of my work.

If I became disgusted with the artificiality of fictional constructions, and the related role of being spokesman for one's own cleverness in making and hiding within a plot, it was not to deny the mastery and personal accomplishment some find in such work, simply to reject that path as a means of my own development and obligation. In the making of the novels, my initial impulses and energies were clearer and more truthful than what they became in the writing, and I despaired of ever getting to them in any pure and intimate sense. Poetry became, then, that lost sense of origin; not all poetry or even poetry as a style and tradition, predominantly the New American Poetry tradition of Olson, Duncan, Dorn, Creeley, Kelly, etc. My involvement was not with their form as much as with their invention of form.

Even the most experimental novelists, like Joyce and Beckett, seemed not to be as serious in their speech as Olson; language was their barrier and opponent, not their path. The accuracy that concerned me, and still does, all traditions and styles aside, was getting at the sense of where we are and what we have to know about being there to retain our consciousness and survive. Not to make pretensions to noble ancestry: but the seriousness of the holyman and magician, the devotion to the fabric and subtlety of the work's evolution of the alchemist or pure scientist concern us more than the specific formal seriousness of the artist, except insofar as that formal seriousness is a literal linguistic, or paralinguistic, measure of the spaces in which all the rest happens.

For a couple of years I wrote poetry instead of prose in pursuit of that purism. Finally, however, I realized that my own roots were in a tradition that was very different in a rhythmic and conceptual sense. When I began writing predominantly prose again, my seriousness took the form of mythopoetic essay, and the first complete manuscript to come out of that has since been published in parts and sections in a number of different volumes, among them: *Solar Journal: Oecological Sections; Book of the Earth and Sky;* and *Spaces Wild and Tame.* If anything, these come closest to being philosophical journals and borrow most from the whole genre of academic writing. I sometimes saw them as mock textbooks, filled with ecology, botany, astronomy, anthropology, geology, phenomenology, etc., out of courses I had taken and was taking thru graduate school, the writing less an attempt to record the development of a scientific awareness and more an opportunity to get all that useless knowledge out of my mind, meaning, to violate and transform it into something more sentient.

A discussion of the ethnographic base of the book also gives me an opportunity to explain some of the circumstances by which I came to be where I was throughout the making of text. As a graduate student in anthropology I was required to do fieldwork for my degree. Although my main interests lay in the areas of myth and religion, there was no one to work with in the department at Michigan in those areas, and when I began publishing my writing, many members of the department took it as a direct attack upon the sanctity of the field and were less than eager to see me get my degree. I had mixed feelings about whether I even wanted it or not, but before any hassles had come up front I received a grant to do fieldwork in Maine, which was ostensibly to be a project on folk medicine and homoeopathy. Subsequent developments both in Maine and my department made it necessary to reconsider the topic; at the same time I was drawn to the coast as an interesting place, it was also recommended that I attempt an economic and ecological study. My total preparation for the fieldwork was in the theory behind different unorthodox medicines, and thus I came to the lobsterfishing study totally naive and uninformed, at lease from an ethnographic point of view. However, I had just finished *The Continents,* and the wharf itself was filled with the possibilities of geography and colonization that book had opened for me. In addition, the fishing itself and the relation of Mount Desert to Olson's Gloucester raised the whole possibility of exploring an aspect of his work that had more or less eluded me previously. Before he died, we had communicated about the area and he was interesting in some "current news" from there, which I initially tried to find at the wharf. This did not conflict with my ethnographic work; the relation of the two made my inquiries richer, especially before I had any specific anthropological goal. Earlier drafts reached out totally into Olson's New World fishing and Dorn's North Atlantic Turbine, but ultimately I came to accept that what I was doing was different, and the ethnography-making became part of the tension of the book.

The study that is emerging from the fieldwork is, of course, a totally different matter than this book, but a statement of its aspects would clarify some of the directions I take in collecting information and locating events. At this point, my paper is divided into sections on: lobster ecology, coastal geography, fishing strategy in general, history of fishing in Maine, lobsterfishing strategy, and lobsterfishing ideology. The bulk of the paper is contained in the next to last category which itself is divided into long sections on: strategy vis à vis the construction of fishing gear and overall cost of hauling lobster traps, strategy vis à vis the marine environment in the setting of traps and locating and pursuing of lobsters, strategy vis à vis other lobsterfishermen in the defining and defending of fishing territories, strategy vis à vis the lobster dealers in the selling and marketing of the lobsters, and place of lobsterfishing on the overall fishing calendar. The section on ideology is, in part, concerned with the differences between conscious and unconscious strategy, and the relation between effectual and ineffectual fishing in the community ethos. For partial elucidation I will quote here the opening passage:

This paper concerns primarily the methods by which lobsterfishermen on the Maine coast catch and sell their lobsters. Other fishing enterprises will also be examined, but only insofar as they bear on decisions relevant to lobsterfishing. In the course of my discussion I will examine the overall operation of the lobsterfisherman as a game of strategy, played under the conditions of fluctuating stocks of marine species, a market in which the value of these species changes frequently, and often unpredictably, and an active competition among fishermen for the more desirable grounds.

The intent of this paper is not to offer a statistical solution to the decision-making processes or to impute the semblance of rationality to aggregates larger than individual choices and goals. I am interested in studying the strategy, or "game plans," so to speak, of specific lobsterfishermen, and how they affect each other and are affected by the ongoing process of the "game." This is not to deny that there may be a "statistical solution" to such matters as distribution of lobster traps, frequency of fishing, percentage of men withholding lobsters from the market, etc. Davenport [1960: 3-11] has worked out a reasonable game theory analysis of Jamaican fishing-pot-setting strategy in which the issue of individual motivation is purposely omitted from the solution. He assumes that the patterns of strategic behavior that go to make up the community fishing effort, encompassing individual fishing strategies, have been evolved in the process of "coping with some of the combined physical, biological, and social forces of their environment" [1960: 3]. It is probable that, over a long period of time, the setting of pots by a community of fishermen will approach minimaximization *for the entire fishing effort,* despite the solutions of individual fishermen. Anything less would lead to a counterproductive fishing effort necessarily supported by some other aspect of the community's economic life.

I am suggesting, however, that a completely nonpsychological solution to a pattern of behavior such as fishing strategy is likely to be limited insofar as selective forces do not always operate in a narrow range or on any single isolated activity. Especially in cases where other resources are available, where the world market is involved (either directly or indirectly), and where such larger redistributional processes as welfare and unemployment compensation impinge on local cycles, it is just as likely that one will find something considerably less elegant than minimaximization in a single and isolated enterprise like lobsterfishing (or even fishing in general). Aside from certain obvious limitations upon community exploitation (no lobster can be caught twice, nor can any spot be fished beyond its capacity to bear lobsters), there is nothing to prevent an individual from taking foolhardy risks, fishing at a loss for great periods of time, and sticking to a nonbearing ground stubbornly, *if* he has other sources of income or the confidence that larger redistributional chains of the society will compensate him regardless of his fishing success.

In *Book of the Cranberry Islands* one can find very few grounds for the above statement or the possibility of the paper described above, but the seeds are there and the information about the paper gives some insight into my own strategy. There are two other aspects to this. First of all, the paper was conceived after the fact of the fieldwork and with the help and participation of other anthropologists. Secondly, *Book of the Cranberry Islands* covers only the first six months of the fieldwork; the final two months, which were much more conscious in their sense of information-gathering, are described in *The Provinces;* and three very important trips back to Mount Desert during the subsequent two years are described in *The Long Body of the Dream* and *The Book of Being Born Again into the World.* For the sake of those who have followed the various journal publications entitled "from Book of the Cranberry Islands" (as well as the four booklet publications of sections by Christopher Books in Santa Barbara, Big Venus in London, Kent State University Libraries, and University of Kansas Library), I might add that the whole manuscript, comprising the four books mentioned above, was originally called *Book of the Cranberry Islands* (Volumes 1, 2, 3, and 4). Volume 2, *The Provinces,* extends the geographical ground of the text to New Brunswick, New York State, and southern Maine (where we eventually ended up living), and develops the historical, genealogical, and etymological aspects more heavily. Volume 3, *The Long Body of the Dream,* translates these themes further into synchronicity, messages, astrology, totemism, and sex, replacing the fishermen per se with Mesolithic man (the original fisherman) and the economics and history with economic history and prehistory. Volume 4, *The Book of Being Born Again into the World,** moves over into trauma, memory, memory loss, numbers in the trillions, the limitations of the nervous system, negative capability, and reincarnation, but it also is a realization of the total theme of the *Cranberry Island* series, so different than and yet so close to the historical fable and mythbed it began as: HOW WE LIVE, both in the devastating speed of the Earth's happening and the fullness of our bodies and the

*Since the writing of this preface and the new grounding of the *Cranberry Island* sequence in Vermont, Volume 5, *The Windy Passage from Nostalgia,* has been written, and Volume 6, *The Slag of Creation,* has been begun.

lands, which cries out for an answer all our lives. *Book of the Cranberry Islands* itself is not only a full statement of its own geographical and local possibility; it is the strong objective base for a castle that is too often built only in the air.

Richard Grossinger
March 5 - August 3, 1972
Cape Elizabeth, Maine - Plainfield, Vermont

gulls

cranberries

debris

CHAPTER 1
THE GLACIAL ISLAND
AND DAUGHTER ISLANDS

a text in geology and hieroglyph

the bodies of lobsters

I

The present powers lie in their disposition. It is perhaps the radio noise of an entire body, no other interpretation is possible. The purebred is now, strain of sunlight and poison, not accidental, Jerseys and Guernseys, and the bull Coelebs who sired a whole state of beef. Lobster world forty fathoms under, their bodies piled like jewels in the polluted harbor, in the now.

A red crossbill, majestic young bird, honking wildly in the corner where the cats have thrown him and cornered him, in the newspapers behind the door, a species. The grasp of another world is upon us, waking us with its voice. We release what we can, what still has wings, back into the forest.

With child in backpack we ourselves go for a walk in the woods, the dark river in gulley, the cats coming to see what they have never seen, born inland, in basement apartments in Michigan, and in Colorado mountains: the ocean, the sea, sniff the salty mussel beds at their feet, tiptoe on rocks, and stare blindly outward into absolute space. No matter how they change their vantage, it remains, is unpassable.

We see the islands in time, three dimensional in utter sunlight, in humpback splendor, in broken field dashes, open gushers, bubble lakes thru mountain peaks, in French and English, its Cadillacs and Suttons, its twice history. Everywhere we look there are more than three dimensions, for the tongues of land go out into the ocean, and the ocean penetrates the lacunae, lagoons of land. ISLE DES MONTS-DESERTS. Champlain's island. One of the Viking islands, so that even Leif Eriksson is buried here.

Mythology. Not that geology shapes geography shapes the biology: with psychology and ecology following up, hewed to the land, BUT THAT All are simultaneously in a place. And though it is reckless to speak of "out of mind and out of nature," I mean here that the connectives are so large that we cannot have them and the matter at hand as well; in fact they are as large as we would have them in wanting to approach the large. Too large for the small. The final substance is astronomy, and upon the large the position of the small is so exact as to be unmistakeable. History.

I come out into sun light. I do not hear the radio noise. I do not see the source. It is all round me, as large as perception, the work of the glacier, of rivers, waves. I see their operation. Brings stone. Washes stone away. Indistinguishable, the present moment. I come out into—suddenly aware that my life neither begins nor ends but is subject to this material, place, and will always be just what it is now. I will never know any more.

It's mammoth, as large as I come into the awareness, exist myself in the historical, in Champlain's time; I exist in geologic time, a base which is shaped, irrelevant only to the degree that I fail to be aware of it, and our lives as large as we choose to live them.

In the age of the emperor's new clothes, the man fears that he will be fooled, that there is nothing beside his personal history, the Freudian temporal content of his life. And anything else, out of mind, out of nature, is the clothes the emperor thinks himself to wear when he is naked; thousands of academicians laugh at him, exhibiting his body on an occasion of state. Then they retreat into their journals of continuous statistical proof, clothes that will keep them warm and in style for at least how many years. We are in the Victorian Age of the imagination, where everything must have its place in mind or in world, where the vision itself of a whole history, a place, is fractured into various diminished subsets: for your counterrevolutionaries look among the academic Marxists, on government grants to prove proof, on which the whole Mafia America-Russia conspiracy stands. Proof of the technocracy. Proof of the existence of the Western World.

Glacial fingers extend in time, in tens of thousands of years. No man wears their watch on his wrist/a fist of ice

3

squeezes from the granite mountains of the Maine coast: an island. Now in the fabled North the work of mountains and sea are daily and simultaneous, children of the same mother. Sea water rushes inland, upland, with the high tide, every inlet harbor cove bay, and fiord itself, Somes Sound, a gash beginning in the center of the island as where the genitalia would be, going out between the legs into the ocean, where the Cranberries lie

In 1754 Abraham Somes

. . . so broken and revealed that we are too, and in living here must explore all the passages. A woman who could be so beautiful.

The first settlers built their farms and mills around Somes Pond and Ripple Pond. They froze the clear water of the lakes and sold it to ships for ice. North of Rockland, North of Gloucester, they built ships, cut away the first growth, went fishing on the Banks, traded with the rest of the old New World, in South America, and the West Indies, and Baltimore, Albany, Portland. We learn from Virginia Sanderson, seventh generation Somes and President of the Somesville Historical Society, that Abraham Somes came back in 1761 with a man named Richardson, to Somesville. The conch shells in the old houses of Somesville come from the West Indies; there are replicas of a mercantile age. After years of college teaching in Ohio, a retired Virginia Sanderson buys the old house on the mill pond and returns to the Somatic, the genetic, to write the same book, of the patrilineal, the self. A History of Somesville. The ducks float in peaceful formation on the fresh water; the gulls hover over the edge of the domestic, wild, saltwater beings of Somes Sound the water pours off the edge of the table into but is refilled under 102 by inland stream.

This is one direction of settlement, known as New England; and the other is Gull, from the Old World by way of the sea: Spurlings, Stanleys, Bunkers, Hadlocks, entering the Cranberries even before there is evidence for them, some of them sheep thieves, others sailors seeking a fishery that was not England. For decades they lived out there, protected from Indians, French, and the King, and then one by one they moved in until whole islands were abandoned, Stanleys,

4

Fernalds marrying all the Somes daughters and taking over the town. "It ought to be called Fernaldsville today," some grumble, as if they were sea scorpions or locusts, breeding in a science fiction plot with the Daughters of Massachusetts and Governor Bernard, taking over the mortuary and burying the islands' dead.

A land of tarns, kanes, and kettles; witches' holes and halfmoons. So the balance between high tide and low tide, in land and out land, is the balance between the glands and bodies of seawater and freshwater, lakes buoying lagoons, upper and lower landlocked Hadlock ponds in counter-rhythm with the salty Pool of Great Cranberry Island, from whence the Hadlocks came.

The material is itself subject to place. The ground, or landscape, under forces as difficult as thought. A river. A tilting of 60° on its axis. Stone lies at the bottom of it, is seed. Four quarts of milk for a pound of butter, seven pounds of butter a week before going dry. River of genes.

"These inhabitants cultivate enough land to provide themselves with potatoes, corn, barley and vegetables, but they spend most of their time cutting wood into shooks and barrel staves which they sell at a good profit to merchants. Each family has a small boat from which they catch cod, and cure it, and exchange it with the merchants for flour, sugar, soap, molasses, oil and other articles that they want. All have cows and farmyards, poultry of every kind and fine pigs. They make cheese which they sell at wholesale. On the day of my arrival there were five ships in Frenchmans Bay, one of which sailed for London, one for Santo Domingo, and three for Boston, loaded with plank, timber, shooks, bark, and even cordwood, which the people cut on the edge of the bays or in the forest." Bancel de Confoulens, 1792.

Enoch Stanley sits on the small public bench in the center of Southwest Harbor telling how his mother lived out on Baker Island, furthest of the Cranberries, a race building great ships, trawling, farming, the women separating the milk, and in another building, made of local forest, the men storing wood for the winter as at 3 P.M. total darkness forecloses day on another island, a Baker, crossing the meridian as it does, swiping away another angle, the men up at dawn

5

after cod and hake. In those days Enoch bought fish on Great Cranberry from the vessels for his uncle's place, Stanley Fish, in Manset. "32¢ a pound for cod," Enoch says, blowing on his pipe. "Now you can get 6¢ for it."

And though the Coast Guard has run electric lines out to Baker Island, lighting up the lighthouse, all the windows are smashed by drunks on motorboat picnics and football players from University of Maine fraternities, and each year one old house that Ene remembers is burned to the ground while they piss on the fire drinking their beer.

Baker Island. Green Nubble in the bay.

Burning down an island they call it, the glacier gone out back to sea, the light of another kind returns and will burn there, till stasis.

Like a forest.

The fire starts here and goes into the cities, recoils from the cities and touches down here, as the demand for, the price of, fish.

There is a flow between the lost nations of America, and in a certain spirit of visibility they are all one.

The grist mills and leather mills of Somesville.

The blacksmith and tannery in Stone Ridge, New York.

The Jackson Whites, soldiers of an ancient war, hidden where there are no roads. Such are the island people, of Swans and Isle Au Haut, connected only by mailboat or ferry, plant their own trees, shoot their own gulls and bears.

Route 52. Route 1. Route 102.

How can you tell anymore the War of 1812 from the French and Indian War from the Revolution?; the war against nature from the war against man? The battles of Ellenville and Fort William Henry and Chateauguay are identical and simultaneous to the battles of Seal and Norwood Coves, and Fernald Point; that is, the wars that were separate have become one historical American war, a family eating off the same plate, endogamous in its genes and museums, hiding beneath the synchronous the jagged clatter of other voices.

I offer you these local events:

Samuel Hadlock who brought Eskimos to English and German fairs and returned with a German Princess to Cranberry.

The hotels of Ulster County, dark brown earth plowed by the inmates of 19th Century novels.

Northeast Harbor: the yachts, the summer cottages of the Rockefellers and college presidents, Bar Harbor cluttered with 42nd Street shops sprung up like fireweed after the fire.

In Vermont: the communes, high on incendiaries and Cuba and Boston rock stations.

In Hancock County: the artist colonies, painting for the

city galleries.

In Sullivan County: the Gheez a black tribe of Israelites camped on a river in Callicoon, a three hundred pound queen they carry on a litter across the bridge.

"The power movements, the Amish situation in the Midwest, the desire of the Acadians in Louisiana to have French taught in schools, the conflict between ethnic groups in the urban areas, all point toward new social concepts revolving around a number of ethnic and racial communities desiring to conduct their own affairs. Even the rising conservative trend in politics seeks power at the local level rather than continued direction from long distance." & Vine Deloria Jr. and Red Power.

Kerhonkson, named for the sound of the geese passing overhead. And Somesville, whose original name was "Betwixt the Hills." The local remains, recoverable; maturing to find ourselves there. The next Ghost Dance is regionalism, tribalism, the return of the buffalo with the return of the cod.

I see those same fairweather clouds that pass over the Hudson at Kingston follow us up the Taconic, the Mass. Pike, across New Hampshire, and drift along the coast of Maine, haut and weathered. "This island is very high and cleft into seven or eight mountains, all in a line. The summits of most of them are bare of trees, nothing but rock. *Je l'ay nommée l'Isle des Monts-déserts.*" Champlain.

And then the Spanish-American War on the Bangor television station. The Sierra Baron returns from Mexico to his estate in Nevada country, finds it surrounded and penetrated by homesteaders and tiny frontier towns, flooded off in bogus deeds until the U.S. Senate decides to honor the Spanish land grants. Now the gunman falls in love with the Spanish baroness, and though she loves him too, and though they are brought to the defense of the same ranchero, and though she kisses him with her more ancient lips, an older order, his name is Jack, and he comes from Texas, near the border, it is to die unrequited, he by a bullet, and she a thousand years later in a convent; and now we find ourselves in Maine, to begin without these archetypal and romantic asides to a world which doesn't exist. The roads fools us. The New

8

World, stripped to gun and holsters, armed and penetrating the frontier, loses the psyche, the kulturkreise of the Old, without which it must lie parched in Las Vegas motels and Spanish-American bars. This because my brother sent me a movie of snow in Colorado Springs, and the bright flashing sign of a caricature Mexican-American. I want him to send the film again, the same images on it, the Rockies, the snow, the Southwest at night, downtown, and I will superimpose on them islands and seacoast, northern conifers and sea urchins, and the lobsterboats returning to weigh in. If there is any rhythm, resemblance, any soul to it, as political parties of United America proclaim, it will occur in the occult interference of patterns, the washout of dyes, the tempo of the fugue itself, as it flees the impossible intersection I am trying to make here. I know that weather passes from one place to another. Cars do, roads. These are diversionary events, superficials, and we are trying to film the real.

A few fishermen sit in the bar in Southwest Harbor, talking fish, *Have Gun, Will Travel* on the t.v. set. We order pizza. They are discussing the price of lobster, the winds to the East. As each fisherman comes in he makes the rounds; the hunters gather separately in their orange jackets around the pool table.

"The Indian outrage at Hickel was a cry to society at large. 'If you destroy us,' it really said, 'you will destroy your last chance to understand who you are, where you have been, and where you have to go next in order to survive as a people.' " Vine Deloria Jr.

And the last time we were here, it was among Hopis, in the the oldest continuously-occupied town in America, Old Oraibi, Arizona. They prepared for the ceremony by capturing a hawk. They prophesied the end of America, the return of the Blue Star kachina; they watched for things in the skies. Here in Somesville's harbors they speak of the dwindling supply of flounder and herring, the threat of oil. They prepare for the ceremony with prayersticks, lobster traps, a stove burning the excess wood.

The t.v. show comes to an end; the baron dances with the widow from Pennsylvania, daughter of the homesteaders

9

whom he marries. A young Virginia Sanderson rows in from Sheep Island to buy groceries for her sick husband.

End of diversionary fugue. Maine is Anglo-Saxon-Irish-Celtic, straight transatlantic, viking and trawling, without crossing the interior of Vinland or the census of the Icelandic nation.

Deep in the streets of New York, THE CHILDREN RUNNING IN THE FIELD BY SOMES POND.

This is a character for the book.

Here lie the Cranberries, pawn pieces, coastal to a stratagem, a nation.

From Bar Harbor to Southwest

If there is a dark avenue on Mount Desert, an occult avenue, it is Ledgelawn. Here is housed the mission boat and the Pentecostal Church, a dark vein holding the islands to the central nervous system, and Christmas choirs that come by boat, to bury and baptize, as above, so below. At the end: Dr. M M Milliken Chiropractor. If it were New York it would be: Flying Saucer Bookshop, and a coverjoint for fags. Or Swedenborgian Reading Room, and within: New Jerusalem, alpha waves. But Doc Milliken adjusts the bones, releases the blood, of old fishermen, to the spot where the nerves restore, the abnormal tissue melts away. Consulting old physiology charts like ephemera, pathways of bones and tissues, locations of nerves and seas. "An osteopath: he just rips one way, then he rips another; he only cares about how tight it feels. I adjust toward the normal. I free the nerves that are pinched at that spot."

Now he takes down his charts of the human nervous system, the early part of the century unfolded, ship-building and hand-lining. "All people have vertebrae out of position. We get knocked around in our daily business in the environment." He draws his fingers along the nerves to the stomach, the spinal constrictions, vagus, endocrine, the trauma ended with a sudden jar under those trained hands.

"A pill isn't very exact. It mixes with saliva and passes with bile into the bloodstream, from the tip of the toes to the nose. But if we know the cells that are out we can go in just like electrical repairmen and restore the signal. All people have had these traumatic events. Everyone has some vertebrae out of position. If you just let me look at your

11

back I'll show you."

This is the distant past, 50 years ago, maybe more, as we stop at the Bar Harbor Library on the way home and buy 41 duplicate books at 10¢ each, including a theosophy, and a 1930's dictionary. 50 years are not enough. The colonial surrounds us; the men with their fishing nets. It is modern, new, with motorboats carrying the ancient gear. It is daily, revealed, bursting out of the occult with the sun in morning, the crying of gulls, the bright-colored paint on the buoys. Not Navaho sand-painting anymore, or the colors of Hopi prayersticks. Not the color symbolism of the tarot or the arteries and veins in a 19th Century medical book. This is somehow my own discontinued sixth grade American history, only this time for real, emerging like a tree from the unorthodox in my work.

I would rather pursue motorboats and lobster-trucks than back-manipulators and antique shops. The chart of the veins has become obscure. Folklore is dated, as even the references in the Folklore File at Orono prove, remedies and ghost stories and recipes, but the coast like a sleeping bear awakes each morning fresh in its icy water, senses the winds; this is more than folklore, this is MYTH. End of the curious, end of my account of astrological botany and the moons of Jupiter. Here in microcosm is the macrocosm, the nation, the stars and stripes, or as Wendell Seavey on the High Road in Southwest Harbor puts it:

"We've gotten out of Europe once and for all. We don't have any more kings and queens, and we've proven that the working men can build a nation from the ground up. Nobody had to be knighted or taken into secret orders. It's just all out there." And he points to the sea.

So Doc Milliken does a rare business at best, most intense where he intersects the Pentecostals, or other believers. We can let him be, for he is safe in the house God has built him, under Yetzirah, and the Parcelsan code. See alchemy and ethnobotany. See unorthodox medicines. We are now leaving the chiropractor and moving into:

Cash in hand.

The gravy of inflations.

The pull of the city market in the country.

Depressions so bad they'll make your teeth chatter. Islands abandoned.

Wind direction, climate, engines and gear, and

The lobster himself.

"And towards night we drew a small net of 20 fathoms very nigh the shore; we got about 30 good and great lobsters ... which I omit not to report, because it showeth how great a profit the fishing would be. . . ." Captain George Weymouth, 1605.

So Andrea Memmelaar leaves her notes on ghost tales among lobstermen in the Folklore Files, where we find them years after she has graduated, unknown enchantress who leads us into this world with her name, and when we try to find her, it is changed to Penny Stephens, a school-teacher in Bangor, dead end by which America sweeps up potential gypsies and converts them into housewives and citizens. She's gone, and all we can do is go to the source of her ghost tales, Mr. Leroy Krentz. We find him at Clyde Pomroy's in Southwest.

"If one dumb dog tells all he knows to another dumb dog, then wouldn't you say the second dumb dog knows it all. So you go ask Miss Memmelaar 'cause I told her everything I know, and now I don't know it anymore."

"Go see Wendell Seavey and Buddy Hooper," Father Gower tells us at the rectory one day. "These are two fishermen as different as any you will find."

Sue Seavey lets us in. "Sit down. Wendell'll talk to you after he's finished washing up."

Now the world begins again, Briah as a fisherman, America a fishing nation, Mrs. Seavey cooking the meal.

Big Cranberry on the Way to Little Cranberry

One road climbs from the water and goes softly down the center of the island, not as a car for there are no cars, and nor cars waiting as the boat docks and the boys run down the wharf to pull her in and unload the groceries, the sacks of mail (*Cranberry Isles, Maine*), but the people leave the boat with their suitcases and begin walking into the morning sun.

There is one known way into Cranberry Isles, one historical way, and the houses sit on either side of it, clustered in spots: utterly stark, utterly mysterious. For there is only one, and this is the most ancient unsolvable mystery of all. There is one way in, and moves so quickly from Spurling Cove around Bunker Head to the Thrumcap that one could begin walking, and walk right thru it, miss the whole thing.

The houses on this road. Are all the houses. The people on this road walk to. And between. There is one main street, flows into the landing, right into the waiting ship. Everything takes this road, including lobsters, rises out of the ocean, goes down into the ocean at high tide. And as in those ancient Atlantic museums, we cannot tell what is above water from what has been sunk or flooded, cannot tell Atlantis from the olden houses in their wisdom, wait like shells on the beach, harmonious replicas of life, for the passage of time.

Great Cranberry is shaped vaguely like Italy. It is not a long graceful boot, but a short stubby foot kicking the other way, all its weight in the heel. And Cranberry is not a foot about to kick a football; it has already kicked, and that is the interest. The mass of the heel is thrown to the toe; the football flies loose like a pail of water, splattering to Fish Point and Thrumcap and Deadman Point (where a corpse of unknown origin rolled in over a century ago). Fragments of the football fly in every direction, but except for Crow Island and its two tiny associates they stay attached to the original mass, meaning that Great Cranberry seems to come to an end at four or five different places, only to squeeze thru a neck and grow fat again, and this whole apparatus, flying off the toe itself at Dolly Hill, winds back around and in, forming one giant pool of still water, called The Pool, hugged into the body of the island itself, and another to the east between the three points of Deadman, Thrumcap, and Crow Island, and another more open to the northeast in The Gut between Great and Little Cranberry using Thrumcap, Fish Point, and The Maypole on the smaller island, and another to the north in Cranberry Harbor, the mouth of Hadlock Cove on Little Cranberry opening into the space between Fish Point and a tongue of land from the ankle of Great Cranberry ending at Long Point.

The road follows always to the thin, a semi-diagonal coming from the leg above the heel to the front of the foot, winding around the toe and into the kicked elongation. All major branches of the road go toward the front, one alone going toward Long Point and the cemetery at Long Ledge branching four times; all other cemeteries lie toward the heel. And what that great uninhabited heel is, in fact, is the name of the island, the Cranberry Bog, The Heath.

And though the houses and people lie to the thin, this is not the whole story of Cranberry, and certainly not the story of ecology among the cranberries themselves. For the seeds and species are blown off and onto every edge of this shore, every tongue of land and beach and point, and penetrate thru the invisible, The Heath, The Pool. Only the thinnest chain of existence, the groceries from Southwest Harbor, the letters from the mailboat, follow the path into. And the path is the only gate into the island for us as people, unless we come as nitrogen, sheer racial thalassan protoplasm onto Deadman Point.

Little Cranberry, Islesford

Between Great and Little Cranberry the boat enters a fog, and we walk into a world where the water drops are blown visibly between houses, close to us on our cheeks, a dew on the sleeping baby, visible shards of mist hugging the fields, blown across the island and back out to sea, and in the distance houses appear and disappear in the wind until we approach and the shore is swallowed in the soft foam behind us.

Here is an island at sea, part of the sea's weather. And the water comes to Islesford, leaving an ebb tide beach of sea urchins and sand dollars, a vegetable garden of seaweed on the rocks, and here in no nation, the lost coins of every nation crumble into soft oxides, sands.

Everywhere we walk we pass into the visible. A woman with dog and fieldglasses is pulled by the setter into the fields. And we do not know where Islesford, the town, begins, except that it is all around us as soon as we walk off the boat and down the wharf, more as the houses are closer together, less Islesford town and just Little Cranberry out by the sea.

A lobsterboat sits quiescent with a dead gull displayed on the cabin, a warning to birds that would come after the bait barrels. This is the sign: a white collection of feathers and lost winged points, scattered as a random disposition, not Islesford or town, but ocean, as the boat sways.

The church, 1898, not Jesus but the American flag in stained glass. Not patriotism, but that history is our religion, America the living form with ocean around it. And the ducks and geese running without flight in their pens, a statue of a cat crawling on a roof, red clover, pepper plants, and *Aeschylus Hippocastanum,* brown in the fall. Spurlings, Fernalds, Hadlocks, Bunkers, and Lester Hadlock singes a duck in the open flames of an old stove. "It's history," he says, meaning right here, even this moment, as hard as wood, written into the streets and where the road turns, the entangling consequences of marriage, the generations, the old homes; this we can never escape from.

Islesford is not nowhere, is not just sweet, as Jack and Bernie thank their friends for a good time on the bulletin board outside the general store, and ask if there is any land available. The island is a house, giant, old, seductive, a house of death, as all houses are in the sexual nexus of beings. The consequences here are grave, and the summer people don't know this. They think of paradise, a quiet retreat from all cities. This is perhaps America, New World, but it is not paradise, not an academic poem or a place for the author to write his latest novel about romance in California, though this is what the cultured summer people try to do here.

The cost of an island is total, and you can't buy an island with money from the city; it's too far out to sea. You can't bring your work to an island; your work is there. Or you leave. And that was clear to us walking down the street, that the rape was on us, on Americans, a forced or enforced recall of the world moving under the world, the ever-compelling psychic which is the poetic space, from Hadlock Beach, thru the Cranberries to Bar Point.

Not Creeley's island, not a place maybe Jack and Bernie can retire to, not a commune, for the cost of freight is finally overwhelming, and the name of all the people on the island is eventually Hadlock, or that was the name it eventually became in the flow from Baker, furthest of the Cranberries. This cannot be escaped, this incessant, this leisurelessness, this space which even more than a city cannot lie without being seized, the work unceasing at the docks, everything twice as hard as in Bass Harbor, the bait brought in each night, the lobsters loaded, unloaded, the groceries taken to the store. Not frontier, but return to the beginning, coming back east, the gulls and ships that ushered us in, living at their own speed the era out.

They say there's no work here for a young man, but the sound is too loud, and it is all around, and there is too much work, and that is why so many leave it, run from here, or sit here pretending to do it, coming back here with cameras and lyrical lines about the ocean, in the only way it can't be done.

VI

The University at Cranberry

Baker Island abandoned, the Coast Guard keeps the light-house. Bear Island, two empty houses, the beach frozen all winter, ice on the seaweed, lighthouse. Sutton Island, the summer homes closed, a few gulls on the rock heaps, and floating pockets of mosslike weeds within the rocks, a long slick shore filled with driftwood, cottages in the hills.

The Cranberries, a sheer New England fruit, a bog, 200 acres of Great Cranberry bright pink and evergreen, rela-tive of the blueberry, the bearberry, the huckleberry, and Labrador tea. And the islands themselves, in New England fishing commerce, launchers of great Hadlock- and Stanley-built ships to the Northern banks, have their own relatives among islands: the Spice Islands and the Fortunate Isles, the Natuna of the South China Sea, the Trobriands and the Bear Islands of Norway, the Aegean Cyclades: Little Cran-berry is the island of the *Tempest*, where women are aban-doned with men as wizards; Cranberries is an economic mis-nomer; they are not the Cranberry Islands the way the Spice Islands are; they are a joke on the Spice Islands, a lightly-regarded fruit growing in a bog, whose real industry is fish-ing, not crops and groves, but from whom ships are leaving always to do their business elsewhere, or in the water around. Knowledge of the Cranberries comes last, as knowl-edge of the Spices; they are first and foremost passageway to Somes Sound, base among fertile shoals, Indian-safe forts, endogamous nations of Spurlings and Hadlocks and Stan-leys; they are the New World Spice Islands, to which the great fish-buyers of New York and Boston and Rockland come, Enoch Stanley a fish-merchant, groundfish is gold, convertible into ships; the Fulton Fish Market, treasury, palace-safe of the common man.

The Cranberries are America, and there is no abstraction in this university, there are islands, integers, events in the life of, the economy holding them together on a string, like Outer Indonesia. The string is broken at Baker and Bear, as it is at Bartlett's, where the laxatives and emetics run wild from their herb gardens, and the Greenland gold rots on the shore.

This university does not teach that the abandoned island returns to its previous state, for there is no such thing, merely a succession of states, of existences, neither primitive nor progressive, neither hake islands nor granite islands nor lobster islands, but the land is forever changed, the trees in the forest, the degree of clearing, the foundations and archaeology, the memory bank and curves of the shore, the types of flowers, the microwastes that feed the birds that fill even the dirt with tiny organisms imported from England and Scotland and Sweden, and wash back into the sea. We teach that the morphology is utterly written by the inhabitants, the cranberries and Cranberry Islanders, by whoever lives there, lived there, gulls, bears, Indians, Basques, Vikings, Europeans, Americans, or Polly Bartlett feeding porgy-oil to her hens, Aramiah Ballou spilling rum on the shore, or Eben Sutton, or the captain of the *Minerva*; inhabitation is never previous, it follows, collects.

We are alone in the old Spurling house, and I film the light as it falls into each of all the rooms, from darkness to sun I draw the lens open, the eye from twilight to blazing morning, from washed-out yellow to deep ambers and oranges, the colored rectangles of glass that border the single clear image in every window, which is an apple tree, which is a general store, which is the stone fence crumbling to stasis, which is a wild field ending at an abandoned fortlike museum, which is in every room a mirror which returns the window to itself, sometimes oval, sometimes square, sometimes blue-tinged, sometimes clear, sometimes with dolls and pillows in it, sometimes with chandeliers, sometimes with the vehicles left in the fields. The crumbling stones, the collection which for a moment is the house and its surroundings, which holds and is the landscape: a perception here.

The proper study of this university is exobiology, and the *Tempest*, planets and islands, way-stations and planetoids, and stopping points in *Odysseys*. And the light, which reaches every planet, reaches Islesford in its way, at the same instant corrected to what we know, reaches Baker and Bear, and there sits on a dormant, a living winged egg. Samuel Hadlock, who was born here with the sea and skies around him, the Cranberry sun in his micro-astrology, attended the university at Cranberry, and it was he who captained the *Minerva*; and though he had not read the metaphysical poets or Walter Raleigh, he stood in the Cranberry house and said: "Thousens of suns multiply without end." Meaning: "From what we know of our own system, it may be reasonabley concluded that all the rest are with equal wisdom contrived, situated and provided with accomodations for rational inhabitentes."

And now the students of the Cranberries are the students of America. All the high schools are one, and they pour into Bass Harbor and Southwest Harbor, and some of them return to Islesford to dig for the remains, Indian and Hadlock instruments of agriculture and fishing, life on Earth restored finally in a museum, as the Islesford Museum of Natural History, of history, which is the nature of the place. We learn that the possible genetics catch like moss on stone, and that the lobsters and gulls rise like Spurlings each generation from the very sea, and grow to seed.

Samuel Hadlock, first Cranberry All-American, dies in the northern seas, on a fantastic and contrived venture, to shoot seals to stuff during the long Cranberry winters to sell to European monarchs the following year. Spice Islands? Eskimo-American curios at best, closer to Greenland than China, closer to George Washington than Confucius. When she hears of his death, his wife, of German nobility, brought to this land and abandoned, takes the whole batch, valuable as they are, and dumps them into the sea, returns to raise her children, to remarry, the generations to go on this far from any home.

VII

Southwest Harbor Town Dump

Blown inland the gulls wait in the burning rubbish for
food, the smoke of turned piles rising all about them, they
perch in the oblivious pride of their white bodies, what they
must eat to stay alive regardless. By the Doctrine of Signa-
tures, they are the old sea captains returning to the garbage
heap of a world sea.

Some of them one-legged, or with a limp, as Enoch Stanley, called to his insurance hearings in Bangor, drags himself out of bed into the taxi, phones his lawyer, and fights
the reduction in monthly dividends. And the men in tractors
turn the garbage under, hiding from these hostile eyes: as
high as you look sea-birds, utterly hungry, circling, coming
down on a piece of garbage squawking, dragging off a piece
of bread or rotted stew in a bag thrown upside-down, and
the rest pecking among cans and dead rats, fleeing from the
cars that drive the circle, without deigning to use their
wings, are herded but do not leave.

These mongers for whom we have taken the sea inland,
depleting their saltwater harvest, our waste containing those
nutrients thus transformed. Sea-captains, with full rank,
defrocked, ocean replaced, shot by kids in rifle practice, their
corpses whiter than anything else in this heap, their wings
broken, until decay sets in and they become part of the mass.

And the unemployed and wounded sit on three benches in
the center of Southwest Harbor, reading the newspaper and
rooting for the Maine Mets, they call them, offering each
other dog biscuits, the nightwatchman shows us his skin
cancer, graft done in Northeast by a specialist. And he's
proud of that. "There's no need for any other kind of doctor.

Soon they'll all be specialists."

So the consequences of our acts disappear into the speci-
alities; the garbage man never speaks of the lobsterman, and
the lobsterman won't speak of the biologist; the mayor keeps
his own private doctor, and the doctors forget the body in
their concern for the disease and the cures. Meanwhile the
corpse grows, so much of this crap they don't know where
to put it.

And here in these gulls is one place where we can see what
we have done to the ocean, poisoning the bottom of the food
chain up, the clams caked in Gulf oil, black gold from Alaska
in the lobster shoals, sardines weired into cans, soaked up
in nets; and when they don't want the herring for food, they
pump them up out of the sea to make artificial pearls from
the scales. The crud of New York carried out to sea by barge
and dumped, a total indissoluble waste, it is we now who
create the animals and the plants around us, we who rule the
ecological nation wisely or squander the conditions of
ourselves,

            and it is mere justice that the mouths of the nitro-
gen cycle follow us in from the sea to where we are, these
gulls paid off by insurance and rot until even the money
clots the drains and the sewers back up into the towns. These
are not alien eyes, but in phylogeny our own, staring out in
the only way it understands; matter, watching, without
judgement, what we have done, judging only by matter itself
what will become of us. The gulls haunt, for in the final
judgement they, or their successors, will not be driven off by
kids with guns.

VIII

In the auto repair shop   the sparks, the sound of metal and air, metal against metal, and the replacement of parts. Here the landscape is more than the landscape, and the parts come in from all over the country to make up this puzzle. How do we get to here from nothing, from nothing to here?, as the drill, plugged into the wall, penetrates, as long as it is plugged, the material removed from the ground, shaped, and altered, the force unrelenting, to drive shape into the axle, the restore the invented wheel to its inventor, each day an operation on the natural sphere.

It is called technology, but it is also a force of nature, part of the landscape and habitat; the materials of man are ultimately the matter of forest and stone, rubber flowers and iron pearls, the geometry contained in the harder forced upon the softer as it is made to flow: the sun on this cloudy day, Hoyt Richards and Sons, Somesville, car screeching on two wheels into the repair shop, is the drill, is the force, no doubt yellow, or yellow once, changing the body of the golem, the car.

The power has its origin in streams, in heights, in the attraction of liquids to stream between jars, in combustibles and inerts; so the Penobscot, the Abnaki countryside is ground out, the stone against stone, hunt.

"If you wish to make a Hand-warmer, you should make in copper a sort of apple, with two halves which can be locked into another. Within the copper apple must be six copper rings. Each ring has two pivots and at the centre must be a pan with pivots. These pivots must so reciprocate with one another that the fire-pan shall remain horizontal. For one pivot supports the other, and if you have constructed it correctly according to the text and drawing, then you can turn it to whichever side you wish, and the fire will never fall out." Villard de Honnecourt, 1235.

How do we get from the visible clay pot in all its forwholeness, the scapula-hoe, the chipped stone point, to the machine shop, so that a man's energy is not needed to put the bolts on the tire rim, but a steel machine muscles them in, who controls a stronger, an inner circle than we. When does the form we prescribe begin to prescribe itself? When do we cease solving nature's riddles and begin creating riddles ourselves, hiding as well as finding? So that in 1269 Pierre de Maricourt can write: "You will then perforate it so that the eye of the ignorant shall not perceive what is cleverly inserted inside the case."

The parts of the car are replaced, and the invisible motor is rebuilt, the violence behind the curtain, under the lyre strings, the metal here of Hoyt Richards, and sons, and fathers too, the steam ship which, off Somes Sound, replaces the sail, and the wind which then replaces with the sail.

The circles run deep thru circles, and the forms are buried under the steel, and then the parts rust in the junkyard on Indian Point Road, and nothing more is known. Rope is replaced with nylon; the lobster trap lasts longer; the diesel engine replaces the V-8 for hauling at sea, and in Islesford no motor cars earlier than the fifties, still run along the one main road between shores.

"In this fashion one makes a saw work by itself.

"In this fashion one makes a faultless bow.

"In this fashion, one builds an angel whose finger points always toward the sun.

"In this fashion one constructs one of the strongest machines in existence for raising weights.

"In this fashion, one makes an eagle that always turns his head toward the deacon when he is reading the Gospel." de Honnecourt.

The workman hammers out the steel, giant strokes, fifty years ago in Halls Quarry down the road from Somesville, the granite, rolled on wheels into the cities, parts of the Maine countryside; the lobsters are hauled from the sea by pulleys, and once again the sun pays the freight, as the aluminum in Iceland, as we will keep shifting materials to create the urban, the village landscape, the charge exacted on the perpetual motion machine.

The first 250 years = the resources.

The next 25 years = the spiritual overlay.

The machine-shop restored in poetic space, and the next 25 years, the penetration of shape by our organs, which for 250 years of America has used our organs to penetrate itself.

The high school rock band draws on the sun, and we all begin to turn soft: the island, the last bullets fired at the last ducks, and peace declared on substance, on chemistry, and the nation which runs on oil grinds, stone against stone, to a halt, the farms deserted, the past, the lights lit then in the present, and return to WHAT WERE WE GIVEN to do, this body, lying behind the violence; and the lines which flow freely between houses plug back into nature; so we can change the ground, but can never change how the ground returns.

IX

From Somesville to New York at Night

In the perfect darkness I walk down the road, not turning on the flashlight I carry, but the depth of concavity I penetrate with each step. There is nothing to see, no haze from cities, no windows or cars, no lightning bugs or stars. Nothing. Utter silence.

Until the clouds break and there is moonlight, and I am dizzy trying to see too far, too sunlike the moonlight now. I look thru a hole in the trees to moonclouds above islands. I no longer try to see short or far, but merely see, how one can become lunatic, dizzy, walk right thru shape, and into trees, and keep going, drunk on its imperfection.

And the streets in the city I remember, lit from every window and lamp and by the density of habitation, screams as loud as the possibility of, the extension of habitability in Somesville, the sheer resonance of human existence. Here in Somesville in New York City I can walk back thru a remembered world into neurons that have recorded nothing yet, filled with the points I rip spreading out, down the road under the moon.

X

The Lobster

Touch, the most primitive sense, moves along sea-rocks, hairs, antennae, the dense shell perforated by hundreds of thousands of minute passages, the sensory nerves played at the roots by the hairs, the twang of sense brushed along the environment, the oils, the sleek hot and cold, noisy silent world, rushes by, the cod

To be in transformation always, never neither to know whether one is alive or dead or sleeping, whether he has a body or a dream, whether the senses join maplike into a network, a mask for predators, or whether splayed throughout the universe the giant world-creature crawls, breathing, feeds on the dead matter of system

Touch floats utterly in water

In the sensorium sensing its way along the bottom, along the body, even in embryo, in hypnos we feel the shape against us, the relentless woman of the body I am, reach out to grab her, to grab the whole lizard, grab whatever we are. The nocturnal emission of shell

Sense: a thousand tailfeathers, loose and responsive, joined to, led by a notochord, a central nervous system pulls like a string right thru the nose, the yoga grand central, out into the suburbs of the body, wings and swimmerettes carried thru knotted at the end

Tailfeathers, swimmerettes, dancing, fertilized, growing oosphere, oolites, egglike mass crusting, crustacean laying its own kind

Touch/hard shell, soft shell, grow in warm water, feed actively, quiescent in cold water, hibernal as the bear and the house-fly. The children build a snowman out of gloved hands

Touch, the most ancient sense, hides in the sea-mountains and valleys, gathering at night the dead fish and mollusks to its cave, ogre belly, hungry for the salt that brings every creature here, covered with it for the ape to lick its chops

A world where touch touches, eats, touch, touch is swallowed by touch, the sense boiled red out of it, a book held between two worlds, unreadable in either, or only partially so

The lobster, whose every part of the old shell, every hair and pore is replaced on the soft red new shell   the map imago mundi

The lobster crawls   touch   as long as sensing, itive, as the moon reaching by weight thru every pocket, cove of the coast, every six hours the weight returning, hidden, filling with water

the fingers running in and out

XI

Fuck: to give shape to in building, to put a stake in the
ground, downward force of *facio,* make, which is not the
root, but the Germanic *fucken,* to strike, move quickly, penetrate, to hammer a nail.

Fuck means that the condition is male and female, the
motion of one opposite snapped into the field of the other, as
the sun fucks thru the trees, moon fucks, or fuck!, the negative constant of failure.

From lips to throat, from breath to glottis. *Fu* which never
ends a word. *ck* which never begins one.

I fuck as hard as, I place the energy, not directly as thrust
or hammer, but into the rhythm, the already-motion being
made, a give of form to, she (can only fuck) gives form to
me, the eternal pull, tidal pull of fluids from their turgor,
the temperature which on one end of the pipe digs it out to
the bone; everything comes just as it is, with as many notes
as it contains, strength of first note, ending at the chord at
which it must end. Leaving only breath.

The shape I cannot have but only make, as the hands cup
around water, her hands cup, her whole body cups on me.

Erotic as shape-liness, or *lines* drawn around me, from
finger to back over the shoulder ass from between the toes to
up the exposed middle stomach chest lips forehead between
the poles in and out back thru the loins, ass and lips and
cock joined in one thrust, kiss, fuck, shape moving in the
current, so water moves in tide.

Know that the weeping bums before the pornographic
throne, October a busty queen throwing her hips thru what
door, would desire shape, end of the thrust, of their un-
shaped-lines, un-penis-trating force. In a cup, foam released
at the end of sea journey, she rounds her palms, loins to receive, shore.

an introduction to lobsterfishing

(we invite Perdurabo to join us at the start

CHAPTER 2

THE MASTER THERION
ON MOUNT DESERT

I

Can a book be a map of the island?
Can the island write a book?
or can I, at the speed of my perception, according to my own movements, construct, with any accuracy, the total sphere of this existence?
If I am encyclopedic, surely I will include too much. If I choose what would appear to be of interest otherwise, I will forget the island and give you a story that could be written anywhere.
There is no dire consequence, only the reality. How to let the island in as map without simply buying a topographic survey and Admiral Morrison's history. How to achieve the *kulturkreise* without being banally anthropological. How to explore my interest in psychological drama, and alchemy, and Lost Continents, and comets, and hollow Earths, without writing another one of those, those Mediaeval paperback histories of U.S. countercultureshock. How to keep the relevance in place, not arbitrary but localized, so that the whole world enters as it bends to this spot.—Integers, not random numbers, for integers orient to a number system.
    The story of this book is the story of our coming to Mount Desert, to live at Green Island Landing on Indian Point Road. It is not Morrison's story, or Champlain's, or Raisz's geological history of Mount Desert Island, though it begins somewhat there. It isn't the *Bar Harbor Times*, or the *Maine Coast Fisherman*, except with borrowings. It isn't even my ethnographic account, though it is the only real ethnography I will offer.
    Pragmatic problem: there is one island, there is a Mount Desert in reality somewhere, and you will find it in any

32

account.[1] There is a relevance, a localism I will not be able to escape as long as I am here. So why let it become trite and banal, news-notey. Why not give it dignity and range and see what it does with itself. The space of the poem, the book, is limited anyway. Let us give it limits known to man, the space of a town, a recognized territory, a mesh of events where the relevance is already internal, like gossip, but not like gossip, except between us and Them, the pronouns of that larger space.[2]

Poetic and Anthropological Gossip

[1]Most ethnographies sound alike because they are unable to overcome this initial contradiction. It becomes an exercise not in describing the Lugbara, or the Chippewa, or the Arunta, but in affirming anthropological literature and precedent. A social science is damned to such truistic jargon because of its base in on-the-spot studies, which are always idiosyncratic, and which it feels it must reject or defang. Attempts to standardize simply blunt the issue and become stylisms. No doubt this is how we get extensive monographs on the association of power with the chief, or modal personality, or the difference betweeen prescribed and preferred marriage. It is as if there were no Africa, no Asia, no North America, no Polynesia, only a vast unexotic ethnographic world composed of harmless culture traits, sanctions, and lineages. Castaneda is banished from the colloquium when his shaman actually does shamanism rather than diffusion or economic role-playing. Similarly, Lévi-Strauss opens himself to mockery by giving the Bororo jaguar some bite. Anthropologists have always felt more secure looking at the relation between patrilineal descent and patrilocal residence, than between myth, cooking, and migration patterns, say. The real questions always seem to trivial, and they end up believing in, as the doctor in Dreyer's *Ordet*, not what's least true (as if that were anything), but what's least worth believing in.

[2]I think I know now why Olson eats on the out-Gloucester side of the diner cut by the Magnolia town line when he wants to relax and chat with friends. Relevance is over the line, is anything which happens there, in the space of the poem, and why poor Ferrini carries that load rather than a thousand other editors of bad verse. Ferrini chose to edit his magazine out of Gloucester (or had no choice), and neither did Olson.

It is territory which fascinates Gerard Malanga as it has always fasci-

I am on Mount Desert to do anthropology, but a poet's geographic problems remain the key. Relevance. Meaning. Without sensationalism. Without indulgence. Telling about tomorrow's water tables, as Pound would have it. Atavism, not modernism. How a man with a hypothetical problem comes to a real place (with a real problem comes to . . .), and finds, to his amazement, that there is work to do. Once the ethnography is cast, the ethnographer sees that no event in the space of THE FIELD is irrelevant, hence fieldwork, following the action, finding in time that the action has a shape; no matter how we follow it in, where we begin, our account becomes the shape, of the written universe, astronomy. So Malinowski pursues the Trobrianders on their trade expeditions around the kula, out into open poetic space, and I will go to Swans as an island where Wendell Seavey says there are marvelous fishermen.

And Gloucester is Olson's fieldwork, though he is not hung up in the Victorian novel, or functional determinism, or synchrony and arbitrary relevance (better to be relevantly arbitrary). His account doesn't read like Firth's or Malinowski's. Olson isn't afraid of wearing the emperor's new clothes, since the tailors are leprachauns, and godlike. Better to wear no clothes than be a clothes-horse, this way like the sorceror to appear simultaneously in blue and red, flashing now the robes of synchrony, now the robes of history; now the robes of determinism, now the robes of the acausal, dancing like a dervish, keeping both feet on and off the ground. This is motion; it doesn't lie there like a dead horse waiting for degrees and diagnoses. If meaning is not the issue, it can't be tested on that score; it's unAmerican. Malinowski fears that he will be caught wearing nothing, and works carefully,

---

nated dispossessed tribes, or those driven out of their own. He comes into Gloucester to count coup, not to free horses or steal a sleeping woman without waking her, but to loot, a few lines while the poet sleeps, and have that stealing be a kind of artistic space. He puts the lines in his own poem, admits the theft, a kind of grace or irony which is itself a geographical act.

34

testing Freudian instincts, testing mother's brother, keeping Trobriand economics out of European economics—except where it counts, in telling what they are doing with their goods, and the bend off this, as hearth-areas and black migrations, to Europe, ten thousand years ago, and again, now. We are left with an example; what we need is world market, the ancient name for money, dollar, shell.

Gloucester is Olson's poetic space, not a Robert Frosty poem mind you, not a kodachrome of the lighthouse on the point, not a guide for visitors except as they come thru the same light passage, being born. It is nothing less than the nation we live in/the national power, as David Smith says Crusoe's island is for Defoe. The whole ETHNOGRAPHIC world. The oikumeme. The larger environment of the world. The Master Therion speaks:

"However we interpret the evidence, its relative truth depends on its internal coherence. We may therefore say that any magical recollection is genuine if it gives the explanation of our external or internal conditions. Anything which throws light upon the Universe, anything which reveals us to ourselves, should be welcome in this world of riddles."[3]

---

[3]The Master Therion says ANYTHING, but he is a quick one to quarrel with the Christian Scientists as sophists devoid of power or notion of consequence; so we shall set our standards within the work, not Rothenberg's *total translation*, but the translation of the immediate data into the manifold synapses of usable space. It does no good to receive a Maori or Tlingit poem in the mail along with a translation from the Age of Malinowski or before and be told to translate the English out of Victorian with the knowledge that it is Maori, etc. To be encyclopedic is to pursue meaning, not to arbitrate it. There is no origin of myth, simply the dynamic that continues to say yes, to open itself from within to the living currents, the changing random environment, the technoeconomic means, the constant exchange of women and goods, and the origin of man in nature. Myth is not cosmological after the fact; it is only as it is.

Send me any flashes from Somesville, Olson tells us on the phone. And now Somesville is being watched. And do you understand this type of Extra! Extra! Read All About It! news that can sit in the Museum at Islesford for 50 years,

---

There is no total translation except insofar as we speak from the deep structure out into the voice. And that deep structure includes the exigencies of environment, technological level, and cosmology learned along with and as part of native tongue. Anything else is simply the latest fashion in misreading text, i.e., the coffee-table book of myths and events, along with alchemy posters, computer dating, and the daily horoscope.

When Olson says we are members of the Navaho culture too, and do not destroy its internal relevance by borrowing from Wyman, or Reichard, or Beautyway, I take him to mean on the level of deep structure to deep structure, in a region where voice achieves a preverbal human syntax, in the whirlwind of proprioception, and can go either way with the material, as we sometimes find in a dream we can speak or read a language we have never known. I take it to mean that when we begin fooling around with morphs and semes and juggling them we are operating in the realm of pure probability and asexual cosmology, algorithm without even the interest of IBM speed. We are merely shuffling the semblance of meaning, the shells of meaning, outside of a realm of syntax. We are in fact destroying the poet who makes poetry, replacing him with what we did as children before we could make our words cohere, taking 'ponies' to Latin class, which is okay if you're going to gallop fullspeed, devil may care, but in *Technicians of the Sacred* they are kept under the desk hoping the teacher won't see, or the public won't care. Like exotic lands, it doesn't matter if you haven't really been there, as long as it looks as though you have. And all their translations sound as frighteningly alike as those Victorian ones they have moved out of because, as Chomsky would see at once, there are no strings, no phrasemarkers, no transformational subcomponents. Which means no poetry and no Indians. What is wrong with *Technicians of the Sacred* is just that *ruleless universal condition*, that makes it impossible to read Jung or Leary also without feeling that the imagination itself is being stolen right from under our eyes, and being replaced by well-trained, well-dressed young men out of computer school, who care nothing for the DANGER, inside the lines, and think that because we have escaped nature with our machines. . . .

3 6

and is still as hot as: awakened as the slumbering giant, the long body in the morgue aroused to, the history and accounts of ships which brought us here, and those here who are now us; the flashing, flashes, as faraway in the mountains as the lights of an opposite shore, yet appearing boldly and naked in daily conversation, as though the relevance WERE gossip, and never receded with the glaciers, the grist mills, the clipper ships, trawls, the eternal directions for getting to that Eastern Muddy Ridge even if the fish no longer pass thru the nets of the Russians to be there. We find the underground continent, the water table; we drink from the well.

The Cranberries hang in medullan medulloid medullific space, just as sun in the trees, stone in low water, or Photo Number 14 of the Planet Mars, the space from the center out as the lens approaches the horizon, as the lines crossing on the Palm are the matter of our world.

The flashing from Somesville is unenumerated, innumerable, *sine nombres,* is the clear historic present past of our condition—the glaciers moving as slowly as that time which counts in which the sun in its place also moves, sashweighting ice. Or is the sun's proper motion in Rodney Collin's room, the axis shifting round the whole zodiac every 25,765 years, a solar breath.

I was here. I built fires. I left clam middens. I lived in Somesville. Our cats shat in the forest. I rolled with Robin in the wet grass. We made love. We talked. I wrote. You wrote your poems. Do what you can, Kelly says. There's not time to do everything. Okay.

And do we know or need to know the difference between Aleister Crowley and Eliphas Levi?,   Aleister Crowley asks.

or between Mickey Mantle and Wendell Seavey?

Pip's convict and Enoch Stanley?

Jasper Merchant and Clyde Pomroy?

Charles Olson and Elmer Spurling?

Can we tell Jimi Hendrix from Father Gower from Samuel Hadlock long dead in God's Pocket?

Is there any price in America as important as the price of lobsters here in the space between Bernard and McKinley?

I will ask a simpler question: is there any price in the

nation separable from it?

It is not the islands speaking to you/you know that. But from that to Robert Frost at Islesford there's a whole country hiding, and it's us.

—

II

At Jasper Merchant's Wharf (1)

This is the beginning of the fieldwork. I come to the wharf and request the permission of the owner to talk to the fishermen. It is a cold autumn day, first snow flurries in the morning, *I Ching* reads, beginning of new things, memory of the old. We can never know what we are at the beginning, we can never know the changes.

"Sure, you can come here all you want. Don't know that I could say anything that would help you. Lobstering's a complicated business. You won't be the first one that's tried to understand it and you won't be the last."

The dealer's shed is a small house with marine supplies cluttered about in uneven piles, a few chairs around a stove, old yellowing notices on the walls, ads and government regulations and nautical maps, no newspapers, no magazines, nothing new. An old rusty fish-scale hanging from the ceiling. A few old lobstermen and a sleeping dog.

Jasper's office adjoins the shed proper, his account books open on his desk, receipts strewn with envelopes in layers. Jasper sits in a lean-back chair on wheels, middle-aged, with a sea-cap, glasses, slightly paunchy and foggy-eyed. Oratorical, like a senator.

"We don't run your usual type of business here. It's an informal place and the men like that."

Why do you think certain men choose to lobster from here as opposed to another dealer, say?

"I don't rightly know the answer to that. After all, your lobsterman is an independent businessman and he can go with his product to whomever he pleases. But I can think of three things right off." He holds out three fingers and begins counting them off. "One, the dealer is a friendly sort of thing. You go where you can get along with the fellows. Two, we furnish them with a workshop and an area in the bait-shed where they can salt their own bait. Like your friend Wendell. The men unload the bait if the truck comes when they're around and they can have it at cost. We also sell them their marine supplies at a discount, whereas the same service over to Pomroy's might cost them more. And, three, in some cases they're financed by us. We own their boats. If the man's a hard worker, brings in a lot of lobsters, we're liable to reward him with a better arrangement. But generally we take a nickel or dime per pound for the boat."

While we're talking, Jasper walks out of his office onto the wharf, where we stand. I'm watching the smoke from the buildings on the other side of the harbor, a town almost identical to the one I am standing in, a vision of being both places at once, or neither place. The space in the middle filled with lobsterboats, clean, white, atop their reflections in a still ocean. This is different than anyplace; it is like the city, but a hidden city, a submerged and entorsoed city. Noise. Activity. The gulls subtend every possible angle, crying from the shed roofs, perched among the boats on rocks and on the floating bait cars. The boats rest in a semi-circle, rowboats marking the moorings from which men have left, tied to the water by a rope passing thru it. From out of the semi-circle radios buzz with the conversation of worlds in and out of harbors, and across points of land, prices, positions, like a ticker tape. An active market. Static mixed with near and far shrieks. Bird calls. All the languages of the world converge. And the bright emblematic colors of the buoys, two-tone and tri-tone, and the signs for diesel fuel, lobsters, marine supplies. A city. on the Atlantic.

Wharf. says Skeat: "This difficult word, with a great range of senses, meant a turning, reversion, turning-place, space, dam, shore, dockyard."

Hwearf: to turn about.

H. W. STURLOW AND COMPANY, LOBSTERS. Proprieter: Jasper Merchant. Influence, confluence. Ships. Money.

"Unless I'm mistaken," Jasper says, "that's Mr. Marlon Bridges coming in a bit early. Yes it is." We go down the ramp onto the floating dock and meet Marlon as he steers in. Jasper throws him a rope and he pulls himself alongside the dock. Then Jasper immediately grabs the first barrel of lobsters and hoists it clumsily over the side onto the dock, rolling it the rest of the way up onto the scales.

"Was hauling traps and a squall hit," Marlon says. "Couldn't see the next trap, I let them go, turn around and come back in, the sun comes out, but I've got enough for today."

One on top of another the barrels go on the scale; Jasper writes down the amount, and then empties them into the lobster bin. He brings the barrels back, weighs those, blows on his hands to restore circulation and does some subtraction on a scrap of paper. "Fifty-five pounds from two hundred and seventy is two hundred and fifteen pounds, give or take a few."

"And a pair of gloves," Marlon shouts from the gas pump, which he is turning on.

"A pair of gloves, and I'll take out for gas. . . ." He gets out his pouch of money and begins to sort bills. "I pay everyday," he tells me. "Now Emery Levesque over there across the harbor, he has a book-keeper and pays once a week. Probably I'd be better off if I did that. Wouldn't have so much money on the books. You pay in small sums they're more likely to keep it all. One big amount at the end of the week they're liable to pay you some of what they owe."

What's he doing now? I ask, as Marlon has driven his boat in along the wharf, closer to shore, and is working heavy barrels on the pulley.

"He's loading bait now while the tide's good and so he won't have to do it in the morning. We've got a tide problem here, and you have to do everything at the right time." He is thoughtful for a second, wondering what else he might tell me. Then he says: "Marlon here's an interesting lobsterman. He's from Downeast, Bucksport originally, went to Maine Maritime, worked as an engineer for a while, had a rug business in New Jersey I think, had some trouble there, don't think he liked unions, now he's back here, doing the thing he likes best you might say."

Is he one of those who goes in one of your boats, or does

he own his own?

"Oh no. He owns his boat. He's independent. We're not in the business of making money by renting boats. There are only a few."

Does Marlon always sell here?

"Far as I know he does. But he can go anywhere he pleases, and I'm sure he'll tell you that if you ask him."

What about the men who don't own their own boats?

"I should hope they would sell here."

If they don't?

"If they don't! Well, I'd think they'd find themselves walking on water."

III

At Jasper Merchant's (2)

"It's a touchy matter, this thing of lobster price," Jasper says. "What we have here is a supply and demand market, and there are certain individuals who, shall we say, have a little more money than the rest of us. They anticipate an increase and begin paying their lobstermen more. Once that begins, everyone else has to follow. The men talk back and forth all the way up and down the coast on their radio-telephones. They know what the next guy's getting. There were a few days there that Wendell was fishing alongside fellers from Swans Island and getting a nickel less for the same lobsters. Now he's not going to tolerate that for long. I've got to put my prices up too, even if I lose a little, or I'll have unhappy fishermen."

The water on all sides of the world is as active, and Bass Harbor is one artery in the tide where, like a clock, land is taken out of, water returns to cover. The gold which is neither precious metal nor produce. Profit reflects that: even the planet, as well as certain areas on it, gains and loses in time. The fish-scales hanging unused for a decade.

Haskell Rich brings his boat in, soft old man, hands two small pails of lobsters to Jasper and keeps the rest on board. Thirty-three pounds, and Jasper pays him at 80¢ a pound.

What are you doing with the rest of them? I ask.

"I'm going to put 'em in my car, hold 'em till Christmas when the price is up."

Do you mind? I ask Jasper.

"Hell, no! He takes the risk, and I get the lobsters sooner or later. Better when there's a shortage and I need lobsters to sell."

Who owns the sea?, but the species in the grip of the web that fills it/Who owns his own boat? The men who fill it don't, but man as a species, commensal, communal, collective, operating under the selective pressure of the Pleistocene though the great world market would seem to lie between here and there, blind, African in origin, Swiss in expression. And man's brain, is it more than he bargained for?, more than he traded in for a fish?

Man the species. Lounging around the stove. Once a sardine factory. Once a pool room. Once a fishstand. The wharf, the body can become anything. As long as they're doing business.

Blended: the bright colors of U.S.A., like flag day, Gulf Dieselect, blue and orange, Petit Marine Paint, with the pastels, oxides, algae of weathering. Unevenly colored wharfwood, crusted with shells, decaying or covered with decay. Fish skeletons, crushed herring, exoskeletons (shells, claws), junk fish cleaned out of traps, old netting and chains; the gulls as plentiful as pigeons in the city hover, screaming their appetites, the ecosystem, alive, and winged.

Commensal or altruistic? Decide. Who owns the land who owns the lobsters who puts them in the sea at Boothbay who takes them out in the lea of Gott's who sells them in Bernard who trucks them to Boston who swallows them chromosomes and all, but others are being born in the template and the gene pool is full. Who?

Man the species, fashioning the traps out of wood, tying his netting in the shed on cold days. Man working from sunup to sundown, or on a blowy day comes in early. In among the Cranberries. Gott's. Placentia. In the map. No longer a hunter, he farms the bottom, and the earth is upsidedown, the buoys resting as the tips of giant roots, climbing, but down, by a stem, the fruit beneath, the lobsters coming after the buds of stinking chum, to be reaped by the fisherman as wheat, as man has always begun off lost continents (these intersecting kingdoms of the Atlantic we call Atlantis), still a creature of the sea.

What are the traps? Who is caught? Where is the market? Finally? Pulling the traps one by one, the price jumping from seventy to seventy-five cents (from somewhere else), as the polar ice caps melting, inches thawing away, the sea going colder, the lobsters moving out to, the fish, the food trapped in the nets drawn between the greater Nations, Soviet trawlers in our U.S.A. offshore waters, of what planet?, but economies have been growing together since the Ice Age, interweaving on these steppes and plains and continental shelves so that every nation lies off every other, and fishermen are fishermen, men of the ocean.

Who between these invisibilities but the species man? What man? Communal or profiteering? Owning what land, what fishing territory himself? What is food for a king who is to rule the ecosystem? And what king to protect the kingdom from itself, the species, as an oak tree rules the forest in glory with its sunshield of sugars and its floating stats?

California Computer? Are they the king? "Providing temperature graphs of all kinds for biological studies. Plotting shifting ocean currents and ocean weather. After studying multiple plots of water temperature strata drawn in exact detail by a CalComp drum plotter, TRW engineers have developed programs to improve the lobster's environment in experimental areas, giving the creatures a new chance to grow."

But are they inside the measure, blind as the breeding, spawning, measureless as the sea eggs, berries, calm as the photosynthetic feeding and mackerel from the surface of sun-star over which winds play, tides?

Haskell has driven his boat back from the cars on the other side of the harbor. The noise of someone trying vainly to reach someone else screeches over his radio. He empties some oil cans and a paper towel center overboard. Thought: this is the sea into which it is happening, perhaps pollution, but I am one man and the world is still large (or is it?). Could medicine arise from this, birth of secret fluids in the harbor that surrounds us, lips on the dirty wharf?

The shore itself is littered with bottles and shells. Upland to human deposit. Weeds growing thru the old laths and netting, fishing gear and broken lobster traps, peeling buoys with crusted seaweed. A tree with black fungus hanging from it like rubber.

Neither a garbage dump nor a curio shop, for the secretaries from Bar Harbor come to collect the mementos and sea-symbols of Downeast, pop art.

Neither an antique shop nor a garden. Nothing visible grows here, but decomposition has begun. Yellows into purples. Rubber swallowed by spiders, rope propping up vines.

I walk with Jasper up to the bait shed where he pours a carton of salt into the heads and tails, and turns it, a fertile stench. In the back another man is peeing on the floor. Jasper pees, taking small pieces of fish down thru the cracks to the mulch beneath. On an island unattractive smells like unattractive women have compulsion, become attractive in having essence, power, shit, decay, life and death as one marches from the sea, everyone seems to feed back in, marry their cousin. You can walk away from anything but a strong smell; it haunts you, calls you back. And we must be at least that strong, our healthy process to capture and convert the lethal to flower. *Ming*: leaving whatever is beyond our control to fate.

An Interlude During Which Enoch Stanley Sitting in His Rooms in Southwest Harbor Watches the Mayor of New York Get Dunked with Champagne by Rod Gaspar

The nation returns to New York,
and it is the end of the Middle Ages, as the Middle West, and the Green Bay Packers, and the St. Louis Cardinals, and the Cleveland Browns, and the Detroit Tigers, and with it an end to Southern California grape-growers and John Birchers and Ann-Margarets and Art Linkletters. It's the New York Mets and the New York Jets, invented in the early '60's, not the giant Yankees or the yankee New York Giants, but the children, the grandchildren who are the grandfathers, the hidden black power backstreets Iroquois Indian New York.

It's the nation again looking back to that city, not for Babe Ruth and Joe DiMaggio and Marilyn Monroe, but Tom Seaver and Charles Olson finally winning those 25 games for the East Coast, taking the Cy Young Award away from Lyrical Poets and Organ Grinders, the Denny McClains in Detroit, and among retired ballplayers in L.A., it's Rod Kanehl and not Chuck Connors, cowboy in Africa, who's victorious; Rod Gaspar, reserve outfielder, called it in four straight, like Namath. And nothing scares your vice-president from Maryland, Mr. Agnew, more than the New York Jets with long hair and Namath knocking off the Baltimore Colts IN FOOTBALL, a tribe of hippies, an entire underdog unregarded league, and the New York Mets, at best a threat to the Republican Party in the '80's, growing by necessity, half the kids in the country throwing harder than Bob Feller, coming from Texas and Minnesota and Iowa to pitch against the Baltimore Orioles and the U.S. Navy. Nothing scares him like this, not the moratoriums, or SDS, or the Vietcong; he can handle those, he thinks, but here in baseball and football he is totally exposed, the world turning back to New York and cheering Jerry Koosman and Tommy Agee and Cleon, and away from Dave McNally with his seventeen straight wins, and Earl Weaver, and Leo Durocher, that other fascist Napoleon from the forties and fifties of Ron Santo, and Italians beating up the blacks. Weeb Ewbank wants to put in the subs, but the players won't have it. We're smashing the NFL, they scream. What, says Weeb, smashing the NFL? I used to win championships in the NFL. But LeRoi Jones could care less about who Lita Hornick used to pitch for and the Kulchur Boys. "Johnny Unitas looks silly with that crewcut," George Sauer says. "I mean it's funny-looking. He should let his hair grow. He'd look good." That's how much vision has changed, so that it looks like blasphemy, shouldn't happen that Al Weis on successive days in Chicago hit home runs, angering the Cub announcers so much they yelled down at the field, "You can get this guy out with a curve ball." Yeah, and with tear gas. That's what they used to think, in Berkeley, and Korea, could smash a fourth rate military power with the all-stars, beat the Russians in hockey, and deliver campaign speeches. But McNally didn't get him out with a curve ball, twice he didn't, once in the first win, once in the last win, a guy batting .215, the lowest average on either team, but it's a new world age, so that Dylan just has to sing, not even 'the times they are a-changing,' and the mayor of New York can get dunked with free publicity by Rod Gaspar. And Art Shamsky, and Jack DiLauro and Wayne Garrett, all of these players whose names are hidden behind those Bart Starrs and Jackie Kemps and Richard Nixons, and George Atlas buying space on the backs of comic books, so that even David Eisenhower wears a Baltimore button, knowing on which side his own chances lie, and they do it, like magic, right before the eyes of Mickey Mantle, Joe DiMaggio, Ted Williams, who know it can't be done, and Mrs. Babe Ruth, who knows it can, and Mickey Mantle says he's even beginning to believe in astrology now, as Swoboda dives blindly in the path of the ball, and meets it, like his fate, and the country's, the World Series of Injustice Abbie Hoffman says, but he's on the wrong side, in Chicago with a Chicago Cubs button because C stands for conspiracy too. We've forgotten the Chicago Cubs and the Chicago police and the Uncle Toms, and the Pueblo, and Mayor Daley, and Ken Holtzman, and Willie Mays; the Blacks in the San Francisco ghetto want the Willie Mays Tot Lot changed to the Malcolm X Tot Lot, 'cause we don't groove on Willie Mays anymore.' The eyes of the nation are on New York again, not Haight Ashbury and the Oracle, but Bethel, and Tommy Agee grabbing it in the tip of his glove as he runs into the wall, synchronicity, and the music played in the mud—which has been coming for a long time, the Rolling Stones in the Labrador air, though hidden beneath the obese bar graph of the middle class and the popular appeal of Lyndon Johnson and George Wallace and Vince Lombardi.

What do we do with it, the enigma of our heroes, the ecstasy of power? The New York Jets are from Texas, and Wayne Garrett was drafted from obscurity in the South to hit the pennant-winning home run, and still doesn't understand New York but thinks it's a great town to play ball in, and Emerson Boozer is back, and Matt Snell is back, and Nolan Ryan is back striking out the side with the bases loaded, his inevitable speed feat, and Tug McGraw is a new man, greeting hippies in the stands even after a stint in the Marines, and all hell is about to break loose in the army high on pot, and Tom Seaver pats a fuming Leo Durocher on the fanny as Leo returns from another spat with the umpires, and says, "How about another Schlitz, Leo," the exact words we hear Leo say on Game of the Week, which won't even show the New York Mets all year even as the Times won't review Olson and Duncan, but this is the year of the *Maximus Poems,* and the return to origins, Robert Frost is dead because he never lived, Donald Hall reduced to offerings at Ginsberg's altar, and Casey Stengel, the Charles Olson of the game if anyone is, is brought back to national glory, and no kidding, just like Charles at Berkeley, it's Casey who's running tonight, W. C. Williams, and old Ezra Pound, first manager of the team, who says, "The Mets have come on slow but fast." And it's true. We all have.

And Gaspar will throw out the one runner he must. Shamsky will hit, as in the mythical past he had one night in Pittsburgh. The wheel turns, the possible returns; Frank Smith says, "To hell with liberalism; let's shoot for the noosphere," and James Brown owns the world. Not Civil Rights, but Brakhage films, the perfect fixed point in the living room around which all other points move. Namath hits Maynard; Swoboda drops a double inside the line; it's inevitable. Monday afternoon Jack DiLauro strikes out Koosman on the lawn of Gracie Mansion, Olson takes a job at Storrs, is in like Flynn, the old President of Black Mountain returns. And maybe Lindy and I, with Io and Robin, will return to Amherst where it began, and begin again without the old fight. Bobby Pfiel is crying, seven years in the minors. Wendell Seavey is a rich lobsterman. It's a new age; it's got to be. You can see it, Enoch. There's no one else alive. It's ourselves.

V

Asa Island, Hat Island, & the Triangles
Gooseberry Island, Harbor Island,
Toothacher Cove
High Sheriff, Ram Island, & Potato Field

these are lands at sea, not known by any earth cartographer, too small to be on any map. they are also lands in the galaxy. spots. and together they: form the separate planetary system plantation of Swans Island, bought as a lot by Colonel Swan from the State of Massachusetts.

The ferry, leaving Bass Harbor, crosses the inner lobster grounds, passes Black and Placentia, to arrive here. And then this is point zero again. The world originates here and goes out again into its own inner lobster grounds, regions familiar to the generations born on Swans Island. Reaching here we look back out to find that the world begins again to sea. And Swans is as large as anyplace, for we cannot see the whole thing at once

world is: forests and clearings. big overgrown fields with reddish bushes, wild deer, and bright yellow apples shining late in October, as knobby, rocky, as the glacial earth.

Our big car pulls off the ferry, could as well be a spaceship landing on another world. Roads run out, toward the quarry, and the abandoned fields, black tarred huts along the shore with lobster traps piled beside them. We drive slowly, waiting for a sign, and then a little blond boy, walking with two girls, this far from anywhere, gives the V-sign, on the road to Swans Island Village, as geography runs simultaneous with the human topos, giant old white houses with windowry as fine as veils, surrounded by turrets; inland are abandoned castles and lodges, the smaller houses lie down along the water. The archaeology is visible without any digging. Farming has turned to fishing. The children run and play in the world, have access everywhere to the coves and the sea. Gigantic rocks lie along the shore, beginnings of a seawall, in the microcosm each pebble overgrown with tiny shells and mussel colonies, slippery with the green slime of protoplasm, spires and sheaths of life, the sea a garden, and the planet fed at the roots, as salty iodiney, as small fish and crabs, worms and kelps: so the planet of Swans Island sits on that organic base which creeps ashore and feeds it.

Out at sea, in the water between Minturn and Swans Island Village, where Harbor Island and its two tiny Hubs sit, is a giant fish weir, black broken wood set in the water as an experiment in intelligence, roped thicket so that as in crystal growth the sides are symmetrical, aimed positionally, and the greater flows into the lesser thru the V-mouth, herring and mackerel, which are used, and also everything else, starfish, urchins, crabs, which lives at sea, the zooplankton, are drawn in by the condition, or so small they sift right thru.

These waters are always around us, with their races of men, each island with its Rip Van Winkle, its Johnny Appleseed, its dwarves. Life in Minturn lies across the Harbor from life in Swans Island Village; and the children go to school on the ferryboat, like the New York City Subway. The farms are gone except for Clyde Torrey who harnesses a horse to an ox and draws a few vegetables. Even Fred Turner's vaunted oxen from Sedgewick, that hauled the quarried granite to the dock, are dead, and everyone fishes.

Much of it is forest, where nobody lives, but it is a community, a living of life in the web of all, the Oddfellow's Hall taken over entirely by the woman's branch, the Rebeccas, for suppers and teas, as any island is, and they do the talking while the men build the traps and go lobstering. Axel Anderson came here from Sweden to work in the quarry. His son married Fred Turner's grand-daughter, turned to lobstering, as his son, and now his son's son. Sheldon Carlson, a native of Swans, not Europe, not America, works in his shed on the point, a blowy wintry day, netting the traps, a white lobster claw hanging from a nail. The waters lie around him like a great familiar road.

They are surrounded by the ancient possibilities of farms and quarries, the deserted deck, invaded by the summer people from the cities. And still the island remains mysterious, a separate event of land in the cosmos. Hidden in the woods from the Freemasonry of an older world, but in it too, eco, in the living web tied to the shape of the ground above sea level, history bearing the cost of the freight. It is that far from here to everyplace else, lies between it and the world of the inner ring. The roads that wind around, and around, never leave, and the cars become domesticated, and symbols arise like mussel beds, in the daily language; 'put a tent over it and you have the largest whorehouse in Maine,' say some in Bass Harbor, but this is the way the local is usually understood, when people fuck what's around. And in the forests the birds and deer, the possible Indians, and there is no way off or out, but on each point a lighthouse or other sanctuary, dressed in the clothing of shape, the gulls hovering about the human smell of land, of people who still live here in this age, doing their business, who neither have their cake nor eat it, and go on, which is essential, the density measured by snail-life on stone. And the names of the families are Joyce and Sprague and Smith and Staple, Morrison and Sprague the lobster-dealers, and the work is hard, but the circle is closed, as with the species that anchor.

VI

Aleister Crowley, Remaindered for $3.95 on 57th Street, is Brought to Mount Desert Island

where the people in the City claimed he would be hopelessly obscure, for there was no initiation and no Magick. But the fisherman, working from scratch on his tools, constructing the experiment from false memory and inheritance of an invisible order: knows his Magick, though not by name. The traps he builds are of virgin wood, and he works by the heat of a self-fed fire, all winter, making the perfect implement, which fools might think he could buy at the store.

And from this I learn: "The Wand must be cut with a single stroke of the knife. There must be no boggling and hacking at things, no clumsiness and no hesitation. If you strike a blow at all, strike with your strength!" And they spend all their lives at it, laying on that single blow.

Outside the sanctum the unadmitted haggle over the price of entry. Inside, the work goes on.

Magick, abandoned in New York, which has absorbed it, and become it, is brought to Mount Desert among the laths and wenches, derricks and tows, as part of the inevitable apparatus of the uninitiated world. Their bodies are links between two worlds, one, of which they are created, one, which they create. Smash the telescope, and the two worlds still lie sparkling and utter, stars staring at stars, external events in search of an external event.

And the Master Fisherman "does not care a scrap of yesterday's newspaper whether he is [the Son of Man or the Devil on Diesel Fuel], or whether there ever such a person, or whether the Universe itself is anything more than a nightmare created by his own imprudence in the matter of rum and water. . . . . What matters is this: True or false (reincarnation or virgin manchild), he has found a symbolic form which has enabled him to govern himself to the best advantage." The City has been built of its materials, its consecration is long past; the fisherman works in the unbuilt Atlantic village, his karma behind him like the whole history of fishing. I did not see these men or the serious and angelic business in which they were engaged till the Master Therion, seeking new territory in the oldest territory of all, led me back to his origins, and the beginnings of Magick in woodcraft and lines.

"(A Magical Operation) may be defined as any event in Nature which is brought to pass by Will. We must not exclude potato-growing or banking from our definition."

Or "Magick is for All"

For those who build traps and drag their nets along the bottom,

for those whose nets are broken and snarl, who must choose between two equally uncertain catches, November to April, May to October,

the rope is tight, and each tug, as the slack is let out or the end of the slack is reached, touches on the Macrocosm, the always-unfixed ratio between man and his holy guardian angels, who have names, who are blind to all other conditions but the calling, who wait there forever as if dead or nonexistent; when properly addressed walk right in the door. Each haul from the bottom, each crab weighed against some larger mass, thrown back or taken in, every claw, attached to the lobster or not, pulls on the cloth of the universe: the fisherman at bay. And the magician on the wharf recalls, and it is recalled to him in coin, that "Nature is a continuous phenomenon, though we do not know in all cases how things are connected." And the wise lobsterman reads his Crowley, keeps his eye both on the motions of the sea and the characters about him on the wharf, weighing motivation of man and beast alike, whom he would seem to fix by his motives and desires, if they too were not tied by strings.

"Every man has a right to fulfill his own will without being afraid that it may interfere with that of others; for if

he is in his proper place, it is the fault of others if they interfere with him." And if he is in the wrong place, he will find
out anyway; he will get blown out of there; his gear and
magical equipment will be smashed; his ropes will be cut;
his buoys will wash up on the shores of Cranberries or float
to kingdom come; his very traps will be emptied by the
planets in their course.

Magick is for All; the Coast Guard at Southwest Harbor
needs Magick, to keep the Navy in order, even to find let
alone to guard the coast, and from what? if its circle be
closed. The Lobsterman's Association needs Magick, to fight
a market as elusive and tenuous as the path and position of
the lobster, and at the same time. Every market, in the Ein-
steinian present, is filled with futures, is a futures market.
"The first requisite for causing any change is thorough qual-
itative and quantitative understanding of the conditions."
When to fish and when not to. How to let the circle fill with
beings. And if one cuts another's trap, the inevitable postu-
late, known on every wharf: one man's knife is as sharp as
another's. Underwater or in the marketplace. At sea with
ropes and traps or side by side on a common wharf, this
double-edged blade we wield, each man for but against the
next man, is society, aware only as we cut out the heart (but
Crowley says both parties are equally born of necessity.
Only in black magic is there torture or dualism. The rest is
single. In which silence the endless motions and counter-
motions have a common theme.

. . . and the Oddfellows, meeting tonight at $1^0 = 10^0$,
the eternal neophytes of Freemason America, God do they
need Magick if they are to escape the American Legion and
regain their order even by the year 2000 here in Southwest
Harbor.

***

Wendell Seavey, son of Frank Seavey, and Sea, brings his
boat in to Jasper Merchant's lobster wharf in Bernard
today, the cold as intense as the sun itself, the wind driving
the gulls who drive the wind, hover, blown, connected, and
stops the engines. Jasper comes down the wharf to help him,

hoisting the barrels of lobsters off the boat onto the next level of the economy where they are turned into pounds on the scale, written down, and from that subtracted the weight of the barrels, and the Price of Gulf, and anti-freeze, and turns pounds into dollar bills, one hundred, then fifty, then some ones, the cold hands out of the gloves trying to snap some life into those hot bills. The lobsters are dumped into the bin, coins floating among each other, their order so changed from active scavengers to items of mint, though not from the angle of their own sharp blades: they are crawling confusedly, giant insects enmeshed in each others', in their own plugged claws, in the confusion of imposed space. So the axiom is proved on the wharf as well: that "Every force in the Universe is capable of being transformed into any other kind of force by using the suitable means. There is thus an inexhaustible supply of any particular kind of force we may need."

Which holds in any biology or physics textbook also: Magick the queen of the sciences even as lobsterfishing is the king of the wharf and the laboratory of social and technological change. Its implements do not have to pass thru the computer; they are all of a kind.

But America $= 1^0$. America is the neophyte. Fools use Magick only to win a woman who dislikes them, Brandolike, as at the movies, wasting their time while the lobsters move into deep water, and they are rendered out of touch with all elementals and gods. Heed Crowley, even in the distance of victory:

"There is opportunity for all kinds of error in the transmission of the Will; misunderstanding may mar the matter; a mood may make mischief; external events may interfere; the lover may match me in Magick; the Operation itself may offend Nature in many ways; for instance, if there is a subconscious incompatibility between myself and the woman, I deceive myself into thinking that I desire her. Such a flaw is enough to bring the whole operation to naught."

And those who ask for sociology of the wharf and shoals, must realize that there is none. The men speak only of Magick; unemployment compensation and illegal deer meat buy off the rest, and what's not bought off by that is bought off by tourism and labs in Bar Harbor raising rats, or World War II moneys left over from then. The possibilities and combinations are as endless as the strings are tangled. It is Magick for learning scallop beds and intercepting schools of fish; with its technological base, its mechanics, is the traditional wisdom of a shipbuilding nation. Even as the American Revolution: "Man is capable of being, and using, anything which he perceives, for everything that he perceives is in a certain sense a part of his being. He may thus subjugate the whole Universe of which he is conscious to his individual Will."

Aleister Crowley comes to the wharf at Bernard to speak only of and to the equal-born of necessity. Remaindered in the city he must return to the source of the resources, Wendell Seavey clear as sea water, a child in his boat, directing his will between islands. Thru many incarnations he will know

A MAN WHO IS DOING HIS TRUE WILL HAS THE INERTIA OF THE UNIVERSE TO ASSIST HIM.

VII

Ron Swoboda (the Mets have won the World Series):
"Nobody thought we were going anywhere, but we won the
whole thing. I guess all that's left for us is to go to the
moon." Or where do all culture-heroes go? How do they leave
their skin and become possible of all things? And better the
moon than Las Vegas or the Ed Sullivan Show, those greased
slides out.

Ken Boswell: "I can't believe this is happening to me."
Better. "Because the entire complex of phenomenal existence
is considered as true as long as the knowledge of the *Brahman* being the Self of all has not arisen; just as the phan-
toms of a dream are considered to be true until the sleeper
wakes." *Vedanta*. "Oh, I guess I'll retire now; *everybody*
seems to be doing that! Anyway, I could live *forever* on
twenty thousand in Austin." Perhaps the wise man retires,
to a commune, or Plato's Republic. Perhaps he understands.

Swoboda: "We're the saints of Lost Causes." But who will
be your saints in your own lost cause now? "For as long as
a person has not reached the true knowledge of the unity of
the Self, so long it does not enter his mind that the world of
effects with its names and objects of right knowledge and
its results of actions is untrue; he rather, in consequence of
his ignorance, looks on mere effects (such as body, offspring,
wealth, &c.) as forming part of and belonging to his Self,
forgetful of *Brahman* being in reality the Self of all." *Vedanta*.

Art Shamsky: "I will light my cigars with hundred dollar
bills." Maybe he's bragging; maybe he's telling the truth.
The sun burns all cash in time; perhaps he knows that. Is
able to say that he has nothing but a match with the words
of America written on it. World Series as *Brahman*, as final

59

judgement.

Gentry: "That means we've won, we're the best; there's nothing else to do, no one to beat. How do you like that!" Unstated is the end of the season, what do we do next? Live?

The matter of Magick is just that the magician's spell is never broken; he is a magician all the time, and there is no end to the game or the season, no end to the one work, no next in the Circle, out of which he will not, he wills not, to pass. They say that God is a Met fan; the Mets are spoken of as magicians. But the manager of the Orioles denies that there were gremlins or miracles; they did it with solid pitching and fielding and timely hitting. They executed, Casey would say. Which is the first and only principle of Magick. The Mets discover the intentional act, the most powerful spell of momentum, of resource within the rules of the sphere. The Mets are magicians, and because the sportswriters in their ignorance refuse to accept this in the most simple sense, they lie and boast and exaggerate. Buy any book on the Mets coming out right after the Series (as Maury Allen's *The Incredible Mets*) splash on the news-stands, or the team album ("The Miracle Mets") and you'll see what I mean. They confuse cars, money, success with the real events of miracle. They destroy the actual history step by step, substituting imaginary events for the fragments of what really happened. Like children who have seen the fantastic, they run into a crowded room and breathless begin to recite, and realize that no one has the context, so they make everything even more incredible to win a few ears. The same quotes are tacked onto ten and twelve different events until they become tall tales. The real story, in which the Mets waste no motion until the dynamo is set, in which the unnamed seizes its intended power, in which history itself is a series of ordinary events climbing towards bursts of cosmic interpretation, is lost, and the Mets become simply the terrible made good, the clowns become kings. The Throneberrys and Chacons and Kanehls are made more incompetent than they were; for instance, I can remember several times Elio Chacon running around the bases while the other team booted the ball. The Mets were no worse than many teams, but they were New

60

York, and re-evocations of the Giants and Dodgers, and simultaneous with the Yankee-General Motors Machine and the Black Revolution and the moon-landing and the Vietcong. Similarly the kings are made more regal than they are, Tom Seaver as Louis the XIV, Nancy his royal queen.

"Selves are of two kinds: worldly and liberated." *Jaina*. But Crowley is a Star in the West, as his biography tells. Like a baseball star or a cowboy, unlike a Jainist, for him the worldly can be liberated, and in fact liberation in the worldly, in one's Western profession, is the true purpose of this world, and the reason for the fantastic technology of the West, the seeming creation of the Holy City on earth, that the metals would appear to be brought to a higher form even as each man; that civilization would be itself salvation. Crowley can accept the baseball player as magus, even as he accepts Pasteur, Thomas Edison.

But the West is also concerned with fragments, intellectual games, how much money one can make after a good season, gross national product, philosophers like Eric Hoffer and Robert Frost, who know nothing of the ecology, the consequences of the world they meddle in. There is nothing wrong with America practical as hoes or fish-nets, but there is also America over-pricing hoes, making too many, letting food rot in the invisible market, catching millions of fish, catching meat but keeping the shell, and turning the nitrogen cycle, the life into rock.

Aristotle here is the winning pitcher for the New York Mets even as he is the losing pitcher for the Baltimore Orioles, the lobsters, and the game warden. He counts his losses; he balances his books without a real measure or fix and comes up with a profit.

What should we offer Seaver after a twenty-five game year, the World Series, and the Cy Young Award? Surely not that his picture and his wife's appear on the promotion seeking pages of the *New York Times*. Not to maximize needless profits, but Confucius, and the world whose profits and gross income are not separate from justice and salvation, a world where nothing is built that need not be built, where philosophy in the realm of economics overthrows Western economic theory; and where we are generous, a rich harvest yields a deeper spiritual life to all, as the morphology of land is by necessity the bone of man and the possibility of man in world: the old alchemical dream, that we be doused in this world and made more perfect by the test before we are removed from it for good.

If we are generous, we offer Seaver, or any successful Western man, that "the elemental spirit . . . . [be] directly built up into the Godhead—the exact goal of its efforts through countless incarnations."

Addison Packing, Southwest Harbor

A sardine pier: the herring are brought by night from Downeast, dumped into a vat of frozen brines, salt and ice and foaming oils out over the top. Life quenched, and the waste of life: the beginning of new life.

They call it pollution, sewage, when it's unmanageable, unconvertible within the economic or other resources of the company, and finally within the economic or other resources of nature. Time runs out, the wharves are covered with oil and black muck, selection flows the other way. The auto graveyard, where cars crash into nature, the very metals die; if only black-eyed susans could eat crushed glass and ferrous wheels. If only the fish could lie in Belfast harbor, outside the poultry plants, sucking up the grease and blood and feathers and ground innards, pure shit, poured out into the sea. If conditions were other the shrimp would not die, the clams would not chew the poisons into their flesh, man would not contaminate. If the conditions were other our totems would not turn into wild horses and streak thru the unknown lands, the women awaken at dawn and brought by bus, the factory set in motion, Mr. Clough and Mr. Wass running the show.

Such is the machinery. That the herring spin in a giant wheel, are fed down a ramp onto a conveyor belt, dense and sliding back over each other, the speed is nonetheless great enough, eventually they climb from the basement to the floor above, past the women on the line who snip their heads and tails. The belt is adjusted to the speed at which they are working, but always moves a little too fast, and the herring that pass thru go back around again, joined by the new fish

on the belt. Such is the full circle, not a car factory in Detroit or Pontiac but American industry, assembly line all
the same.

The herring is turned into a sardine, the heads and tails
coming down a separate ramp into the back of a truck, pri-
vately owned, pays the factory for the right to be there and
gather the refuse, drives around to the lobster wharves
selling it as bait. When the truck is full, the ramp is closed,
and unknown to the women above, another ramp is opened,
and the ends flow down into a truck which takes them to
Rockland as high protein chicken feed. Mr. Clough points to
the watchman, sitting in his loft, sleepily watching the first
truck fill at the switchway of the ramps.

The bodies themselves flow in another direction, limp as
swimming fish, still burning protein suns, are put, some
with mustard, some with tomato sauce, some with soy bean
oil, into the cans of different companies, the cans into the hot
retorts. Such is the crude cycle that flows back into Belfast
harbor and out the bellies and sewers of Detroit. Such is the
wheel of karma that turns round, and these people must
operate within that wheel, forever and ever, until. But it is
also the wheel of American economy, in which matter is
made indistinguishable except as mass, cash per ounce, auto-
mobiles and sardines.

The Master says that "any living being is a storehouse of
energy varying in quantity according to the size and health
of the animal, and in quality according to its mental and
moral character. At the death of the animal this energy is
liberated suddenly. . . . . The animal should therefore be
killed within the Circle, or the Triangle, as the case may be,
so that its energy cannot escape."

And with the lobster the signal is that his dead flesh turns
toxic instantly, losing not only power but edibility. Thus the
living beast is thrown into the boiling water, eaten upon
emergence, perhaps not soon enough, but sooner than most
flows are stoppered. Such is the wealth and magical luxury
of the being, and the task of the lobsterman to bring them
ashore alive. "The whole potential of its original total energy
should not have been diminished in any way."

Here at Addison, as at Pontiac, the strings are lax, the

64

ramp leaks, within a margin of error that profit allows. But what is profit, Confucius asks, if the wealth is not returned to the land? If the exercise is not done within the circle. All thru the factory herring are falling away, squashed beneath boots around the vats as they drop from the ceiling, down thru the floor-boards back into the ocean below.

IX

At Jasper Merchant's (3)

"Magick takes every thought and act for its apparatus; it has the Universe for its Library and its Laboratory; all Nature is its Subject; and its Game, free from closed seasons and protective restrictions, always abounds in infinite variety, being all that exists." in the words of our guest.

The warden is here today, on the spot, busy sorting the lobsters, pushing up the wider wriggling tail of the female to look for eggs. He puts his measure on those close to the limits and finds nothing wrong. "Fine. Fine," he says to Aubrey Fowler, and turns around to wait for the next fisherman, who is Wendell. Clarence Hawkes, Department of Sea and Shore Fisheries, Augusta, a brown suit with an emblem and a police-looking cap, takes it off and brushes his hand along a flat top. "Hello. Hello." he says to Wendell.

"How are you today," Wendell says, and helps him haul the lobsters over to the bin; then popping his big gloves together and holding his ear-muffs down: "Yes it's cold, yes it is. Richard, I'm glad to have my traps spread out. Yessir. There were a lot of places I couldn't haul today, so I went to the ones out around the back of Gotts Island. Glad to have some there."

"The warden comes down every once in a while to help us unload," Jasper tells me. "He works for free." Hawkes smiles, hyperactive, hand to hand, in his job. "You never can tell when the warden's going to pay us a visit. Sometimes he comes two days in a row, sometimes not for a month."

"Oh, I bounce around," Hawkes says.

Now Jasper turns to Wendell. "Wendell, I wanted to thank you so much for the scallop soup I had at your house last night."

Wendell: "I bet the warden would've come if we'd asked him."

Jasper: "Nah, the warden was too busy with his own scallops, and he probably had a little bit of deer-meat on the side." Hawkes laughs, unbroken in his pace, lobster after lobster tossed away. "Come here," Jasper says to me. "I want you to see something." He points to the extra claws lying on the dock from Wendell's catch. "You can learn something about the difference between dealers. The lobsters that belong to those claws will get eaten by the others. Some dealers weigh out the claws at least, and some weigh out the whole lobster. I'm not so picky, and the men appreciate that."

Meanwhile the warden has bounced away, and Ralston Cleaves, waiting a little off the dock, pulls up. Jasper counts the lobsters and gives a nickel less per pound, or so it seems from my own multiplication. I wonder whether or not to say anything. Then I figure that's the game. It's now or never.

Jasper, how come he got a nickel less a pound?

Jasper: "Oh that's a screwy business. You don't want to know about that. It ain't lobstering or anything like it. It's just plain screwy. If you write all this stuff down you're going to get a bad grade on your paper."

But, Jasper, unless I write down the crazy stuff, my paper will sound just like everyone else's.

"Well this whole matter of Cleaveses and boats is just plain screwy. You can't say nothing else about it. Sometimes I think I must be crazy to be doing this. I sure as hell am not making any money." Ralston has walked up behind us. "Why don't you ask him?" he tells me. Then to Ralston: "He's doing a study of the lobsterfishing industry, and he wants to know about our arrangement here."

"I've been sick," Ralston says. "I couldn't keep up my own boat if I wanted, and Jasper gives me the best lay I can get. Now actually I do own a boat, or at least the construction company my son and I have together owns it, but he goes in it. My father Emerick fishes for Jasper, and he has his own boat. Then my son George, he's just back from Vietnam, Jasper's buying his boat for him, and he'll fish for Jasper."

67

"I just want to make sure your boy works for a respectable dealer. He was thinking of going over to a Mr. Sewell Alley, you know." There are a few chuckles. "Now Ralston, don't forget to give your cousin Charlie a call and tell him I've got his rope for him." Ralston gets back in his boat and tries the radio-telephone. Meanwhile Jasper turns to me and says, "Now Charlie did let Sewell Alley buy him a boat, and maybe he's happy with the arrangement over there, but whether he is or isn't he's going to have to live with it. I'll just point out to you that he still buys his marine supplies here, which should say something."

Ralston is calling thru the static, trying to get Charlie, or someone who will pass it along to Charlie further out. Finally he is able to tell Jasper: "He'll be in for his rope tonight."

"That's good. Cause he owes me some money, and maybe we can clear the books."

Named America-World-History. We're in it for keeps. Repeat. *We're in it for keeps.* Sea and Shore Fisheries, Earth. Micro-Cranberries. Perfect construction of a circle which the men, from which we as men, cannot escape.

To what end is the lobsterman a stand-in for man the species, the whole American, the world economy, BLIND? Using Magick to turn boats into lobsters and lobsters into color t.v. sets and electric stoves, the mortgage guarantee-warrantee always projected outward in time, as the female with eggs, the unborn crustaceans, investment in the forge.

Man is the only visible link between these forms of matter, the only one standing up, steering his boat, his will, practicing Magick every moment of every day. The warden may be arbitrary, the dealer may deal his own deck, the sample is arbitrary, as I take it, but this is our blindness, for there is nothing arbitrary about the game we are playing. To make out of wood a barrel is irrevocable as law is; if you don't believe me, watch it, watch them do it, building traps, setting weirs, collecting the heads and tails of herring, and burning fossils in their diesels, utterly bound to the steering wheel. Sea. Which is land. Under ocean. Stake in the ground marked by buoys, color of the present owner, the lobsters passing thru that land claim. This is endless, and inherited, lineal, as the symmetry of the operation is cyclical, the trap/ the lobster's body, the path of either, the map we leave of the conditions which draw their map in our flesh and balls. Ralston fills his pails with newly-salted bait and walks out to the pulley.

My thoughts: Are the lobsters going to hold out forever?

"I don't know. There isn't as much good bottom here as there is in Canada, and this new gear and unlimited traps— I don't think if I was young I'd—ah, I guess if I was young, well I wouldn't know any better either."

How to eat our cake and have it too, how to be independent businessmen and keep our soul, the energy of our proper motions, which wastes away anyway beneath our fingertips, as even the lobsters will dwindle when the basic sustaining energy of the lobster world is gone and the circle broken.

"When man obliterates wilderness, he repudiates the evolutionary force that put him on this planet. In a deeply terrifying sense, (he) is on his own." J. H. Rush.

The world of the spirit has its counterpoint on earth; we have come from the dark of the animal kingdom, our path lit by the fire we have stolen, and the name we have given to sun and moon. We have to live to see the world we make, whatever it is, and here purgatory would be identical to Darwinian consequence: that we suffer to know and suffer to live as the formal result of our actions: Dante as ecologist.

Is it shrimp, or the sun itself they seek as they rig their boats for a new kill? King Crab off Alaska. Salmon stolen by South Korean pirates. Danes draining off the gene pool of seals. Because there's also belief in an unlimited supply and the money's there to make, and if we don't catch them, somebody else will, and if no one catches them, they'll die of overpopulation. *Ming.* The California gold rush. Mariculture. We cannot see the Earth, for we are on it. And our guest concludes, and rightly so:

"At the same time, it is most necessary to study the business, whatever we may be going to do about it; for our ethics themselves will naturally depend on our theory of the universe."

X

The Territory

crabs
redfish
brine
and the hungry lobsters move thru the rocks, establishing
their territories. Every island has its lobster population. Not
on the island. But all around it where the sides drop off into
ocean. Every island, no matter how small or desolate, is
habitable, inhabited, on the lobsterman's map, named.
Trumpet Island
and Goose Cove Rock
Black Island. Duck Island. Heron. and West Sister.
A photograph taken at sea shows only an island in the
background of the ship. We could be coming from any direction. The shape changes. The landing. The same place is
made of many different places. The uninitiate cannot tell
where, whether a Moose or a Porcupine, a Drum or an
Eagle, a Masonic Ledge (or Lodge); that is, he has acquired
no history of the local regions and appearances. The student,
Crowley says, acquires a general intellectual knowledge of
all systems, but this is of no use among planetoids; the Neophyte acquires perfect control of the astral plane, turns
from a greenhorn into a fisherman, identifies the island and
the lobstergrounds, knows the old halibutgrounds that lie
within them, goes back as far as Egypt, or here it would be
Penobscot and the cairns of a lost race of magicians.
The territory underwater is invisible, but there are signs
in the atmosphere, sudden flash of a porpoise a mark, seals,
birds on the point, and the herring suddenly sprung in weir,
locked in the microsphere for greater or lesser powers. The

conjury, the congery has worked.

So in geomancy, mariculture, the names repeat from sphere to sphere, concealing the differences from fools, who do not see that the same angels are different angels, Green Islands everywhere you turn but only one in an invocation, only one in any event, and its living creatures are by name invoked.

A man learns the sphere of the bottom as any ancestral realm, and returns there with his knowledge. He drops his traps into the underwater map, the mythosphere, the unseen but orientating, Opechee.

The bottom is not the Holy Qabbala, but everywhere the magician returns to the sacred land, the source. Black Island.

There is a Black Island by Swans; Fillmore Turner fishes there. And a Black Island in Blue Hill Bay, around Gotts, and Little Black Island; Jasper Rich fishes that one. A Black in Western Bay too, its shoals dragged for scallops.

We have Seal Cove on Mount Desert Island, Seal Cove on Bartletts, and Seal Cove on Swans. They all face the same approximate source of seals in Blue Hill Bay. Yet are three utterly different places, worlds, each in different relation to the inhabitation of the land around it. The seals come in with the dream-quests, bearing names.

America lies microregion by microregion in the occult. As we change maps, so the focus changes, from large islands to ever smaller island systems. Within any one of these the focus may be drawn to tiny rocks, necks, and fragments of buried lands, eddies of an underground disturbance. The world grows smaller and more complete, down to the very lobster shoal, as microcosm takes hold. The names begin over again in each quadrant, like Main Street in any town, or you know there'll be an Elm Street, for one reason or another. Black Island is Main Street. And the multiple names bring out the distinctions between towns at sea, keeping a person in his own mythologic (and economic) region. No town wants two Main Streets as thoroughfare shoals.

The lush planet: is Green Island, or an island owned once by a man named Green.

An island thick with spruce: Black Island, or Mr. Black of forgotten years, or far enough back these are the same

71

name, for the same thing.

The island with spits: Ram Island with its horns.

Trumpet Island.

An island so small it was a folly for the claimants to go to court over it: Folly Island.

A name is simultaneous with a meaning it can never reveal in advance. When the land is named, a world is constructed, true or false, and the treasure map, the lobster and gold map, drawn, genealogy of the Turners, before which: nothing; men can only fish where there is world.

Great Duck and Little Duck, sitting out past Great Cranberry, look like birds nested upon the water when seen from Seawall, sitting ducks. They are also islands inhabited by ducks, gulls, and other birds, and are now formally bird sanctuaries, though fair ground for lobster-hunting. Are they named Ducks because they look like ducks or because they are inhabited by ducks? There are those who will say either, indicating that two deeper structures rise thru syntax to an identical and harmonious designant on the surface. And this is why poetry is history, as who will not agree that a Trumpet: is music. To know America is to know a thousand or million islands and rocks, for only in the microcosm is there a world history to speak of.

So is Bear Island a bear or a home for a bear?, whose ancestors swam there during the Pleistocene, and who awoke from centuries of hibernation to find men, Englishmen at his door, and fled into the woods, or a hibernation of granite, and was never seen again.

And Crow? Is it for Mr. Crow? If so, how was he named?

An island named Locust Reach, no one can remember why, but during the Revolution an American vessel is chased aground there: becomes Ship Island, and the two islands beside it: Eastern and Western Barge. So is the world created from nothing, and the map drawn only by those who have been there, the learned.

And though we are not immortal, our mortality is itself a myth, an immortality in the universe. Whatever home we build, love we make, we are not separate from the universe that made us, sexually also. We are its power to be on Earth, to fish in Earth's seas.

The Earth at large is nowhere, but every place on the Earth is a place in the universe, and history is utter, blind, perfect, and Main Street passes thru the center of it; Green Island is the name for Earth.

XI

The Book Itself Becomes 25

Or is it me?, that the steady wind-blown rain of my birth-day recalls the burning mark of Scorpio, the unfulfilled promise stung beneath the nerves of my backbone. Each second, as I age, aches. Moving irrevocably toward an ending as obscure as the beginning. But not the same.

Because I have been here, born and grown, it will never be the same for me, or for copper or the imp of gold. Even as time passes over me, it is copper and the copper man who must remain here till infinity.

Between these vast obscurities, the rain keeps the men off the seas. A few of them go out and are back by noon, Jasper in his yellow raincoat counting out the diminished early cash.

And Buddy Hooper is a fisherman who seeks no company with the other men; he sells his lobsters in Stonington, an hour and a half run by truck. True he gets up to fifteen cents a pound more, but some say that's not the only reason, that Buddy Hooper has used up his human credit in Bass Harbor and Southwest: the ancient fear of reprisal mixed with the daily onus of pride.

It's Buddy who says come at 3, and then he's not there. I wait, as I did at noon, and noon the day before. He comes at 3:15 in a pick-up truck. I get out of my car and stand in the rain talking up to him in the cab. "What do you want to know?"

"Just about fishing."

"Well, come back at four."

I leave Buddy's place in Duck Cove and go back to Jasper's. It's no sense not working today, even if I do get drenched, because there are some men, like Buddy, who are never around on a half-decent or even half-rotten day. They fish from dawn to dusk, dinner, and bed, and dawn to dusk. But this November 3rd: about the worst day possible, not just rain but thick rain, not just winds but gale winds, and cold, and muddy underfoot. Walking down the wharf my umbrella is blown to the precipice of inside-out, and my feet slide on the crushed fish and sardine bait. This is too dangerous, to be holding up a sail with the sea below, so I return the umbrella to the car, and walk thru the rain.

After a few moments with Fred Beal and Haskell Rich, while they paint buoys and net traps, I go into the office to call Lindy and tell her where I am now. The phone rings ten times. No answer. I dial again. There is no warmth left inside me, even against the day. Seventeen rings. No answer. I am terrified, as if a forgotten curse is and always has been upon me, suddenly revealed that I never even had a chance, and it will all come to an end now, on a day I am told, I am supposed to know I was born.

What is to happen to me? Finally? Irrevocably? What is happening to me? I race down 102 into Indian Point Road, to get home, to find out what has happened to her, if I still have a life—confusion, wife!. The tires slide on the road, and I encounter the inevitable prophecy, that I will die on the day of my birth, thus breaking the cycle of karma and freeing myself from countless transmigrations. Which is giving up, making end and beginning the same, casting myself from the world of events and catastrophes, the alchemical world of deed into the Platonic, as I inscribe a perfect, November 3rd to November 3rd. circle in the heavens. It is not that I don't know what I will find out in the end: that the phone was in the other room, that she had a record on, and the washing machine too, possibly even the dishwasher, and Robin was crying. I know that. But the drama is old, precedes this Island in the Druidic hills, brought to America along with everything else irrevocable, as seed, as clone. And all the rest is a superficial wave of emotion laid upon the archetype, surging to false hopes that are identical to the unbased fears. Beneath there is a rock that can never be broken, whose power is thru and piercing of the emotions as a sine wave, an ocean wave, whose imprint can never change or cease.

The terror becomes one with the car, and where do I go?, will I still be the same person when it happens?, how long can Lindy and I be together anyway, can I hold it, if my powers over my body decrease to the same note?, how long can I hold or be or be loved by anything?, what do I want?, do I even know?

Do I even know that the ultimate magic is any more than invoking and meeting the terrors, passing thru them at the speed of assignation and one? And even if I get free now, it will not end: passing on a curve, November 3rd in its hours, which I am outrunning, what karma am I in, Perdurabo?, what mad world consigned to, cannot free myself from?, what chains of possibility thrown over other chains?, crying like a child, hugging Lindy, choking on my voice, my flesh.

A bowl of soup and I am out again, rushing to make Buddy's at 4. For the ritual is not ended.

Drunk in his lobster shed, first day in off the sea in months, he offers me whiskey, I take a sip, he fills my glass to the top. Here the sun is setting, the sun which we couldn't see all day anyway except now the degrees of total darkness, the great wind and waves crashing into Duck Cove, gaining momentum, icy foam sucking the sands, making old men out of the rocks. I think of previous lives frozen wherever there is ice.

We talk about fishing. Buddy brags about his scallops and how they're the only clean ones on the island, without shit on them, he says. He brags about his enemies, how quickly he makes them, how he can be friends again tomorrow. He talks about what a real nice place he has here, his, Buddy's shed, and how anyone's welcome, as long as they're straight and don't put on, and breaks the wood, tosses it into the stove, dark shadows of fire on the lobster buoys, uncontrolled as flame itself on the walls. "I'm a real rough guy," he says, rubbing his hands. "There aren't many like me left. In the old days a bunch of us would have tied you down and given you a shave and a haircut."

So that's why Buddy wouldn't talk at noon, and wouldn't talk at 3 after he said to come back, and waited till 4 thinking about it. Should he talk to me? And then whatever he decided, we're here now, and there's no choice left, filling the glass because you have to be there and drink with him, and he's cursing every soft-ass fisherman on the island, naming himself among the few good ones, and how many dealers have told Buddy to take his lobsters and shove them up his ass. And Buddy says that's just what he did, except for shoving them. And if they tell him they were just kidding, he says, "Well, I'm not," which is how Buddy Hooper ends up off wharves.

And Buddy says he's not like Wendell, and is proud that the priest thinks they're two different men. Buddy's not precise, he's not conservative; when he goes fishing it's tearing up traps like hell, or setting his traps right between Swans and Frenchboro, leaving a mess of trouble and cut lines behind him, regardless, screaming his bloody head off, singing obscene songs, like the cowboy riding the H-bomb down to the end of *Strangelove*, bareback, waving his hat as she bucks, right down to the end of the world singing "We'll Meet Again." Maybe. Maybe when the world returns.

"Is there any other way?" Buddy says. "I mean do you know another way? It's not that I'm a hog. I give twenty dollars a month thru the Catholic organization to some kid down in Mexico or New Mexico. But you can't save the world goddamnit. You can't save everything till there's nothing left for yourself. And I can't take these pussy-assing fishermen. There just ain't time."

I get sick of drinking, but Buddy keeps filling and one more, one more, and the fire burning, I think it's burning the whiskey, a clean fuel or whatever heat's left in here, and this is hospitality in Buddy Hooper's lobster shack in Duck Cove, is initiation. And Buddy says, "If you want a name for me, you call me a weirman, I'll take that. Because Buddy Hooper's the best damn weirman left." It's Wendell who says that being a weirman today is like being a Model T Ford or a clipper ship pilot. And as Buddy said, Wendell's precise and all, and Buddy's not. And I say that being a weirman's like the first order in a Masonry, without which the rest can't come, is learning the behavior of materials in the astrum, at sea. Though it doesn't amount to much money,

Buddy says that you're not a fisherman if you're not a weirman; you're not a man. So Wendell laughs and says that if Buddy needs being a weirman for his confidence that's all right with him, but he has enough pride without it. I would say to Wendell: don't tell the initiate that there's no pride where there's law, for one man cannot see into another man's magic, and even Buddy Hooper will tell you DO WHAT THOU WILT IS THE WHOLE OF IT.

And what does it matter if they misread Crowley?, or thought only for their lives, their experiences, equals experiments, and not for their souls, or the law? What if they attacked the sacred for their blood: the woman full with child, the girl hot with love?, climbing down the back stairs of apartment buildings for Holy Sacrifice, and Black Power, and Black Magic, and Lobster Power, and unscrupulous muscle on the wharf? Who is to say what is the whole of the law until his power breaks and he is free? And Buddy still works seven days a week for cash.

It gets late and dark and everything begins to change. Until I'm having to talk his language, cursing back, and why do you do whatever you do?, and fuck it, Buddy Hooper, don't you agree that there's just one thing in this world and there's nothing else you can do a thing with or about, and nothing else that counts, and that thing's use. And he says, "Goddamnit, yes! The best makes the top."

Dark moon passes over the fires in his face, not because he doesn't like me, but because he does, and I'm having to stay. It is getting near the time I was born, I think it rained here that day too, and Our Guest reminds me that without the microcosm the macrocosm could not exist. Everything down here is there too, and so the sphere cups its hands around my life, the world, and Duck Cove, Maine, is the whole of the world, Buddy Hooper. And the sphere of the lobsterman, Our Guest reminds me, is filled with lobstermen, even as the sphere of the Qabbala is filled with angels and the sphere of the I Ching with Chinese philosophers, and if we press geomancy, we gain converse with geomantic elves and daemons, and so we come to the sphere of the lobstermen, also for wisdom, for the incredible knowledge which is anywhere, that they both lie and tell the truth, and this is their custom, but is their total ability too. It is me, but it is also fear of death which comes on November 3rd to the sphere of the lobstermen for wisdom; and it isn't the silent majority except as most of America is silent and unknown, and Buddy Hooper is the only god in Duck Cove, and even Perdurabo would warn me about that, and about going there at night without preparation. My preparation is November 3rd, for I have no other.

I am drunk too, and learn my body, an ease with which I see myself sitting here in this halfway house, meeting a man, as I couldn't lying in the easy chair with the book of magic, closing my eyes to rise above my body and see it in space, not caring if it is mere memory or sight from the astral sphere. Now I see that I am sitting here, and the stars pour out into this moment as they do into all others, but this moment I can see.

I struggle against all the dross, the hazy web and armor over my life, whatever has held me down, blindly or consciously or both, to know that nothing matters because nothing can be kept from happening, even by warnings and signs of putrefaction in the sea. This is the sheer light of one light shining in Duck Cove. And when I tell Buddy my wife has cooked dinner and I've got to get home, he pours another drink and says, "You ain't scared of your wife, are you?" It sounds like life again. I am scared of my life because just now I discovered that for all my will I have none, and I won't end it, and still I won't make it perfect. I will go on like this, a neophyte not even, and will not, cannot somehow snap the chains of this creation. I cannot even love her at 3, in broken terror, though now in semi-calm can make a magical link and sit in the kitchen with her ten miles away? What is Magick? What if I am perfect and can't tell?

I don't know what it is or what I am, but in the end it would seem that for one second at least I could be a magician all the time, every second, and there is no escape from initiation, second by second, as it happens.

I stumble out of the lobster shed into a world of utter black, but this is the world when the lights of man are blown out by conditions and at sea. The sound of the sea. The giant furnace of trees. So many things burn I can neither set fire to nor put their fires out. How far we have come from nature now that we are so close we know that everything we do and have done is coming back in the wind. I try to live in the black, stumbling over buoys and traps in the mud. Buddy comes to the door and opens it, looking out after me, who is escaping his realm. He is the only light in the doorway in his Cove, his form there, the whole rectangle raised, it seems, into the sky, a Body of Light. He floats there, total in his covering, light as spinning air, able to levitate at any angle, and laughs and says, "Come back after dinner. Come to the house with your wife and kid. You can't tell what a man is like without his wife." Now he sees that I can't see. "Turn on the headlights there. On the pickup."

And the battery?

"No damn light's gonna burn out the battery on Buddy Hooper's truck."

I pull on them, reaching across the dashboard, and suddenly see the mud pouring down the hill into the cove.

"And even if it does, who says Buddy Hooper can't afford another one!"

Further up the hill, looking in darkness for my car, and he calls out, "You're gonna have to work for what you get out of me."

And so it is, not that it ever begins, but that it never ends. Though finally we get to go home because we have made one. As from the beginning the warmth over the distance between. And driving back in the fog, weaving, I'm not, I know, one ever to be drunk driving, or driving drunk, but the car is irrelevant, I'm still in the sphere of the lobsterman, there's no way out, even on the state highway. I do what I don't do and am what I'm not, and in this exercise I remember that it always was this way, that this way was always possible.

Home is: replenish my previous strength, as a man with Lindy. Then hunger. For water I must have a lot of seawater. I take clams, throw them all in, steam them and gobble them. For earth I roast, I even burn chestnuts, even burn my hand. I eat them burning hot. I eat Maine coastal waters. I eat New York stove-vendors. Lindy frosts the birthday cake, the smell of candles is the smell of the years.

Sure we go back after dinner and his wife gives him hell for his manners and drinking and everytime a four letter word and her hand over his mouth, but he laughs and tackles her and lets her know who's boss, and in any case he has almost forgotten the powers of his sphere, drunk out there in Duck Cove, and the operation is over. We are drinking black coffee and Robin is playing on the floor. But he knows and I know and we all know that even with the bluff there's no way out, like when the bottom falls out of the market. Perhaps that's when the lobsterman in his sphere returns to the fisherman = the first degree, the weirman. Lindy says, "I would just walk away," but you can't and never could, and that's my birthday present, coming back around again thru all the shit of a year, to be born again here on this Island. Such is the nature of birthdays from 25 on.

XII

61

Day after day the storm continues. The weather is blown across the island, thru the trees, matter passing between matter, rain, wind, and there is no way off the island, the Earth, no way out of the loose Earth economy of parts, however many parts separate, that many, they always come back again.

Wendell brings his boat in early, 61 pounds, having fished his furthest traps out by the Duck Islands. Jasper watches the ocean around him fill with dark fresh water, poison to his crop, undoing of the salty effluvium in which the condition of their life is born.

"Damnit," he says. "Fresh water isn't even good for the lobster bait."

This is the sea, and its beings are sodium, chlorides, iodines, manganese, and a Liberian freighter off Nantucket is split in two, and 61 men lost, the number repeats. And the pleasure yacht Whisper is lost between New England and Bermuda. No one would set out willingly into such a storm, the newscaster says, but nature accepts no excuses, not even the best, and this is her nature, her karma, why Proserpine is not released even though it was *only three* seeds she tasted; a mistake is a mistake, a poison a poison, and certain mistakes are fatal, though how is a man to know this, the lethal choice, as he blunders among unconscious obsessive possibilities, none of them important, and makes the wrong decision, thinking it to be trivial whether he goes for a swim or not? In the end this is the most consequential part of psyche, what a man doesn't see, either for lack of knowledge, the proper synapses, from sheer bull-headedness, or in the difficulties of his personality; he can scream bloody murder, but the sea drags him down still. Even as we try to remain conscious, to choose our fate, the unconscious, the unchosen moves in, and numerology is at once the most conscious form of perception, seeing the planet from end to end, and all the cards, the six-and-one-are-seven's it draws, and the most mindless form of idiotic rhyme. And we never know why or when, but even the consequences of consequences have consequences. Even the lobsters can expect no better, and if there is no other, this is the root of 61.

XIII

Around the Leg

The fog grips the island as it has the ocean before as it will the ocean after. The boats stay in, and one side of the harbor cannot see the other side. As the houses melt into, soft as the drizzle, melting more of the paint off *St. Andrews by the Sea*. In Seal Cove the children play in the marsh grass; Andy Butler walks to a friend's house. A couple on horseback. A deer hung on the front door.

Out by Swan's Island the buoy clanks out the three different notes. Frightening how this one possibility of sound endures, and endures, as the ferry passes, three metal arms striking into the circle, like one tiny Telstar among islands. Here in the Atlantic, the Gulf of Maine, as in the asteroid belt, the forces of nature, volcanic and glacial, have splintered a possible planet into thousands of little ones, islands, the outer ones calming the waters inward in the intricate crosscutting leas. Isle Au Haut. Burnt Island, where Fred Beal's grandfather was born. Marshall's Island, where his father was born. And Fred was born on Swan's. Vinalhaven and Hurricane, sheer granite masses: though they have trees and churches, mined for their stone which is returned to the continental Earth. The shatter zone of Deer Isle and Stonington, a web of hundreds of tiny islands, dense lobster territory filled with as many traps.

The fog darkens Bass Harbor, at low tide Sawyer's Island melting almost to Anns Point, boats pulled up in the mud. In Bernard, Jasper's place is closed; the ramp creaks, and the gulls sit on the roof. In McKinley, Levesque's is closed, but young Torrey stands on the edge of the wharf, just looking out. Dead fish everywhere, cleaned out of traps, the wharf slippery with their skin. Lee Tracy roasts a pail of crabs and carries them back to his place of business. I have never spoken to the man who buys crabs and scallops and shrimp, so I stand in his office and ask him about his business. "There's no business today, no fish, no shrimp, no scallops." And how does he know what to pay the men? "This isn't my own outfit. Hook makes all the decisions. He sets the prices. I merely work for him." Hook of Boston, the man behind the scenes behind the prices for the coast of Maine, a shadow on the waters. What's he like?

"I don't know. I've seen the man twenty minutes in three years."

And what did you do before you bought for him at this wharf?

"I worked for Stanley Fish in Manset cutting 'fillettes.' Yes, I know Enoch. He's one of the great old boys."

The mailboat slips off Clark Point into the soft warm rain, carrying Carl Mellon back to Great Cranberry. I stand on the wharf, having missed him, having spent part of the day looking for him, first at his house in Seal Cove, then at Bartlett's Island Landing, five years too late or fifty years too late, and then five minutes.

Fred Beal talks about the old days, how a man'd work the high seas dragging out of Portland in the worst weather and make not a cent. Haskell Rich shakes his head and smiles. "Foolishness. It was damn sheer foolishness, and in those days a fellow took it out of his hide for nothing."

They sit in the warm shed painting buoys, all the old Ronald Gott's calendars on the wall with middle-age porn-queens, one Playboy calendar, the youngest girl in the room. In the bar in Southwest Harbor the hunters are singing and waving their red caps, checking each other for blood. We sit there waiting for our pizza to come.

And it turns night. The back of the power lines broken by a falling tree. A meteor burns from left to right; then clouds cover even the starlight, closing the island to the sound of the trees blown in the forests. Somes Pond is dark, the ducks asleep under a bush. A car screeches out of Hoyt Richard's down the road. Saturday night, the cars lined up at the Somesville Social.

A deer leaps out of darkness into darkness.
Across the road.

We Come to Stonington

having driven along the coast, thru small towns, Blue Hill, and back out to sea across bridges joining one island to the next, Stonington on the point, facing the ocean across which Swans Island. Or as at Swans Island when I asked if they ever had trouble with traps from another area, they pointed to the Northwest and said, "Some of the boys from Stonington and Deer Isle come up here because it's awfully crowded there, but we cut them off." I look out across the same ocean, here as there, realizing that there is always land to the West, or South.

In Stonington the houses are densely clustered, reminiscent of an older day of South American and Transatlantic voyages, a small Boston, up on rocky hills, roads winding right down to the shore itself, the backyard as ocean, even for shops. The character for Stonington is a mass of Granite (the Stone) sloping down into the body of a lobster, its feelers upon the sea.

We come here on the advice of Buddy Hooper. "Stonington, now that's a real fishing town," his words. And I know already that Stonington has a consistently higher lobster price than Mount Desert: the sociological question is Why?, and here like Sherlock Holmes to find out. Buddy is here today too, by phone, auctioning off his lobsters to the highest bidder after fourteen days of storm and rain, choppy seas and no lobsters brought in. Where to begin? Stonington doesn't ask the question; it simply sits there, Stonetown, an utterly different landscape than Mount Desert, but the higher lobster price, this is simply part of the commerce that flows thru its streets as individual fishermen, women to the shops; it holds the town together, even like the old Near Eastern City, the price of bronze, the temple surpluses, sheep or granite farming at the base, the fishermen of Boston and Ur. The price is invisible: stare into the face of the gods; their masks lie opposite fish in the dynasty. Stonington has its gods, from the days of cod and mackerel and granite, to the marketplace for lobsters, hidden under the tablecloth, while money changes hands.

In Stonington, we learn, the older fishermen have lots of traps, setting more than they can possibly fish in a day: 800, 900, 1000 or more. The younger fishermen are way behind, and it's too late to reverse the trend. Reduce the number of traps, and it will open the grounds to newcomers, as at Mount Desert where a man with 50 traps has a start. Here he has nothing.

At Frank Townsend's lobster place Vance Sawyer says: "I'll talk to you cause I'm young. I'll tell you I've got 300 traps, but if I had any more I'd tell you less, and maybe I do. Anyway, I'm building more. I'm building up slowly. But I'm not in debt. I'm not sold to anyone. Those guys with more than a thousand traps know us younger ones are coming along. We're not going to starve. And then when they get old and can't fish that many, that's their problem. They're the ones who started it. The old ones. They always do."

Joe Turner sits by the stove, toothless, gentle rough soma of the old sea, Bear Island body but unable to fish in these water since he came here, all his traps cut, slowly bled, a cold stony silence on the shore, whose only testimony is territory, to a carnivore.

Vance: "No. I don't think they let anyone starve here. I think some drink. Then they ain't got nothing."

I ask Vance whether he's going shrimping during the winter.

"No, two or three from here are, but I'm going scalloping with my brother; he's got the boat rigged up and I think we'll do pretty good."

Is scalloping enough money to keep you thru the winter?

"Yes, I think it is. I hope so. I think I make pretty good at it. Shrimping: now you can't go around here anyway; you can't live in this town and go out of this town shrimping, no location, no nothing, you can't sell your shrimp. About the only thing left is scalloping. There ain't no money in lobstering in the wintertime."

Don't some people get four or five hundred pounds a day fishing traps way out?

"No. Not a day. Because they ain't been out for a week that I know of."

Okay. Not a day. But when they do go out.

"Yeah. But that don't make no big money."

Do they buy scallops here?

"The lobster dealers'll buy scallops. There's a good market for them. They buy all you possibly could get."

Are there better places for scallops?

"There's scallop-bottom. In places where it's muddy and all there ain't so many scallops."

Who gets to fish the good bottom?

"Whoever gets there first and gets the best of it, that's all there is to it, see."

If someone's dragging in an area, then you don't go there?

"Yes. I go there just the same. They go there. But, see, it isn't a little area. You don't get in anybody's way cause you can steer clear of them. They drag all winter at one place and they don't get 'em all. You can't catch 'em all. There must be a lot of scallops on the bottom."

Do you get in trouble scalloping around Swans Island?

"Yeah. We go scalloping Swans Island. They don't bother us too much. It ain't no big thing. It don't last too long. We go North Haven, Swans Island, they come here. It's really lobstering people are interested in."

Do you have any trouble with lobsterfishing territory?

"You mean fishing together? No. I don't have no trouble. Cause I don't fish around people. I don't go that close to them."

What is your general territory?

"From these islands right up to Stonington, right down to Spoon Island they call it and Isle Au Haut shore, right down thru there."

How about within that?

"My license says I can fish anywhere in the State of Maine."

Do you ever get cut?

"No. Cause I don't mix with Swans Island. In the area I fish the fellers from this town are the only ones I fish with. I know every one of them."

Why do you think the lobster price is higher here?

"The price went up when Dureeay came. He's a really big dealer who buys all the way to Nova Scotia and sells in New York and Long Island. He wanted men, and he had to lure them away from other dealers. He did it with an extra nickel a pound. Now all the dealers give that, and they call it a bonus."

Another fisherman claims it's the Lobsterman's Cooperative that's forced all the prices up, but Colby Pratt, ex-graniteman, manager of the Cooperative says: "We have nothing to do with the price. We just split up the profits at the end of the year. We get a higher price because we catch better lobsters. That's all there is to it."

I repeated this at Jasper's and it brought a great uproar of protest from the fishermen. "You tell me how they manage to catch a better lobster," Wendell said.

Jasper added: "The only reason they're getting a nickel more is that they're a bunch of damn fools down there, and the lobstermen have them over the barrel, and they don't know how to get out of it. Dureeay's selling his lobsters in New York, and you know how much your Manhattan lobster dinner costs. Here everything's above board; I pay one man ninety cents, then I pay every man ninety cents that day. There they've got a different price for everyone, depending on where he's from, what time it is, and how many lobsters he's got."

But George Spurling on Little Cranberry counters: "The only reason that the fishermen don't get a fair price in Bass Harbor and Southwest is that all the dealers are related to one another and they keep each other down."

Finally I advanced the problem to an arbitrary judge, Merton Hinckley, a lobster-buyer who trucks from both places to Boston. "Pratt is telling you the truth. I'll pay more for Stonington lobsters myself because they have more selects. I can mix them in with my others and get a better shipment.

I don't know why a pound and a half is better, but that's what everyone seems to want in a restaurant."

Back to Vance. "The lobster dealers are even worse liars than fishermen. And that's pretty bad. Now you just listen to Frank. He's not here now, but when he shows up, oh, will he complain; you'd think he was hurting or something. He'll cry so much you want to go over and loan his your last dollar, but each year he's got a new pick-up or a Catalack. So I figure Frank's not hurting too much. He's a shrewd one. No one's going to get an extra nickel out of Frank."

Do you sell to him?

"Very little. I sold over to Graves' mainly. He uses me well, has stuff when I need it so that you don't have to wait half the winter, and he'll give credit so you have something for your lobsters. He doesn't own me though. You come in to a guy twice, three times in a row, he gets it into his head you owe it to him; the next thing you know he's expecting you, and then before you know it he's bought you. I don't want to belong to nobody. I'm just a young guy starting out, married. It's hard. But I make a living. Not a hell of a lot more. Now I'll tell you: I may be coming in one day to Graves' and the wind may be blowing the wrong way, or I may just get it into my head as I'm steering in to steer my boat around and go somewhere else, like Frank here, no reason, just cause I felt like it."

Now Frank comes in, complaining that he's going to go broke if no one goes lobstering soon. Vance chuckles. "I'm clear out of lobsters," he complains, whiskers twinkling, like a little English Santa, goes and sits down behind the books and is instantly involved.

"You don't want my lobsters anyway, do you Frank?" Vance teases after a bit.

Frank looks up hurt, mumbling. "That's what I'm here for. To buy lobsters. What else. What else. Course I want them. You got lobsters I want them. I want anybody's lobsters. That's my business." Everyone in the shed laughs.

And the men, across their territories, emerge, each of them made of the ground, the visible genetic ground of these islands, that keeps them here, so they'd think of putting out more traps before leaving, Sawyers and Seaveys, Stanleys

91

and Spurlings. islands that move with the speed of stone. As Spider Fernald leaning against the counter of his place on Little Cranberry, puffing on a cigar: "Our fishermen try not to mingle with the boys from Southwest Harbor." I find myself looking out to sea into a mirror, myself at other wharves, on other islands, as in 19th Century poetry about the soldier who sees that the enemy is himself. But here in American commerce it is all the same, the reflection, and though they cut traps, hopefully, in the end, there is enough to go around.

Fishermen don't mix, and yet I cross from territory to territory, making friends of each other's enemies, who have slashed each other's traps in the invisible biological war. It would seem almost cavalier, unfair, and at base a more difficult question than lobster price, which is academic, after the fact. It's not that I'm above it all. Literally speaking it's because this isn't where I have my traps down, at sea. I stand on language, and if it is cut, I will go with the wind, seeking new forms, as when Brakhage once told me I'd be a fool to keep writing novels, back then six years ago, and here I am.

Or seen another way, as poets and anthropologists wage war: I'm ready to cut if anyone plays around with my lobsters. So Vas Dias better watch it. I don't want to get used without being used. Not even scalloping. If a man is too soggy a thinker, knows the territory that poorly, and has to come in hauling from my traps, he's going to get cut off, the knife as sharp as, made of the same thing we are always doing, right here.

When a territory gets too crowded, those that know the bottom win out. It's summer people, like Lowell and Madame Y who try to buy islands, then hire lobstermen to take them out and show them what they've bought. It's men like MacLeish and Donald Hall, without a real knowledge of territory, who put out too many traps and snarl lines. A good fisherman, like Duncan, knows the land marks. A Seavey. But a bad one, like James Dickey, claims, in his enthusiasm, the Moon, where he has never been, just because the astronauts were.

"There ain't no rich fishermen," Vance sums it up. "But we get by."

XV

Integers

The Museum at Islesford is filled with these, fragments of
events, preserved not in consciousness, but the conscious
mind recognizes them and returns to blood:
the account book of the old general store at Cranberry
a train schedule from the Bangor Railroad, now defunct
a postcard of the inn at Cranberry
archaeology showing that Baker was the first of the Cranberries settled
old farm tools and ice-cutters
paintings of the ships which sailed from Cranberry Harbor
and records of their voyages, their cargo, owners, shares
And today we cross a choppy sea to come to Islesford, the
boat radio blasting with prelaunch newscasting while we
rock heavily in Earth's ocean, utterly subject to the moon
and sunspots, instantly out to sea the radio switches to a
local channel, the most local, a conversation about ribbons
and the price of linen in the harbor itself, then two fisherman back and forth about the weather as it comes from the
East, not just integers—but   JUNCTURES,
                                        as the astro-
nauts, neither East nor West of us, are struck by lightning
a wave takes us up top and drops us into a hole; sea foam
runs across the window blurring a vision of Sutton Island,
the trees running into the water that there is even land, that
there is even   ISLAND
Today is different from all other days, juncture with this
storm, the twenty-first day of rain in a row, someone's windows for Big Cranberry tied down to the mailboat, the wind

rips at them, they rattle, and Wilifred Bunker says he won't be responsible if they break. They are unloaded by men, faces in the rain, walking down the wharf at Cranberry Isles, walking away, with the mail sacks too, and several cartons of food.

some meteorites that fell on the Cranberry Island during English settlement

Abnaki remains

a bone from a skeleton washed ashore

the genealogy of all her kin in a child's schoolbook

credit issued to fishermen on the Banks

Today that in 1750 settlers on Bakers Island, in 1754 Abraham Somes, repeated in the Museum, that the Gilleys married into the Hadlocks, Samuel Gilley left Bakers Island, Sawtelle pasting the families into his book.

"We're all twisted around like checkers in these islands," says Spider Fernald's sister. "The Cranberries are all one family."

Today Gordon Spurling, Jr., brother-in-law and partner to Spider Fernald, shoots a gull out of the sky, picks it off the wharf and tosses it dead into the corner. George Spurling comes in cursing the weather, and says, "Those astronauts were smart, they got off the whole damn Earth."

juncture

Merton Hinckley arrives at Spider Fernald's wharf to take the lobsters in. His own boat burnt out, Spider Fernald lends him one, and a man to take it in, from Little Cranberry to Mount Desert, and back. 3400 pounds Hinckley collects, two days of lobsters caught in the Cranberry shoals, and the boat, loaded down with crates, disappears into the drizzle.

juncture

We switch from the general to the local, from the atmosphere of the Earth to the single migration, the ship entering Baker waters, the visible gulls. The astronauts lie in a darkness or desert beyond ocean, the checkers scattered like the dead stone of space. They seek commerce with the living bions, the angels, to steer them home, as they approach the maximum, the moon. And in Sawtelle's Museum, where the Cranberries are hottest, and flash with their known body, the sky visible of its meteors, we pull of necessity from these

94

ledgers, consciously, the very integers of the historic present, sustaining the windy whitecaps come upon this, Hadlock Cove, Gilley Beach. . . . .

XVI

Man was made to subdue nature, Wendell says, and I think you'd have to consider lobsters nature, just like copper or nickel alloy.

In Stonington the men are angry because the Park Service, which owns inland Isle Au Haut, won't let them shoot off the deer. Those lobstering around the Isle see the deer on the shore, driven from the interior by hunger, eating the seaweed during low tide, and the rest carcases. Vance Sawyer says: Why don't they let us shoot them, at least for an orphanage. It's painful to see.

Let man in. Let man subdue. The warden says that man is just the issue, whether we can have any places left where animals live and die in their natural cycle. "It's according to whether these men want to let a deer die a deer's death. Or whether man has to deal out its fate."

It's a question of man. And it's a question of what kind of consciousness is going to run this planet. Finally. A sign on the back of a car: "Czechoslovakia Has A Good Gun Control Law." Hanging in every house like pool cues, protectors of the republic.

We're okay, they say. We don't kill gulls.

But that's only because gulls clean the ocean.

We wouldn't think of hauling a female lobster bearing eggs.

But that's to plant next year's crop.

There's a quota on the amount of deer one man, or one town, can shoot. But that's to enable man to balance the deer population.

Conservation is a funny word; it means conservation of metal, not of souls.

Remember Ivaluardjuk's words: I have spoken of them

before. It's because the beings we kill have souls, souls that seek revenge, that we lie in this greatest of dangers. A danger we cannot see but which the Master Therion will guide us to: yes, a man's ethics *are* determined by his view of the universe, and that's just where we need the most help from every creature, the lobster crawling along the wharf, escaped for an instant, its eyes turning in beady propelled sockets, its legs moving, its feelers in sensation, measuring the distance among created worlds, as doubtless we shall have to do before it is over. So if you're going to live like this, you damn well better know what you're doing. Which is the difference between Aleister Crowley's magick and Norman Vincent Peale's power of positive thinking, or Dale Carnegie's how to win friends, or Eric Hoffer's self-confidence on the wharf. Norman Vincent Peale will catch you a lot of lobsters. And a crew of Eric Hoffers'll transform a countryside. But what do you have, in what zoa, zone are you, with whom have you made contact, with whom will you have to live an eternity of Mother Must I Be Born Agains?

Why the lobster must die and the men dressed in orange caps go with their guns after the deer. Why the Hopi kill the hawk and within the circle spill his blood for crops. What of a man who would spare the whole Earth suddenly, if he could. Such a God. War cleans the bones they say. War frees where the grass clots the surface where the pond can't breathe, blows up blood, because the stars blow their horns and must have their say. And whole galaxies collide. And lobsters wander among the campfires of stinking wrecks, thru the bright cities of decomposed food, so dazzled by the light that they eat even their kind.

Why should Ted Williams with his great batting eye, the last of the .400 hitters, go out and shoot the last of the zebras. Williams looks up in amazement at the sportswriter who asks that:

"You love the lamb but I love the ceremony." (Confucius).

Which is the only answer the ritual murderers could give her when she asked to be allowed to live and see her baby born.

Eskimos and lobstermen alike in a cosmic bind. There is no way for the mock turtle not to stew in his own juices. So he may as well sing the song of himself.

And there is nothing gratuitous about ethics, that is, about one's view of the universe. It's how to live with the unending consequences, how to receive in the fullest, as "Gordon Gray, from Tolland, Conn., proudly displays the nine point albino buck he downed last week while hunting on Long Island. The buck has eluded hunters for years—or, superstitious hunters have eluded the buck, depending on who you talk with. Gray was hunting with Arnold Allen, Mount Desert." *Bar Harbor Times,* Deer Season Issue.

Kelly asks:

When we take life—what do we give?

What about the men who went crazy when they saw a woodcock in front of our house, couldn't look at it, or where it was, but jumped out of their car, the two of them, to discharge a round of pellets in worship, just missing our cat, and the bird, while Lindy cried, and they left apologizing: Gee lady, we didn't mean any harm. It's just that—well, that *was a woodcock.*

How do you get out of such a temple: to the honking manteia of the geese south?

Or into the body of a fish, as Merlin placed the child king?

Or into an owl hooting in the darkness of this forest of stars?

How to get out of ourselves?, back into, where it all comes from: the animals living currents of, willing to speak to us, if only we will reopen channels, they will give themselves to us, as well as their words, in our time of needs, we may eat our gods, our friends, even ourselves, as consciousness anyway chews on and wears the body of armor into which it is born.

Is our use imperfect? the gull shot anyway and put on display atop a boat in Islesford, to scare the rest of the species from the bait-bucket,

and ducks bred simply for shooting gallery, senseless of, our imperfect use.

(for a closer look at lobsters yet

CHAPTER 3

STONEHENGE

(the Master Therion remains, though his attention is elsewhere absorbed; he is replaced in the main body by the Irish,
and by the Greek masters of the star-temple, those first sailors, fathers to our Cranberry Isles

Wendell Seavey: LAND MARKS

(Western Shoal)   Little Duck just starting out by Long Island and Black Ledge on end of Marshall Island.

(Pencil Shoal)   Schooner Head hid behind Richard Head and Western Sister 1/2 + 2/3 out by SW Point.

(Meeting House Ground)   About 5 or 6 feet of Long Island out by NE end of Big Duck and Baker's Island on Schooner Head.

(Lad's Shoal)   Baker's Island lighthouse on Western crotch of Western Mountain and high part of Long Island by Mer Point. To set down, hold the mountain mark still over the stern.

(The Middle Ground)   Schoodic Mountain out by Little Duck Island and Gooseberry Island on Placentia Head.

(The Reefs)   The two Duck Islands together and Gooseberry Island on Placentia Head.   [hard bottom].

(The Cottle)   Blue Hill Mountain over Placentia Head and Mer Point on the mountain just to the westward of Cadillac Mountain.   [hard bottom].

(Gorge Hen's Reef)   Baker's Island light on middle of Pemetic Mountain and so you can see water between Mer Point and Long Island.

(Bull Ground)   Have the house on Gott's Island head out by the little Island and Green Island so you can see it on the NE part of Big Duck.

(Aberner Ground)   Placentia Head on big Green Island and the beach on the little island out by Mer Point. [hard bottom].

(Shell Ground)   Big Camden Mountain on Southern Cove and Mer Point light is on the mountain just to the East of the Bubbles. It is about SSW two tubs of trawls [6 or 7 minutes running time] from the Aberner Ground.   [There is not much bottom].

(Robinson)   Blue Hill Mountain on Placentia Head and Mer Point Light is on the flat place on Schooner Head Mountain.

(Bank's Ground)   Baker's Island light is on the western part of Schooner Head Mountain and the Quarry at Black Island is on Mer Point.

(Clousen)   Blue Hill Mountain Head and Baker's Island light out by Mer Point.

(Handline Place)   Baker's Island light on the mountain west of Green Mountain and Black Island just coming out by Mer Point.

(Eastern Muddy Ridge)   Baker's Island light on the middle Dog Mountain and so you can see water between Long Island and Isle Au Haut.

(13)   Have Baker's Island light on the Bubby Mountain and Mer Point light on the Quarry of Black Island. You can run in 5 minutes for the Bubby, then set off tubs and bring Baker's Island light onto Green Mountain.

(Tucker's Rock)   Baker's Island light on Eastern crotch of Western Mountain and the high part of Long Island on Boat House Cove.

(Picked Hummok)   Trask Point out by Long Island and Baker's Island starting out by Mer Point.

(Gilbert Hummok)   Sargent Mountain in the V on back of Long Island and Johns Island run down with Swans Island.

(Marks for the Outer Peak)   A. Ock Hill over Mer Point, and one leg of the bell-tower hid behind the light.
B. On an ebb tide set, set for the light. Good for two or three tubs.
C. The Inner Peak is about a mile or more inside.

(Marks for the Outer Pratt)   A. Blue Hill Mountain over Mer Point, and Baker's Island light in the middle of Green Mountain.
B. The Inner Pratt is the same except Baker's Island light is in the sag of Green Mountain.
C. For a flood tide set, set in for Green Mountain.

(Marks for the Western Muddy Ridge)
A. Have the point of Black Island down by the quarry just out by Mer point, and Baker's Island light almost on top of Pemetic, the third mountain from the eastward, but just so it is a little to the eastward of the top of the mountain.
B. Ebb tide set, set just westward of the Rock.

(Spurling Shoal)   Green Island out by NE point of Big Duck and Blue Hill Mountain on western end of Little Duck

(Wall Shoal)   Just so you can see water between Little Duck and XXXXX

(Grumpy)   Camden Mountain in Western crotch of Isle Au Haut and Carver's Harbor out by Western Ear. [Good bottom with Blue Hill out by western end of Long Island and Burnt and Spoon Island run on].

(Good Places for Halibut)

A. Just south of the Rock with the three chimneys lined up. Set one tub of fine gear.

B. Go SSE of the Rock for about 7 minutes. When you're in about 45 fathoms of water, set up towards the Lodge. Good for two tubs of halibut gear.

C. (The Millician)   Green Island out by Rich's Head, and with Schoodic Point just starting to come out by Little Duck Island. Eastern end with Gott's Island Head on the eastern end of the fourth mountain.

D. Have Schoodic between the Little and Big Duck Islands and Green in the notch of Black Island and Placentia Western end. Eastern end, the lone tree on Long Island so you can see it.

E. Eastern end, have Bass Harbor Head onto the sandy beach on Placentia Island and Mer Point light out by Green Island set for Long Island harbor.

F. With Johns Island touching on Crow Island and the field out by Green Island, the South end.   [two tubs].

II

Bartlett and Black from Green

"Every historical event must happen, not anywhere, but in some particular place, at some point in space, in some locality or minimal unit of space in which its unique causal factors operate." Malin via Irby.

The machinery at each place would seem to arise separate of an unknown world. A bridge, an airport, a road, even a village, has location in the real world as well as the geographical subset of it. Central place theory is the beginning of an acknowledgement of what ethnogeography and migrating people have always known, that when you get there something is there, even in a myth. The conditions may be multivariate, but we can sense the oscillation of factors choosing a place, seeing that as the river narrows, we approach the bridge. A Penobscot village lays the ground for an American settlement; one system of commerce is generated by another, always leading back to the pregenerated conditions of the land, the genes, attendant species, access, freight, marriage possibilities. We can come to the exact place and find it there.

Swamp. River. Lookout. Nuts. Berries. Maple Sugar. Lee of hill. Furs. Tillable Soil.

The village grows to include harbor and tidal mill. The navigable river. The settlements in the country. The hexagon of human existence replaces any prior geometry. But as Plato taught us, maybe it was there all the time.

Somesville is properly specific, function of prevailing winds and currents, arable land, grazing, protection. Betwixt the Hills was waiting there to become Somesville.

And Stonehenge, whose sheer purpose is to impose a right

angle, a geometry on the motions of sun and moon, is built on Salisbury Plain where, alone, that purpose is served. The giant stones carried across water and sledding along ice to a spot within a few miles of the one latitude, $57^0.17$, where the azimuths of sun and moon at extreme declinations are separated by 90^0. This is the Stonehenge that preceded Stonehenge; a bit further to the north or south and the rectangle becomes a parallelogram, the planets cannot enter the temple. The rugged geography, that issues from a Platonic condition, never loses its perfect origin, which is revealed in the works of man. The visible rises from the visible, the solved and the being solved are one. And we would seem once again to be in the world of the known.

The conditions of Green Island are not perfect, not geometric. It sits in the bay out beyond Green Island landing, at the cable crossing, its shore clearly visible, as if one giant step should place us on its world. To our left, in the passage between the beach and Green Island shore, which becomes Bartlett Narrows, we can see the hazy edge of Bartlett, as in history, blurred into its superposition upon Mount Desert.

It is not so easy, as Clayton and I found, rowing in a small plastic boat, while the tide grew high and the waters full; we seemed to be getting precisely nowhere, as hard as we pulled on the oars. We hung there between the equally visible, the trees of Green becoming more and more our immediate environment, the gigantic size of Mount Desert and the great creeping edge of its forests becoming a distance, as a vision from airplane. We had been fooled by the nature of the space between.

Taking the oars from the oarlocks, we stroked on either side, jerking the boat there like a canoe, receiving the ground as Matthew ran ashore up the rocks, as a place to stand on, as the next place we will stand on even before we are there. The names change with the optical field. Green becomes the shore, the mainland, and we look out at sea to Mount Desert. Carrying this condition to its extreme we realize that every piece of land is an island of some sort or size, but the name itself, *igland* in Anglo-Saxon, the Latin *insula,* is given without awareness of this fact to the inward: is a word to the outward, proven only by sailing completely around. But the original Teutonic phenomenological was simply a space belonging to water, *ahwa*, or aqualand, a meadow by a stream.

We walk up a hill thru trees, away from the water, past the giant house, and continue into the forest of the other side. What we know from the map is that Green Island is shaped like a molar, one crown point missing and the other two elongated toward Bartlett Narrows. In between them a quiet stream of green water, rich with ebb tide grasses, comes at high tide, leaves a damp meadow at low tide, a bathing spot for seals, and Pearces, who now own the island.

We walk out on one of the molar crowns and find ourselves in a new vista of the immediate lands. No longer is any edge blurred or superimposed. Outward we face straight on the blunt edge of Black, rounded, bright and visible stand of conifers, no houses, no sign of anything but depth, climax. Beyond and below Black, hazier but larger, the edge of a giant landfall, Christopher Bartlett's Island. Here the remembered darkness, the foreclosure is total. We have been thinking of islands we can hold in our heads, the shape of, land in, history thru. Bartlett is a Jupiter if Green Island is Earth. Called Hog Island once, it was settled by Christopher Bartlett in 1762; the homesteaders live there, fishing, farming, with their cattle, self-sufficient, yet part of the legal town of Mount Desert, and the larger fishing nation, an outer parish abandoned during the depression, now littered with bones and tombstones and the foundations of houses. In the distance I feel the pull toward the larger hidden, the previous world, distance at sea, distance of my memory, where all the islands no longer inhabited consciously are recalled in their ancient names. As the key drops, the music falls off to sea, and we come to eternal Atlantis, buried on Bartletts beneath the cattlebones of the depression and Abnaki arrowheads, or Bartlett is one province of the old Atlantic kingdom, is Jovian, abandoned for all its miles by those who have fled to the backside, the harbor behind the sun, flow of light thru Mount Desert, where civilization is as small and local as the Jovian moons. Bartlett was a kingdom, has grown old and into ciphers, while Green is subclimax, forest flowers, without the dark forest and the ghost town. Here on Green there is an alchemical text, green, young, and the house is filled with butterflies and herbals. I feel the cold saltwater with my hand, straining out the rich strands of seaweed, original food which I eat when I eat anything, which I remember even from the vendors of it in Central Park, as orange soda, as chestnuts, now the climax forest in the youth of the sun.

It is not geographical determinism, but each of these three islands fulfills an absolute condition. Its place, which does not determine anything, is nonetheless irretrievable. Bartlett is a colony; Black a hermit; Green is a family. Mr. Ellis, the original owner, had a stable built by the landing, and a bell which rang across the water for the servants to come by boat and get the guests. The island itself is a map for children, a giant gameboard, its orchid bog and hawthorn trees, a cut thru the forest to make Blue Mountain visible from the verandah, the rabbits and deer who cross on the winter ice floes, the baby otters sunning white on the rocks, the ducks, the gulls on that neck of land, collarbone broken off the island, a thin line of rocks, itself with a few trees and moss, a place for Webster Peace to swim to and sulk, sitting on the long bony mantle of the earth, an island imago, mansion from which for Mrs. Pearce, matriarch of the family, there is no escape.

The house itself has been changed by the Pearce children, the lower floors filled with games, the upper floor with so many rooms no one knows what to do with them, and one whole room a child painted the Black Hole of Calcutta Black to hide in, one room with its head in the trees, a giant vegetable in the stratosphere on an island in which sunlight crackles, and an old wooden bed to dream in, the vision itself surrounded by water as the leafy perception with blood.

This is to own an island, to buy the Map itself; the kingdom is Ellis' handiwork, changed by the Pearces with their money paying the freight charge, for washer and dryer, and thick rubber hose underwater carrying phone and power, tiny joint of the transatlantic cable, exposed in the scallop beds at ebb.

Green Island is Green Land, Earth. Its mansion is owned, its guesthouse in the ecosphere. Its shape is a swimming pool; its seals are pets; and the animals and seeds that cross ocean to get here find themselves in a garden or a preserve, as long as this decade lasts.

Houses cost more money than islands, and Black Island has no mansion, no pool of water. More than twice the distance from the shore, its gold is other. There are Black islands all along the Maine Coast, but here we have a man named Black, not a dense growth of spruce, though that as well. Black was a hermit, in the early 1800's; twice a year he came into Somesville to purchase supplies with golden guineas gathered from the wreck of a British warship. This too happens at a particular point in space, the crossing of winds, trade routes, and a sudden shock of highland, mountaintop of the shoal. Now Black Island is owned again by a wealthy eccentric who goes there only on rare and unexplained business.

And Bartlett, once an independent colony of ranchers and farmers, is owned by Dead River, a development company in Bangor, which is turning it into an exclusive cultural retreat for wealthy businessmen. Who owns the land, or as Will Rogers said: they ain't making any more of it. We who do not own the land own vantage, place, and watch the land return to its origin on the chart, the Neolithic *hanging stones* locked to the sky.

Cranberry Stonehenge

a year's work in a week
                    they call it
the storm having passed, the lobster price thick at 90 cents
and the men stay out long past sunset, the lobsterboats returning as stars moving singly into the harbor
these deliveries of giant insects, crab bodies, the moon in
        winter leave at sunrise into a world afloat
        with markers
        traps windblown
                        who
                        are the visible
                        gods here
at Cranberry Isles Stonehenge
                        where the rising midsummer sun
                        touches the visible
                        between two stones
                        is led with the moon
                        in and out of chambers, angles, cradles
                        sepulchers, is led
                        to its death, from its death
                        in and out of a trap
where the lobster
having penetrated the head
must stay, is one moon
locked in the season of its growth
a tub of moons, insects swimming backfeathers thrown in
                            ancient revealed motion
even thru a cage, the powers which of
man's will must enter man's order, hungry, and leave

sanctified,
        the sun to swim in and out of a trap
        and its seeds replaced on the female
        stone after stone locked in the invisible netting
        of numbers
                as the price of having a creature
                appear where he must
                in his named time

At Jasper Merchant's (The salesman. . . . .

says to Jasper: "These lobstermen never had it so good. The price is high. There are so many lobsters they can't catch'm all. And the gear's so much better that once they have their traps made, what does it cost them a year in supplies! Yessir, Jasper; they never had it so good."

Jasper says: "Yeah, but don't go try telling that to them. Don't tell a lobsterman that. You know it and I know it. But they don't."

"And what's expenses gone up, a fraction of the profit I bet. So gas. What's that? A penny more a pound. They can absorb that."

"Well, it's a little more but still. . . ."

"I see you got a new net Jasper. Where's that from . . . no . . . don't even say. I don't even want to hear the word. That's just Brand X to me. That's all I call them."

"They have lots of odds and ends over in their warehouse to Manset."

"Lots of junk Jasper; is that what you're saying; they've got lots of junk. Hey Jasper what's that. Do you see that, floating across the harbor about halfway between here and that boat."

"It looks like the piece of a wharf from'ere."

"That's what it is. That's what it is for sure. Who do you think cut it loose?"

"Well we know damn well who cut it loose, the people up thataway; why they'd let their whole dock go out to sea without noticing it."

"Pretty dangerous aye Jasper. A boat go over that at twilight it'd rip out a pretty good chunk."

"That it would. That it would. But do they care about the next fellow. Look at this water and you can see how much they care about the next fellow. Look at all this oil and shit. Why they dump the stuff overboard up there."

"Yessir Jasper it's something being downcurrent from them. You get a whiff of it; it'd poison a batch of lobsters fast if the water wasn't moving. I tell you."

And good day.
And damnit if he didn't get in his station wagon and drive right up the harbor to the competitor, carrying America in briefcase.

V

Stonehenge
 and sun and moon
pass between within
between
. . . . . the Islanders cast off with stars
                             to pass beyond equinox, the archway
and farm there or die
                             to be blown onto Great Gott
          moving to Black the next spring
these refugees of England,
                     these Stanleys Spurlings Lawsons
Who were the builders of Stonehenge?
                             the Bronze Age
                             itself the Beaker People
                             Wessex culture, lords
                             from the North German forests
Who were the settlers of England?
                             the Stone Age
                             the Azilians, wielding reindeer bones
                                              and harpoons
                             Cro Magnon from France
                             and Russian hunters
                             the Windmill Hill farmers
                             in Kent and Cheddar and Yorkshire
but this which is English
which is Celtic and Druidic
which is the tree alphabet and Stonehenge
                             is also Crete
                             and Mycenæ
                             is Egyptian
                             Baltic

                    Norman
                    Scottish
is the Neolithic pan-culture, the oikumene
of Homer and Plutarch
Brendan and Bran

                    into which our Cranberries come
                    by Hadlocks and Fernalds
                              Who built Stonehenge
                              on Cranberry?
                              and the moon visible
                              between the rocks
                              land marks of the Hyperboreans
                              whose god returns to the
                                   temple each 19 years
                              whose people recall
that there was no Atlantis, but a Cronian Age
a Neolithic wise in the art of stars,
                         who brought stones into a puzzle already
                              built
                         to build upon the outer circles
                                        (Stonehenge II and III
                         an even greater puzzle
                         to encompass the outer islands of the
                              Atlantic
                         the Neolithic wisdom of Odysseus
                         the Neolithic which becomes Druid and
                              encompasses its stars in a mystery
                                                            play
                         which becomes Arthurian and in search
                              of the Grail
                         which fishes the banks of Newfoundland
                                        in great sailing vessels
the Neolithic of Hadlock
returning to England and the Continent with Eskimos
to reclaim his German princess
                         to build the ancient site
                         of Spurling Point and the Maypole
                         of Placentia Head and Baker Island
                              Lighthouse
                         into which sun and moon rise and set

                    114

                    and summer and winter come
              and the great spawning grounds of fish
is Stonehenge
built of the quarries of Swans Island and Black
              and STONington and ROCKland
the Neolithic Atlantic city
                    to this purpose we return to the University of
Cranberry and our guest, silent to now, reminds us that sun and
moon still pass thru the gates of Stonehenge, and sun and moon,
the same, pass between the gates of the five Cranberry Islands,
                              for the heavens, an asymmet-
rical operation, cannot be captured in a symmetry of circle and
rectangles,
    but how the land falls:
    Bear, and its lighthouse
    Baker, and its lighthouse
    Great Cranberry Island
    Little Cranberry Island
    and Sutton Island
    and the outer gates of Little and Great Duck
    Little Gott and Great Gott
    Black Island and Little Black and Placentia
    the Drum Stone, the Crow Stone
    and Rum Cove
              these markers of an inevitable
              way of an inevitable world
              of the inevitable hanging stones and Woodhenges
              and Mohenjodaros of Atlantic
thru which sun and moon will pass
as an oracle or farming calendar
to whom the god is Apollo and origin in the East is Greek
on whose sea sunset and moonset are stageset
the rocky landscaping skylining sea-and-land-vista
and every inch of the coast
of this world
              sunrise and moon rises,
                         plants in wound set
"No intelligence of the type that operates divination is a complete Microcosm as Man is."   AND DIG

                              115

VI

At Spider Fernald's

Spider Fernald sits with the boy, the woman, the little fat man, the tall man, and Merton Hinckley, the buyer, drinking coffee and chewing on stale doughnuts.

"They're good anyway," Hinckley says, shaking off the rain.

"They're doughnuts," says the boy, a Fernald.

"Well, you must have your brights today," says the woman. "Yes, he must have gotten to bed early or eaten a good supper."

The men move, in and out of the shed, having their coffee, having had their coffee, moving the lobsters into the boat, while in a different rhythm the Cranberry fishermen come in early, one by one, throwing off the rain, hoisting their barrels onto the scale. This system will go on   The wind blows the rain across Islesford, white caps visible right up to, then crashing in upon the shore. The woman, Spider's sister, keeps the books. One of the men is her husband, Spider's brother-in-law. "Is it that one?" I ask, as the fat man throws up his rainhat and goes out.

Screeches of laughter as the door slams, and I stand there with the pen, waiting to fill in the genealogy.

She: "Him! That thing my husband!" Spider is slapping his knee, an old cowboy with a broken face from laughing, puffing a salty cigar. "Why he's nothing," she says. "It's the tall one. He's my husband."

The boy, still aroused, says, "Him? We don't even let him live here. He has to live over to Big Cranberry."

Time doesn't move in Islesford, and the chocolate bars have molded on the candy shelf, and the raincoats sit there

unsold, gaining two dollars on the price tag with each inflation, and when the boy goes out the men sit and talk about
his hunting ability. "You should hear him curse when he
misses. What a streak!" says the brother-in-law. "He's a
good boy, though. You just can't go out without practice and
hit a bird on the wing, you know."

Everyone agrees, the woman vehemently.

The wind steps up, the rain is blowing hard, the town of
Cranberry Isles votes not to buy his wharf, builds a new one
instead at Islesford, and Elmer Spurling sits there thru
another winter, not buying any lobsters, but running the
passenger boat, not moving to Florida either, with the
wealthy lobstermen of Great Cranberry. This world age
comes to an end, Cranberry I, on Cranberry, as Marilyn
Hadlock nurses her chubby babe, and Lester Hadlock singes
a duck, Lindy sits by the fire holding Robin. "It's history,"
says Lester, as he takes the family records from a trunk.
But Marilyn is not interested in lobstermen, and wants to
move back to California, end of intaglio, of Hadlock rocking
with a Hadlock child on the island of their ancestors, while
the wind and influences are at sea, and all the rest of America is hidden from here, until they penetrate the veil of
weather and ice and rejoin the races of the interior. No
doubt the Hadlocks are the beginning, and that's history, but
no doubt they can't stay here anymore, their homes sold to
private school teachers from New York, and the boy headed
for the Navy, somewhere like Minnesota; the Hadlock fleet
broken like the ice, and the Fernalds part of another scenery.

End of Cranberry I. Olson's first wife has a home here,
he came out on Elmer Spurling's boat, visited his daughter.
"Who is he?" asked Sarah Spurling, keeper of the Cranberry
social news. This giant Indian poet with pig-tails, who
spends a few days in the museum and tramping thru the
population, long gown of the comet behind him, the aura.

"Oh that's the new poet of the young people," says a
teacher: Sarah Spurling serving us the last of the clam
chowder, and I pull a soaking wet copy of the *Maximus
Poems* from out under my raincoat and show it to her.

"So this is what he wrote."

And on the wharf the rain is so thick we can no longer fight it, Robin lying asleep in the infant seat, warm inside the complete snowsuit, while the cold water runs along his face. "That's a baby," shrieks old woman Hadlock, not recognizing us.

"It's only rain," I answer, seasick as hell, while Lindy attempts to pay the fare.

"That's a baby," she continues to say, passing the information along the wharf, where the remains of summer people come to pass comment on our incompetence.

"They shouldn't be allowed to be parents."

"Child neglect."

It is all like the rain, has voices, no time left, Cranberry Island disappearing.

* * *

"He drank all the time he was here," says Sarah Spurling, pushing the book aside. "Some parent."

And there is nothing we can do but stand here on the wharf, with Robin, and let whatever will happen, happen, and roll off, because eventually it will end, not with atomic fire as some think, but just with the rain blowing like this, no Hadlocks left on Cranberry, Spurlings gone, rolling down the broken glass, the baby's face. We are given little choice, and it happens so quickly. I find myself standing there with Robin, my head spinning, the invectives out of another world.

The wharf out of Hadlock Cove, fills with money, new blood in the deme, Hams from the West, and the Spurlings fly South out of Cranberry, gone from Spurling Cove and Spurling Point on Great Cranberry seen from Islesford, fixed in the sky, leaving like a species of bird. In later afternoon we pass the old Spurling house, old woman Spurling sits in her wheelchair, a shadow against the door.

VII

Chamber

The dream is in a museum. We have entered its halls, awaking in the room of the sarcophagi. And the soft voice of the narrator begins, like the sound of the bird behind the spotlight, naked Indian poised with bow, background murmur of the subway. He describes the castles of Europe, and we see them all about us. We are in Lascaux. We are in Neolithic Vardoe, near the North Pole. All around us the men are working, constructing new exhibits, the life of the bee, and hanging Arabian tapestries. My uncle, an historian of pre-Revolutionary France, is running about checking the dates. The curtain is about to go up.

Stageset. Platform floor. Now the voice of the narrator: Is it Geoffrey Ashe? Is it Gerald Hawkins?: begins again.

"All about you is Europe. Beyond is the North Sea. Now, as the lights begin to dim and the sun passes to the West, you see those mountains, and beyond them the exhibits end. There is an empty hall. Beyond those mountains lies the Western Wilderness."

Across the platform, as if it were water, comes a lobsterboat, the man hauling his traps. Water and platform are indistinguishable, but both remain, planet invading stageset, the boat moving thru the exhibits.

It is either catching lobsters or laying the groundwork for new structures. The Greek alphabet is taught to the Cranberries, lost in the woods. The sun has passed to the West, and the known world is totally dark. We are in a cove and cannot see land or water, either or which, but the lights of many boats, and the harbor village. And the men are rolling on a continental vista, a new horizon, with kings and queens of undiscovered kingdoms, like wallpaper. Spurling Point is a star in the sky.

My uncle sits in an office, reviewing the chronology, calling to see if his prostitute will be ready on Friday or Saturday, or both days. It is snowing out, and the ancient sledders, neither children nor real, come out upon the world.

It is Europe. It is getting older and older. It is closer to morning. I think I know that something lies on the other side of the Atlantic. The museum has become a planetarium; the lights are out. The bird behind the sun calls; it is only a recording. The Indian will never pull his bow. The bird has been shot and mounted. Behind the exhibits: a stagelight, the men working after hours to complete the show. My uncle leaves his office singing an opera in a loud voice. The children are opening their Christmas presents. The gold store windows on Fifth Avenue the alchemists knew. It is like an old fifties movie, a couple walking thru the city park, lamp-lit, along snowy hills, the baseball season over and the snow falling on the Plains, and in the Eastern Woodlands, the music is "walking in a winter wonderland."

The boat hauling traps lies in a cameo in the distance, in a lake at the bottom of a valley, seen from a mountain. This is one crevice of the Old World, or the New World.

The sun moves into the Western Wilderness, setting the forests on fire.

VIII

At Jasper's (5)

2 P.M., and Jasper's sitting in his office going over the books. It's too early for any of the boats to be in, but some of the men are around the wharf, Haskell painting buoys, and George Cleaves working on his boat alongside the dock.

I thought you ran an informal business, Jasper?, I say.

"It may look that way sometimes. But everything has to be taken care of right here. Uncle Sam requires it."

I ask him the lobster price today, and it's down to 80¢. Why?, I need to know.

"Well now, your Grand Menir season has started, and your Nova Scotia and New Brunswick lobster's about to start. Down in those New York restaurants where they're trying to make money off lobster they're not going to begin paying 90¢ for a lobster they can get for 65¢ in two weeks."

George Cleaves comes up the ramp looking for a certain size of nail; Jasper finds it for him, but he decides to sit down and talk.

"How are things in Frenchboro?" Jasper asks after a few moments.

"I hear Floyd Phippen's gonna sell out. Don't know how he stays in business anyway. The wharf's rotting right out from under him."

"I know it. And you'd think a fisherman'd know when a man's running a good business. He keeps up a boat and all. It's a wonder he's got any fishermen, isn't it?"

"Well, there's Williard with him now, and Williard's boy Donnie, and Albert Gascon. But Ray Teal I hear's getting rid of his boat. The bottom's gone."

"Figures. You know Floyd Phippen tried to sell his lobsters to me. But I said no to that. I figured I'd have to pay him Stonington prices and then ten cents a pound on top. I mean if the dealers out at Long Island want to pay Stonington prices that's their business. I'm not going to tell them how to run their business though they're a bunch of damn fools if you ask me. But I can stay the hell out of there!"

"Does Floyd owe Spruce Head money?"

"Let's put it this way: the last I knew Floyd was still getting paid for what he bought. So if I went in there I'd have to pay them the $2000 they set him up with."

The conversation continues on about Frenchboro, how the young people don't stay and the lobster dealers are gradually going out of business. Haskell, coming in for a fresh can of lobster buoy paint, sits down and adds: "Frenchboro—that's a fine fishing place in the summer. But it's a hard place if someone gets sick in the winter."

George: "It seems to always happen on a stormy night." George's wife is from Frenchboro, and he fished for four months with her uncle. "I would have moved there if I could've gotten my trailer over on the ferry."

Would you fish there now while living in Bass Harbor? I ask him.

"Fish there and live here?"

Yes.

He laughs. "I could try. Wouldn't expect to find my traps. But I could try."

"No sir," mutters Haskell. "That's a way to lose a good piece a' gear."

Jasper rises from his chair, tightens his belt. "I think I hear—that must be Aubrey Fowler coming in." Just at that moment the warden breezes thru the door. Jasper breaks off a yawn and manages: "Well, how are you and where've you been?"

"On vacation." The warden always has a big smile, the happiest job in the world.

"Well, I guess you're going to see Mr. Aubrey Fowler. Now you haven't seen him in a long time."

"Can't say as I have. I think I've checked him maybe once in the last two years."

Jasper and Clarence Hawkes walk down the ramp, I trail.

A quick hello to Aubrey, then Clarence helps Jasper cart the barrels onto the scale, everything very polite as if the social relation were measured in micrometers too.

Suddenly Jasper is howling and cursing a blue streak. By mistake he has taken a barrel and dumped it into the bin before Clarence has had a chance to check them. "Jesus, I'm sorry Clarence. Just by force of habit I . . ."

"Don't worry," Clarence calls back. "No care bout that. Shit! You think I'm gonna check every lobster in the harbor."

"I'm so used to taking the barrel over and . . ."

"Hell! I wasn't gonna look at it anyway. One barrel. That's all I want to see. And I'm sure Aubrey's got nothing to see anyway." He is hastily tossing the lobsters into the bin, hardly even looking at them.

"Jesus," says Jasper, shaking his head.

"Shit! What'd I want to see those lobsters for anyhow. All lobsters are the same."

And finally comes to rest. Jasper and Clarence return to the office, rejoining Haskell and George. I break the silence with some questions.

Are the lobster dealers on Little Cranberry getting eliminated like the ones on Long Island?, I ask, citing the case of Elmer Spurling.

"Elmer's got lots of money," Jasper says. "And I don't figure he wanted to jackass bait anymore. It's a different business if you're buying lobsters out on those islands. You've got to pay the men the same price or they'll take their lobsters elsewhere, but you've got to pay extra freight on supplies. Now Floyd Phippen's a kind of irresponsible fellow if you know what I mean. But I don't think Elmer wanted to work his rear end off for nothing, and I'd do the same. Hell, he spends his six months in Florida and runs a mighty profitable sightseeing service in the summer."

George: "Now that Spider Fernald's another one that's not hurting."

Clarence: "I hear he married a rich woman."

Jasper: "You might say that."

Is that how Spider got his money?, I ask.

"That's how," Jasper says. "She just kept coming after

him."

I asked him, and he said he sold his life insurance, I say.

Everyone breaks out laughing. "Hell," says Jasper. "He didn't sell no life insurance. He married just about the richest woman in all of Cranberry. She could buy everyone out there twice over. That how he got into the business."

"Aubrey's having a good year," Clarence throws in.

"Well, let me put it to you this way," Jasper says. "Do you know anyone who's not? I mean anyone who wants to work for his living."

"Guess not."

"That's right. Everyone's having a good year, and bitching just as much as before 'bout the dealer. And he's the only one not making any more money."

Fred Beal comes in and points at me. "There he is," he says. "Watch him. He's out after the income tax. Don't let him write down how much I make. I don't make this everyday."

"Now does he look like an agent of the Internal Revenue Service?" Jasper says.

"I don't know. They're getting mighty tricky these days. Gotta watch out."

Fred goes up to his shed, and the men sit around talking about hunting deer, and how to write off a boat on your income tax. When they start comparing engines I get up.

"Where you going?" Jasper asks.

I'm hungry, I say. I'm going home to eat.

"Well jeez, we ain't done nothing yet. We don't start working till 6 o'clock, do we?"

"No sir," Clarence says.

IX

Here in the dark mud the seaweed drips like blood. Origins. Even the earth grows like wheat, where the water is salty, fishy, the sands filled with it at low tide. The rake cuts a scar, goes down into the clam-bed, dragging out the Venuses, the margaritas, white muscle split by a steel point: the essence of life, which is only in position, which is only what we are. There is nothing more here but to rob the grave and the cradle at once, to maraud and spill blood, to be unable to tell blood from muscle, earth-plant from sea-plant, not to know where the food chain begins, but wherever, it is all around us.

The weight of our own bodies crushes life; we expose a bed with the steel we have invented. Venus lies open everywhere, in her bed, on her bed, covered with the sheets of full tide, open at ebb tide. She sits in a pool colder than moonlight, held by rocks above water. My hands freeze and numb in catching her, scooping in the pool while the sky darkens until I cannot see her and cannot feel her as different from stones. Her organs are covered in the blackest mud, the healthiest non-oil non-smoke black, the original salt and scum of the biosphere. The beginning of thought is here in the clam-bed, controlling an atmosphere fizzing, spitting, kicking their strong legs nothing *more* conscious, and the returning-to-cover-the-bed sea

So in a science fiction story we dream of returning to Earth, far across the dry southern skies:

"Imagine trees. Imagine leaves—vegetation dropping uneaten to the ground. Imagine water pouring by the tons, no one greeting it with tears of relief or happy laughter! Imagine Earth. Old Earth. Manhome itself. . . . think of a whole planet inhabited by Hamlets, drenched with music and poetry, knee-deep in blood and drama."

This is a world we have never left. Though it grows drier everyday. Though the smokes weigh heavier, and the shots of the hunters, and the ducks falling, come from Negro Point and Indian Point and the direction of Alley Island. The knife still exposes the clams, the smell of decay and change in the soil, as the cycle at its nether ends joins its nether ends. The smell of an asshole. Going in and coming out. As the Earth grows drier, so we think, our thoughts of it grow wetter and more nostalgic, orgasm as salty as the sea. Is the cunthole filled with, the pure white interior of, the heart-shaped lunule, violet zones about the muscle-scars, clams, living   to live.

Imagine Earth women!

"What terrifying and beautiful things they must be! Dedicated to ancient and corruptive arts, surrounded by the objects which Norstrilia had forbidden long ago, stimulated by experience which the very law of his own world had expunged from the books!"

Robin and Lindy sit on the rocks, wrapped in snowsuits. The mud gets into my gloves with a winter cold and I discard them. Everywhere ice is forming, water left in the shallows, in pools of facial surfaces, leaves frozen, eyes in the stare of, the Earth takes under, and its odor, its perfume is change. So we learn our seductive poses, to open, to take in, to eat, to swallow, to gather in a box, to open to the insides, to look under, to move in a sinuous shape, to fly up off the water splashing into costumes and wings. To find ourselves as naked as any designs we could have, the pure stone-cold wisdom that there is no more, like vomit, and the frozen, sun-frozen imago of a tree in pouring-down-upon, poured-onto. Is a world we never left, and spit out its guts. From body or foodchain there is no escape. I carry this weight. I run. I run these muscles thru a vector, which drags a rake, exposing, water filling pockets, revealing muscle itself, continuity under and under and within, a remaining of substance, an aging, a formation of strata, a revolution, tide by tide of a fertile sexual Earth. This is the economy into which the lobsterman sinks his gear; this is what his money is invested in, right up to the eyeballs. This is the source of old coins, and seaweed, and the Greek line. Terra firma: an old pot.

Cordwainer Smith is with us today, his novel bought in Bar Harbor on Friday, or just yesterday. *The Planet Buyer*. On the cover is a naked man, his body violet and glowing, like clouds and seas. In the center of his chest is the Earth, showing the tips of six continents: almost all of South America, Labrador to Florida and Texas, the white North Pole, Europe, the hump of Africa, a hazy Antarctic. His eyes are water. His hair is wavy and gold; from within the arc of his shoulders to above his head, a circle of jagged electrical currents. This attraction then to me of the macrocosm in the microcosm, man within book, planet within chest of man. The day begins slowly, so I open the book and read into while the sun crawls across the low sky, and do little else until we walk at three P.M. down to the sea.

So from a dry planet we are always trying to return to a wetter planet, trying to awake ourselves, to douse ourselves, with cold, with motion, with the mere sight of the water running between islands and rocks, out of the cove into itself. Macrocosm trapped in the microcosm, always flowing out, escaping drop by drop, while we pull it back in, standing on the rocks, the three of us a family, recalling ancient history, carrying a cold muddy box of clams.

"Manhome.

". . . The sky itself was not so different from the false 'sky' which had surrounded the ship on its trip from Mars, but there was an aliveness and wetness to it, unlike any other sky he had heard about.

"It was not the sight of the Earth which surprised him— it was the smell. He suddenly realized that Old North Australia must smell dull, flat, dusty to Earthmen. This Earth air smelled alive. There were the odors of plants, of water, of things which he could not even guess. The air was cooled with a million years of memory. In this air his people had swum to manhood, before they conquered the stars. The wetness was not the cherished damp of one of his covered canals. It was wild free moisture which came laden with the indications of things living, dying, sprawling, squirming, loving with an abundance which no Norstrilian could understand. . . . . This *was* his home, no matter how many generations his people had lived in the twisted hells of Paradise VII or among the dry treasures of Old North Australia. He took a deep breath, feeling the plasma of earth pour into him, the quick effluvium which had made man."

Don't believe it. The month is November, and we are still on Earth, and the lobsters are out to 80 fathoms. Robert Torrey has moved in from Swans Island, but it's the same sea, and his lobsterboat rigged with nets, he goes out looking for shrimp in the soft mud. He pulls up his mesh anxious, hoping for that gold strike. It's flatfish. They're full of flounder. At 6 cents a pound tossed right back into the water. A day lost, but not a lifetime. And one day's pay don't count for nothing. Not on a wet planet. Not on a you-know-it Earth.

Married Irene Davis on Swans Island, her father Richard Davis, a boat-builder in Frenchboro, and her mother Ella Tinker, daughter of a lobsterman on Swans.

Swans is an island. They live in McKinley now, a town, just up the road from H. G. Reed's General Store. It's coming off the island. It's coming back, as always, to where they are. So the kids can go to school. And McKinley isn't Swans Island. You can't cut down a tree on or run across anybody's land, or tame the deer, or walk along clear shores. In McKinley, the stage lights but on Swans the night falls closing you off from the whole planet; and the stars in the universe, the visible gods, return to Stonehenge where it is; on Swans Island moon seen between Harbor Island and the two Hubs, seen entering the fishing weir of Selden Wentworth, seen leaving it thru the closed end.

And if this were a science fiction story, or a story about returning to Earth, I could do better. But it isn't. We're still here. It's still *Book of the Cranberries*. And Olson stops in here on Saturday evening with:

"that we are only
   as we find out we are"

X

At Clyde Pomeroy's (1)

The three Pomroy brothers sit around the t.v. in the office, variously working on the books and watching the recovery ship in the Pacific. Down and thru the window one can see a further stage of the operation, Merton Hinckley standing boot-deep in, his boots lazily open, the harbor water. The pulleys reach from where he is up to the open back of one of his trucks, and the boys standing there hoist up the crates he attaches to it.

Norman Pomroy, protecting his fishermen, refuses to answer any of my questions; finally bites on: why is the price higher in Stonington?

"The dealers are all bucking each other there. At least here we've got some friendliness. We're not so piggish."

Merton Hinckley comes in shaking his head, his dog behind him whining. "A whole crate of lobsters busted, 25 of them, fell off the rope and went right back into the sea." He turns to me and says, "Now that's what you call shrinkage."

"And they're gone" is all I can offer him.

"Oh, I reckon I'll see them again. The fishermen'll catch 'em, and I'll buy'm twice." Now he calls out to the Pomroys. "Hey, did they get those men down out of there yet?" It's a parachute dropping over the Pacific, the t.v. high up against the window so that two oceans are imposed on each other, both stormy, one in black and white, shaking, waves mixed with static, the other in color, with the sun setting, bright yellow above the clouds, and the gulls circling above the houses. "How's the sea?" Hinckley asks. It is all the same. The astronauts will land, and come into Clyde Pomroy's with their lobsters. Dressed in their great yellow moon raincoats they'll pour them out of their barrels into Pomroy's wire containers, stand in the refueling spacecraft while the weight is written down and the band plays *Anchors Away*! It is all one ocean and one price. They are bringing back precious stones from their traps, rigged over centuries in the application of American invention, one giant consumer trap in which we sit, watching it come down, an old Western, or Flash Gordon, Maine on the bare edge of the nation. "They're gonna wish they hadn't eaten," says one of the Pomroys, and then the splash; just at that moment the two boys who came up from below to watch run down to catch the two boats coming in. First one is John Leonard, and his boat is called, ambiguously, the *Karl Mark,* and I hear his his name as John Lennon. He's talking about the wind.

"I've seen a lot of days but not many like this," says the old man. "I reckon I'll see more if I stay with it."

Alongside him the Pettegrows pull up, a father and son team loaded to the hilt with five hundred and sixty-six pounds. The two work at a terrific speed in perfect non-opposition, the son taller and darker, the old man with glasses just as spry, their partnership carried over from traps, a profane silence cast by the technical motion. They've also got a barrel of crabs, and those they pour into an extra lobster-crate, ticketed straight for Boston, the thousand legs squirming, the moon rising on Southwest Harbor, soft in daylight. It is all connected, without any need to talk. The environment in which we haul, to which we return from the great jewel theft.

Now the other boy, Jamey, almost dumps a barrelful into the bin without weighing them.

"Watch that shit, Jamey!" fires the older Pettegrow.

Up above the three brothers Pomroy work together, each holding a big hollow pipe, trying to reconstruct the path of the hot air into the shed.

XI

At Jasper's (6)

It happens day after day, and this is the story, as I am putting it together, the motions that are apparent and necessary and. . . .

Today the brightest sun on the harbor, Earth. Jasper stands alone on the floating lobster bin, filling the crates for the eventual arrival of the trucker. I take the opportunity to ask him some questions while he works.

Did George Cleaves sell his lobsters at Frenchboro the other day?

"He did. His wife's from there. He has famliy there."

Even though you own his boat?

"Oh, he asked me first, said he was going to be staying overnight. Now we're not like a bank or anything; we're not going to be unreasonable."

Let me ask you this, if it isn't too touchy.

"Go ahead. I'll let you know."

Well, I've noticed that Emery Levesque has the most lobstermen of anyone. Is there any reason for that?

"Emery has more fishermen than I do, but he also employs two men and a bookkeeper, so you'd have to say the profits were spread around a little more. You also have to remember that Emery has a bigger wharf and he can handle more traps when the men pull them up for the winter. Also he can afford to buy lots of boats and handle their lobsters. Remember; he married a Pomroy."

Let me ask you something about Pomroy's. I noticed how they have two boys weighing the lobsters and working down below with the fishermen while the brothers are upstairs.

"I don't know whether you've got a different type of fisherman in this harbor, or what, but you couldn't operate that way here. The fishermen want to see their dealers working. They want to be sure they're honest. They respect somebody who knows if their lobsters are legal—someone who knows, shall we say. at least as much about the business as they do. So I haven't been able to hire a man for that reason."

The Pettegrows brought in 566 pounds over there yesterday. Is that a lot?

"Another year you might say so, but you've caught us here this year in a very unusual situation. We're having a spurt the likes of which comes along about once every seven years. We had people hauling single and bringing in 600 pounds yesterday. At Islesford they hauled 250 traps for eleven or twelve hundred pounds. It's just an odd situation. Anyone who wants to work is catching them. And for those that aren't, well I don't know, so I won't say." He puts the crate on the scale, fills it until it balances, then a cover over the lobsters and the whole crate into the water—forming a long string of crates pushing one another out from the end to sea. I ask him why, if both he and Pomroy, as well as Spider Fernald, are after the best price, he sells to Hook most of the time and they sell most often to Hinckley.

"If you're asking 'is there more to it than price?', then your answer is *yes*. I'm paying out two thousand dollars a day to my men, and I've got to be sure someone buys these lobsters from me. Now Merton wouldn't take them today; he wouldn't want them, and he couldn't get rid of them. But Hook's the biggest dealer there is. I mean you're talking about millions of pounds, and what little pissy ass lot I've got right here," he says, gesturing to the string of crates, "he'll take, whether he can sell them at a profit or if he has to take a loss. I'm not as rich as the Pomroys, and I can't afford to have seven days worth of two thousand dollars piling up here while no one will pay me for my lobsters."

Across the harbor a boat is turning in toward the wharf, paint peeling, an old man standing in it. As it comes closer I can see the boat is filled with crates rather than traps. Is that a lobster boat?, I ask.

"That's Floyd Phippen, coming in here to sell his lobsters. Now if you were doing a really enterprising study, you'd look into these Spruce Head people who set him up in business, because word is they're owned by Dead River Oil, and financed by the Market in Boston, and they're attempting to take over the lobster business."

Floyd Phippen pulls in alongside the wharf, Jasper chuckles. "If Floyd don't watch it, he's gonna get caught by the tide. He doesn't have all that much time to unload."

Do you mind him using your wharf?

"Well, I don't imagine there's any other place he can unload."

What about Alley's?

"He'd have to have three or four men to do it there. They'd have to haul up on the dock and then cart it across. Your answer is: they just don't have the unloading facilities there that we have over here."

Do you have an agreement?

"Not of the formal type. He'll say something to me every now and then, see like how he gestures up there. Shit, I don't care. As long as it doesn't bother me too much. And it doesn't today. I'm not going to put the man out of business."

Don't the buyers pick up out at Long Island?

"Some of them do and some of them don't. Lunt's buyer comes out with a smack, and fills it with lobsters right there. I imagine Spruce Head doesn't have the facilities. So Floyd has to bring them in here. I wouldn't do it, but then he's sort of a half-ass lobster dealer, and I don't think he's getting back a new dollar for an old; maybe they're paying him ten cents a pound, but then they're taking back three cents out of every dime for what he owes them for setting him up in business. No, I wouldn't do it."

Does he have to?

"Well, how to put it. That's his set-up. That's his life."

Can he survive off that kind of profit with only three or four fishermen?

"He couldn't make it off lobsters, but Floyd's a jack of all trades. He sells kerosene out there, gasoline. He's an unlicensed plumber and electrician of the type who can work out on the islands if you know what I mean. It's just a different world. Things aren't as rushed. The men come in, they find Floyd's off on another job, they weigh their own lobsters, crate them up. If I did that here, they'd be madder than a hornet."

Now the Spruce Head truck has backed into Jasper's driveway by the bait shed, and Floyd has his initialled crates piled all over the wharf while he and the man on the truck work hurriedly to beat the tide, making their job harder with consecutive mistakes. The mess on the wharf expands. The man on the truck unloads the FP crates and returns them to Floyd. Floyd rushes up the full ones. Grandville Pierce, grumpy, comes in puffing a cigar, unloads his lobsters, curses the price, down to 70¢ on this the first day of Nova Scotia buying, walks up the ramp to get his bait. "He doesn't leave a hell of a lot of room, does he?" says Jasper, as Grandville slowly winds his way thru the crates. Now he comes back down, still cursing. "I can't help it, Grandville. You're gonna see'm less afore you see'm more. They're going right out by you."

Do you mean less money or less lobsters?, I ask.

"Actually I meant less money; that's what I said, but I meant both. He's going to sell less lobsters and see less lobsters too. He's not what you call the enterprising lobsterman. Like yesterday he had six lobsters hauling traps for a half hour. But he's got enough. He can buy and sell you and me two or three times over. Don't tell anyone because he doesn't know I know this, but *there's* a man who doesn't believe anyone should pay income tax. He was born and raised out on Cranberry where they're born to wait on summer people, you know, these rusticators, and that's what he does all winter here in Bass Harbor; he takes care of estates, cottages, and they pay him a salary alright, but more of it's just like gifts and bonuses; he prefers a Christmas tree filled with dollar bills to a salary check."

Grandville Pierce's puffing his cigar carrying the bait pail down the ramp, staring all about. He looks the part of a summer person's lobsterman, a caretaker, a rustic for the rusticators. But another boat's in. Terry Smith: no lobsters because he's put them all in cars. He stands in his boat whistling, waiting for gas, and Jasper runs up and turns it on. Casually I pick a sea urchin off the side of his boat and bring it up with me. "That's a whore's egg," says Jasper.

"At least that's what we call it on this dock. The Italians like to eat them; they cut them open and suck out the meat raw. I don't see how, but they do."

What do you think of the idea that offshore dragging for lobsters in Massachusetts is going to kill off the Maine lobster business? That's the idea of that guy John Reeves at Bar Harbor Trust who did a paper on whether the bank should finance a one man lobstering operation.

"I've been here since '47, and I haven't seen a year when they're catching more and getting more for them. My question would be: when's this supposed to happen? The economy and the population are going up nationwide, and people are paid more money and can afford more. There's always some expert who's telling us what's going to happen in so many years. But I can tell you what I see down here, and I expect to be around a while."

Up above the wharf is really crowded, and things are getting tense. "He doesn't have too much tide left," Jasper says. Now Fred Beal comes down from his shed, and, limp and all, he's helping Floyd Phippen, working the pulley so hard that he virtually swings up off the ground with every pull, watching the tide with the other wary eye.

"Now don't let her scrape bottom, Floyd," he calls down, and Floyd looks nervously about, poor old Floyd, cornered on all sides. No one can get thru, not Grandville Pierce, or Terry Smith, nor Aubrey Fowler, or even Jasper, who says with a little snap:

"I guess Fred thought it was a bit too cold to go out today," and walks into the bait shed with Ralston Cleaves, Jr., unzips his fly, and pees on the floor and thru it while Ralston loads redfish skeletons for bait. Jasper gives a deep sigh, and Fred, still in a rush, comes in:

"You still around here?" he asks me. I tell him I am for a while, and that I even spoke to his brother-in-law Robert Torrey. He's vaguely impressed at my thoroughness, so I ask him:

Have you known Floyd a long time?, trying to sound sympathetic.

"We were neighbors you know, Swans and Frenchboro; I knew Floyd since he ran a sardine-boat, that's a long time."

They're done and Floyd's getting out in a hurry; he slips Jasper a few dollars, then comes over to Fred, a slight embrace, and stuffs some money in his hand. Fred begins to protest, but Floyd says, "Buy yourself a bottle of beer."

"Okay," Fred grunts, "and I'll think of you when I drink it."

Was there an exchange of money between Floyd and you? I ask Jasper.

"Oh, just what you'd call cigarette and candy change, a few bills."

I was just curious, I say to him. I thought maybe he paid you something for the use of the wharf.

Fred Beal, who is climbing the stairs back upto his work shed, stops and shouts down:

"Curiosity killed a cat!"

And is gone inside.

a woodpecker with flaming red hair knocking the wood on
the top of a dead tree.
the gulls screeching.
the sun between, as always, islands, as always, shadows.
the small winter arc across the sky.
there is no trap, I recall, for fire.
but here in the deeplands I come back
and you open a way for me,
between pasages of your body
into the old sense
without which   nothing
no island
no new place
the sun, without which, silence
on the market

         no supply
         no demand
         no profit
         no loss

it is a good patch
one I can walk
it is not a trap with strings
     even without which the sun must go thru its seasons
     on earth

XIII

At Sewell Alley's

Here on the wharf the Neolithic art of trap-building goes on winterlong, hammering together the wood, tying in the netting. The piles of them grow daily, the old ones brought in from the sea to drain, the new ones built in the sheds.

A road of another era, grown over in part, hidden in the trees, passes directly from Jasper's to this rival operation. Roger Ham owned it when it was a fishing wharf, before the fleet went sour, and Charlie Colwell cut the fish for him. Now Charlie buys lobsters for Sewell Alley, and Andrew Robbins, who sold out, comes in early from a day of fishing, shivering dramatically while Charlie weighs his catch. "Charlie my boy, I don't know when I'll go out again. But I imagine I will."

Crowley stresses ethics, not power, with release from will as the final act of will. That the consequences of life are grave, and in the West, we the stars of the West, are industrious, and work in the open channels of a pre-existing world. We of the optimistic gnosis, not the Buddhist veil of sorrows. The belief that somehow the influence of the stars is not lethal, and the Neolithic was a spiritual ethical gain over the Paleolithic, the Twentieth Century over the Neolithic. We think that we can chase, in motorboats, the ancient world-source of our life.

I fear the lobstermen will go on and on without rebirth; that is, I cannot see that they will be born again as anything but lobstermen, or perhaps as lobsters, to fulfill the ethics and balance the system.

The unceasing ocean around Britain hugs and hides Bass Harbor, its earlier Neolithic crafts, magic, fishing, and building a trap, which we now return to, building a city out of as many crosscutting symmetries as will appear a symmetry in motions of sun and moon. Each new age adds a circle to Stonehenge, a door to the trap, or an extra lath or angle. The present age is busy with fresh-cut wood, building sheds for new fishermen, adding planks to the wharf, extending the landscape into which the sun rises.

> "Thus do aviators regain daylight
> after the sun has set.
> So in super perspective to us
> do the stars,
> moving at thousands of times
> the speed of the 'Twentieth Century'
> seemingly hang motionless in the night sky."
>
> —R. Buckminster

Fuller, an old Maine sea-captain himself.

The tide rests upon a step, retreats a step to ebb. There, on Saturday night, Walley Gilley, the three hundred pound lobsterman, took the step off and ended up in the water.

"Walley the Walrus," says Andrew Robbins. "Standing there in the water with just his head showing."

"And he blew like a whale," says Charlie.

Into this era march the stars of a previous era, the thousands of them, we can see them wherever we look, now the winter sky at ebb tide, and I think we have nothing to show for it but our actions, which go on and on from life to life, like one of Wendell Gilley's carved birds, a replica of a species whose name we shall never know, or who shall never know its own name. We cannot see far enough. We cannot see beyond.

We do not know if we will survive.

If we do, we do not know what our survival will mean.

XIV

In the cabin of the ferry returning from Swans Island. It is totally black. Here above the ocean. Here where the sky would seem to be. The world below is the sea.

Captain Lee stands at the wheel, three seaman around, call him captain and obey all the other formalities; the formal property is that we are at sea.

Before the ferry came, we stood at the wharf in Atlantic watching the sky darken, the early winter night. The ferry late, for having taken a piece of well-digging machinery to Long Island, and we, its only passengers, waited. In the distance, across water, the spruce makes its stand, long lean vertical tiers, an utter thicket as landscape. To the right we can see Black Island, and to the left we can see another Black Island, and the sky darken behind a world where no one lives, Placentia, with a few white houses in the trees, long deep forest, at high tide hardly a shore. The wind ripples like goose pimples on the incoming tide, another, an external skinning process of water, while the internal brings it nearer and nearer upon the shore, the rocks where it crashes, and out in the sea, breakers until they blur into a foamy white.

The great apparatus of the ferry terminal stands against the sunset, as on a planet only partially inhabited, stark, moans in the wind. The Earth, in the end, makes no peace even with its children, and wears them down, and this is an icy sea, a biting wind, a haunting cove, even if it is home, and as hard as I fight it, there is a longing, strong, almost like music, to get back inside myself, into the warm of the house; yet there is the warm I carry, my cheeks and eyes sparkling, and allows me as I walk against the cold. I carry planet into planet, where they meet.

The ferry comes around North Point, past Fir Point, now

appears, lit like a Christmas tree, says one of the men in the terminal who is not used to seeing it that way. And Mrs. Lee sits joking with the minister about heaven and hell, and speaks of the Captain's sea-faring, and they listen for the rumble of her out on the waters; she comes in, discharging the school children into the black. Boy grabs girl's hat, wears it down the wharf, running; she chases him, grabs it back, and into Swans Island itself, home.

In the cabin the body fights it, that driving our car onto this, being here floating in the hours of measured time, we should be on land; but we are not. Captain Lee knows how to stand on the water, high in his terminal overlooking. In front of him sits a red ball, and within it a hemisphere floats with all the directions; North, Northeast, NorthNortheast, and so on, float in the menstruum before him, as he stares down into it, a partial abstraction, floating to maintain the level as the ship sways, hence floating as part of the ocean's body. Everything up here is down there also, and the visceral motion in the ball is no different than the sea's motion, though it counters that in a man's head. It is Captain Lee in the darkness, it is that we cannot see him, that he cannot see but looks into a red ball, floating, alive and fluid, for the line of his approach, that we cannot tell if this is airplane or seaplane or spaceship, floating vehicle of what sort, among what directions, what orientations. We cannot see Captain Lee or the men, but he asks for a chair and they pull a high stool under the Captain while the ship unsteered bucks a few heavy waves, and they throw the great light onto the sea, searching among whitecaps for the buoy, and pick up its fluorescent squares, and pass outside it, long before we hear its three notes in the viscera of the sea. This is blind but not invisible, frozen but senseless of the cold; this cannot hear but speaks in a regular phonology, is made to live here, a gull, a floating piece of steel, and Captain Lee staring into the red ball because the Earth is a circle, even since Ptolemy, staring into the planet on whose seas he has floated, staring within from this impossible purgatory, where the shapes remain Platonic and utter, and Captain Lee cannot escape the circle, nor can the ship, and that is why we move thru it, and why it is round, and why the Earth is magnetic, recognized here at any point on its seas, as we float and are drawn towards, the motive power under us, as we are repelled by, as all action is reaction, as we fight the weather being on top of it, as we use a stone to the North to come to the Northeast. And the radar turns, lighting a map made in penetration of the hard substances, a land given radiance in choppy sweeps; we are within the limits of, passing always within the limits of, four miles, one mile, we see the buoy pass, made of light, cut by the circling line; we see the slow movement of Black, Placentia, and Gotts past us as if thru us, and the omnipresence of the shore. Above Placentia the light of Mount Desert Rock scans, passing us once in a circle, as one of its divisible directions, chained there, Promethean, against the tides which rush totally across it; "not much real estate there," says Captain Lee.

It is called seasick, and it is deep within, as I find no place to stand, as I lay back into my body, and find it is close to water, and then sink dizzy into whatever motion, neither home nor far from home, simply sick. I feel the red sphere move over me and thru me; it is no longer separate of my body; its fluids are passing thru my system, all its directions afloat there; I am in a Mediaeval laboratory, and the alchemist-astrologer is trying to find the way among the planets; the directions float thru me, trying to find Northeast, to come home. I stumble into a chair, keep one eye closed, my other eye on the red ball; my eyes keep falling at the speed of moisture; my whole body sinks into the sea and returns; the directions are an abstraction; the danger is merely directional. I think that this is the well-known theatre of terrestrial astronomy, where the sky turns on pedestal within the ship, and all our hopes ride within the circle, and the light scans, revealing that the known lands are finally made of it, so soft that we could run into them and disintegrate into light. They are discussing a new beacon above Bass Harbor, wondering if we would hit Lopaus Point running right into it. Captain Lee says he could run it into extinction and wouldn't hit the Point but would miss the Harbor; it is an almost hypothetical question, as though at this point we could do it or not. But formality prevails, and I see the light bobbing up and down, thru my horizon on the ship, coming closer and closer. I feel that in the darkness the charts prevail; I feel I am in the planetarium, the lights have gone off, and all the stars and directions and islands are visible, scattering out from where we are. I feel that extinction is soft, is the inevitable crossing of beacons with ourselves, the passing thru that will come into harbor. In the darkness I watch the red ball precede time and glow with directions, places invisible but from where the stars can be seen. And if we get outside of time, there is but one fix, one body, and we are drawn irrevocably towards it. I feel that there is no chance, that we will always be in between, and I know that most of the Earth lies in such darkness, and waiting, and men work eight, ten, twelve hours a day, in the factories, or twenty-four hours a day as sea-captains, and return between dusk and dawn, waiting for the cities to sustain them, to remember them, to return the time their body uses, as there is no city on Swans Island, but the islanders wait in the price of lobsters, in heat blown thru vents and the living room, in the names of heaven and hell and whether they have to meet their Creator at death with the Baptists or not until the Day of Judgement, whether the Baptists or Adventists give a better price: here in the closed isolated community, where local means everyone, and over-rides the parishes.

The seasickness, like the darkness, is an admission of utter dislocation, also of willingness to float, not to steer, but to swallow the red sphere and fall easily back into the astral ages, to let the directions guide because I have chosen to be in them, turning, circling, loose, guiding, my intestines wound around. This is a psychedelic theatre, and all that is lit is the globe, all that is at stake is body, is the world, the Captain in total charge of the lights. I am in the belly of the planet, and the pangs shoot out the directions, from stomach to nerve, thru muscles, and the memory itself; the Captain reads my body, steers me inevitably as I lie back against the colloidal wall, in my sickness I fall totally into. The shards of broken color floating thru it, I cannot tell my body from the planet, and for the first time I see visibly that we are never outside, no matter how clearly the disk, the chart lies before us, we must swallow it and steer from within. Someone is shouting over the radio: "Viva. Viva Romeo. Viva

Romeo Romeo Romeo. Viva Romeo. Romeo Romeo. Viva Viva Viva. Romeo Romeo Romeo." "He's got nothing better to do when he knocks off work," says Captain Lee, and the voice falls back into the static as we bend away from the direction in which it comes.

The organs align to their recognized order, resonance in the motion they feel. My body knows even as I don't, what it is, perhaps even where it is. And the continents, like the liver, float in the loose lit boundaries of the dish.

CHAPTER 4
THE CITY AND THE FARM

Lars Andersen sits in the shed turning the buoy on the paint brush like a top, black half over the white. "I came here from Sweden; it was more than fifty years ago, to work in the quarry. They were doing piece work, you know, so much for a rock."

Had you heard of Swans Island while you were in Sweden?

"No, but I heard of all the quarries in America, everyone knew about them. They were cutting the stones for the cities being built and there was plenty of work for a stone-cutter. You could go anywhere and get a salary, Swans Island, Hall Quarry, even down in Georgia. Swans Island isn't special; they cut granite on a lot of these islands."

Did you work in any others?

"You know Hall Quarry? I cut stone there, and my brother, he was killed there in 1937, in a car accident."

Was stone-cutting like lobstering? Did you have a dealer who sold to a buyer?

"Well, dealer and buyer was one, and that was Meehan and Son in Philadelphia; part of that city's built out of Swans Island. We did have a boss, and he was quarry-owner, but he had his contract with Meehan and Son."

When did you stop cutting stone?

"The depression done away with granite. 1929 was the last year, and there were three hundred quarrymen earning a living here then. A lot of them left. I stayed here. What's the point of going to the city anyway. I figure it's best to make my own food where it is rather to wait on food lines somewhere else. I mean we could fish, and dig clams, and raise our own vegetables, and we used to shoot birds before they came out and made a law against that. You were your own boss, and I still am."

What did you do after stone-cutting?

He smiles. "Fishing, steamboating, cutting wood, trawling, dragging, scalloping, seining for herring. The steamboat to Rockland used to stop here and buy our saltfish. When we went to the mainland then it was Rockland, not Mount Desert."

The door crashes open and two jolly men, smelling faintly of whiskey, stumble in. "I want to see if you got the right size of nail for me, Lars. Hey, you being interviewed? You going to be famous like Wesley Gore? Maybe we'll let him think you're popular around here like Wesley. We'll let him think that, won't we?"

Lars looks for the nails, and I turn to the man talking: Kenneth Beal. "Yes, Fred's a relation; he's my cousin, I guess."

Why do you suppose he moved in?

"His wife didn't like it. That's what they say. But I don't have a wife." Cherubic smile, mild voice, teeth missing, short and chubby, shirt open to undershirt, Swans Island male. "This is a real friendly place here. You see on a blowy day we can come over and bother Lars. And we can go scalloping in the winter when we don't want to lobster....."

Are there any disadvantages to living here?

"You might say the winter's dull, but the summer is good; there's lots of dances and suppers. Would I leave here and go to the mainland? Never."

"No," says Lars after scouring his shed, "I don't imagine I have what you want."

"Well, that's okay. We just wanted to visit with you anyway." And they're gone. And Lars slowly takes up his seat again. I sit on the barrel. "Now maybe you can answer some of my questions," he says.

Okay.

"Can you tell me why all the kids are acting like lunatics and communists burning everything up and breaking up their colleges. In my time you couldn't even get an education. And here it is given to them. Maybe that's the problem. They didn't have to work for it."

It's not that they think it's bad to work. Without taking anything away from you, I'm sure that if they could come

147

out to an island like this, far from the city, and live with their friends, they'd be glad to fish and farm and share things. But you yourself said you wouldn't want to go live in the city. They have to live in the city."

"Well, I know this government's not perfect. There are a lot of things wrong. Like I don't get my social security just because I'm working and making money, while some fellow who doesn't want to work gets the money I earned. Do you think that's right?"

I don't think it's right that he should get your money, but not everyone can work as easily as you can. There aren't enough jobs. Maybe the rich people should pay more taxes.

"All the rich people do is they make foundations and give money to people in the cities to start trouble. They use that money to buy guns and get drunk."

What about Sweden? Do you like Sweden?

"I haven't been there for years so I couldn't say, but they're supposed to have such a good socialist system and everyone's committing suicide."

And the war, that has a lot of people angry, because almost everyone knows that we shouldn't have gotten into it in the first place.

"I don't like war. But they'll always be wars. Communist China is just waiting to take over and kill all those Catholics in South Vietnam. That's what's going to happen if we leave. As long as we're fighting wars, we might as well fight them there."

And it is true that the city in America is inescapable, inevitable, the usury at sea and on the farms, so that the good farmland on Irish Point, or out to North End and Mackerel Cove, isn't used, is moved in from by Lars and his kind, quarrymen, turners, but not subsistence farmers, restless cowboys on too small an island, making prairie of sea; and Duck and Hen, inland thru Buckle Island Harbor, are abandoned to the foundations, for the history of Maine agriculture has ended on Swans Island, replaced by inflation in the grocery store, and boats running back and forth picking up cartons of Coke and oranges and celery, and T.V. Guide, the television linking the community thru the winter. It is not possible to leave the city, whom Eldridge Cleaver calls *the*

148

Black Man, whose body IS the political body of this nation, not just the Ultramasculine Lobstermen, his frozen white cock, his 18th Century manliness, but the Body itself now urban, where the real dirt, electronic slime of kulchur Americana collects: city as brainfield, as fertile human implosion, nuclear hive, lit of cosmic prebiological possibility, to which Swans is provincial mimicry, at realpolitical distance, no longer sturdy out-to-sea and back into wintry oblivion, healed by the degree zero Atlantic waters of all other civilization and spiritual responsibility, but now the market, the Twist, the Mashed Potato, the Swim, the central ecstasy of meaning, so that even here on Swans it cannot be escaped, in the children, it will have to be the coming of the city, twisting, rhythmic; Black, and they will be devastated by its heat; they will not understand or be equipped; they will not make any difference, this time; they will turn on. What Eldridge Cleaver calls, believably, *the Balls,* or Flower of Africa/Queen of the Nile over Swans Island, over its once granite and lobsters, over its wasted inland fertility and profundity, its communal sentient potential, seducing the sea birds to their ceremonial hearth, using fully, with Nubian Xhosan splendor, in a dance. Or which Vine Deloria calls *the Red,* muddy rich nitrogen soul the Indians of many worlds still cultivate beyond the city, Navaho sand and pure Beautyway doctoring, Cherokee sperm, Iroquois scapula farming, moving here to what was the summer middens of Penobscot, Abnaki, and Passamaquoddy, proper seasonal use of, without destroying, without inflating, without failing to keep account books of, the island, what comes into it, what leaves it, how the morphology of the landscape, the phenomenal village, changes each year, and cannot change back, is the Indian who would silently return, haunting Lars Andersen, putting his shit back into the cycle, the Black Urban City Land from Philadelphia to Swans Island Village, which John Lennon would call the young people, Chardin the noosphere, Yeats the grinding of the gyres, McLuhan the computer-linked visual-tactile-aural, what needn't be called Black or Red (but can) in order to invade from the city and touch Swans Island and all the land of the coast of Maine, what is the Reawakening, seen as America or world, or the Final Doom,

which is in any case the end to imbalance, usury, waste and
endless import of junk, pollution, trashfires, which is not
just a book for the city but must be read by Chauncey Somes
in Somesville and Lars Andersen, and the descendants of tall-
tale hero Jones Tracy who stuck his finger up the ass of a
deer, (white man beating up all the animals), and now the
animals return, the theosophical dance in another reading,
the inevitable consequence if so many wisdoms are right; the
book is *Soul on Ice;* the book is *A History of Maine Agriculture, 1604 - 1860;* the book is *Jones Tracy, Tall Tale Teller
from Mount Desert Island;* and if you think these three
books can be read, the reality in one held separate of the
reality in the others, you are wrong. Urban is America, as
Farm is America; as land is, per acre, land; and there are
no lines drawn within nation where this siege can be carried
out; the belly of the army is where the army is, and food
doesn't appear magically, in stores; food is joined by roots
irrevocably to the ground there is; and though we are talking of lobsters and rural American, and the seacoast and
gulls, we have not forgotten the city, nor could we ever leave
it, the one reality enacted in time-space in the costume-
shells of where we are.

II

On the island where we know no one, Annie Beal becomes
our blind date as we drive past her walking along the road
from Minturn, taking her own sweet time. Our reasons for
anything are flimsy, almost non-existent; we're not related
to anyone, and the traditional excuse in that case, as Lindy
points out, is keeping in circulation, in high school going out
with some boys only to get to meet others. She invites us in,
and we sit with her at the kitchen table. A man who was
waiting outside in a running car now comes in and stands
silently in the doorway, dark, Indian-looking. Annie is short,
rocky face, boy's haircut, brash in manner. "Oh. Haven't
you met? This is my husband, William Beal." To him: "You
can sit down."

He shakes his head uneasily. "Guess I'll stand."

Do you like living here?

Annie: "It's okay, I suppose. If I had the money I'd leave.
But I don't."

What do you think the advantages of living here are?

"If you're a fishermen you have your own shore. Of course
now shore privileges are a thing that's changed. It used to
be that all land was open to people long as they were resi-
dents of the island. A hard winter comes along, and we could
dig up some clams to get something to eat, carry us over to
the next day. Well, these city people come out here and buy
up choice lands. First year the sign says: 'Open to Swans
Island people only.' They're trying to be friendly, let us know
how good they are to us. Next year it's a new sign: 'Closed,'
or 'Private Property,' and some even specify 'Island People
Keep Off.' "

Since they're not there during the winter, do you still
clam?

"You better believe we do, if we've got two legs."

What do you do for a living?, to her husband.

"He works at the power plant. There isn't much to do for a woman here. I clean houses a bit; in general we have to scrounge a bit to get along in bad times. Like five or six families band together to make wreathes to sell in Ellsworth. I mean the brush is here. There's plenty of that. But there aren't too many luxuries."

William: "I'm gonna go now. I better fix up the engine before I miss the boat."

"That's up to you. I hope you make it on time. Addie'll probably go with a friend if you miss her."

"I'll be there." And he leaves.

"That's my husband alright, but we've been separated about six months. You'll meet the man I'm living with, Walter Turner. He owns this house. Say, where're you from?" Lindy tells her. "So you're living in Somesville. I go to Fernald's store all the time. Bob Fernald. He's the undertaker, the big undertaker on all these islands. I tell him he better be nice to me if he wants to lay me up."

We're all victims of sex and family, and it becomes closer and tighter out here. The winter rural creates a haunting magnetism that draws people together, and they wake up in the morning strange bedfellows, unsuspected lives buried in each other. Ethan Frome. Peyton Place was a town in Maine, not a city or suburb. Almost everyone looks pretty after a while. *Woman* means *pretty*, as I discovered when Kenneth Beal told me that if I went to a certain wharf I would see this beautiful girl. We went there and saw her, and in it the strange cult of Swans.

But Annie Beal is the Ava Gardner of this island: as Walter Turner comes in, sparkling like a Shakespearian elf, or is it the certain variant of the Swans dialect. Perhaps half her age, or as Mrs. Wentworth puts it when we try to get off Annie onto a neutral subject, like how old would you say she is?: "Old enough to know better!"

On an island there are no girls, only dreams, and wandering thru them men find that endogamy reaches deep into another kind of sex, a hidden sacrament, and they flee in horror, as some Beals, or find they can't, as others.

152

The daughter comes home, having missed her father, as much make-up as her eyes, lips, can hold, but school-girl dress.

Do you want to live on Swans? Lindy asks.

"I guess so."

"And last week it was no," Annie says. "What will you find to do here?"

She shrugs. "Guess I'll have to be a lobsterman, won't I?"

Fred Beal, a farmer, married Augusta Stinson, one grandchild, by Austin, who was a cabin boy on a streamer, is Annie Beal; and another grandchild by William, Sr., a lobsterman, is William Beal, Jr., and these are the parents of the girl. After Augusta Beal died, Fred married Genette Turner, Arthur Turner's grandmother.

Time, which is dispersable, which is seemingly lost between generations, scattered with genes, is recovered, circular, in the endogamy of a single house. Not to lose their origin, is a compulsion that drives people too, a lust: doing with their bodies what would seem to have been undone long ago, in the galactic beginnings, and in this sense we are all incestuous, homosexual, drawn inevitably to the island, the deme, reunion in the primal egg.

III

Looking for the old Swans Island, looking for perhaps the occult, perhaps the colonial, looking for leprechauns, trolls, elves, skraelings, looking for the village, the homestead, the Mason Jar, the plow; looking for the horse and ox yoked together, the stout and the sleek in single gait, across a snow-covered farmland, hauling wood toward the sources of fire, which is light. I ask Lare Andersen, as he sits and paints the black stripe on his white buoy, whether this reminds him of Norway. "Except for the trees," he says. "The homeland never had so many trees."

The quarry is abandoned since the depression, the entire edge of the cutting exposed, and giant boulders all about. The quarry wharf is used for storing traps by those who don't have shorefront. And all around Goose Pond, grown in with woods, and nobody knows what happened there. The old carrying place beach of the Abnaki is a winding road thru the forest, here where the Indians carried their canoes after debarking into the place of summer clamming and fishing; and this road runs out at the Fine Sand Beach in Toothacher Cove, before reaching Irish Point, where the old foundations of burned-out farm-houses lie amidst the escaped vegetables. Swans Island is lobstering, scalloping, seining, and today's market; there is nothing old but puzzle pieces that don't quite fit; the bottom could fall out of it; it could cease to be a boat and become a farm again. Or do these further islands lie on the border of another country, still invisible in the prime of lobstering: Swans, Frenchboro, Isle Au Haut, Vinalhaven; still inhabited because of the lobsters, while the inner islands, Bartlett's, and Long Island in Blue Hill Bay, and Hardwood, though giants in their own right, have diminished to a few summer cottages, or nothing, waiting between habitations?

If we are looking for the old Swans, they say to go see
Wesley Gove; he's the one who yoked the ox and the horse
together, which was the standard Swans Island post card
for years. "He's not representative of the place," Carl Andersen says. "He thinks he's popular with us; we let him
think he's popular," Kenneth Beal. And Leon Power: "You'd
think he had nothing, living over there like that, but he'll
pull out some words so long you and I'd need a dictionary
for them. He's so stuck up. We call him King Wesley the
First."

Instead of turning right for Swans Island Village and
Minturn, we turn left, and into the town of Atlantic, passing an old white Methodist church in the sun, the defunct
Atlantic grade school, coming around the corner at a grove
of trees, and an open space beyond them, a giant series of
fields up to the shoreline forest, several rows of apple trees
bare in the winter, and four old buildings falling down,
held back up by fresh birch bark, and stuffings of rags,
newspapers, burlap, plastic. Wesley Gove stands in front
of the barn, working over an old car. We pull in. He is nod-
ding: "Yes, yes, this is the place." As though we could be
come to no place other. He is hobbled, hunchbacked, moves
broken, the only man on the island with a beard, an old
overcoat. He beckons us to follow him to the barn;
there we peek in, a dozen kittens running in and out,
black and white, and soft grey, winding thru the legs of the
old stove, and in the corner, among cans and papers and
sacks, where nothing definite can be seen, and in the dust of
the old desk. There is nothing new here but the kittens, not
even the sun, which hardly gets in, and the bit that does
turns that dank color; it smells, it is dark; the indoors is indistinguishable from the ground outside, but it is the beginning, changed by circumstances into a slum. Here he refuses
to change; here he sits among old press clippings, and letters
from professors; here he is history itself. "My nephew Minturn Smythe owns the place now. You know Minturn, don't
you; he owns the world. He lets me live here, but soon as
I'm gone he's going to burn it to the ground. But I keep it,
and I'm not going to outlive it. It may outlive me; then Minturn'll burn it down. I thought that was going to be last

summer. I was awful sick, didn't even plant a crop."

He hands us a pair of binoculars, sixty years old, and we step out into the field and look across the Bay; visible without them: the mountains Champlain saw when he called it Mount Desert, archetypally giant and snow-covered, enormous glacial horns whose visibility is the total landscape of Mount Desert from sea, which we could not know for living there, what Champlain saw from slightly closer in; and to the right, Wesley Gove says, is Black and Placentia. "Placent, we call it here, a localism." But they look like one long island, no angle to kick a field goal thru, merely strands of forest, a view which is lucrative to Minturn Smythe, with picnic grounds right down toward Joyce Beach, and this great embarrassment of an uncle who comes in to bother the campers with history, and his press clippings, and a cigar box to take a tax collection for Percy, America's most photographed horse.

Even age itself has turned sour on Wesley Gove, though he would consider it redemption, vindication. After being laughed at for forty years, out comes Educational T.V., Marshall Dodge, Yale boy of Downeaster jokes and record albums, microphone and cables, and newspaper reporters with photographers. "Just yesterday they were doing the follow-ups," Wesley says. "I went out there and mowed that hay, and I rode the plow, and—" laughs uproariously, "Percy, that Percy, ruined one whole batch of pictures by walking over the cable. But you know they asked me what I thought the most important thing in the world was right at this time, and I said President Nixon and his domestic program and his ending the war, that's the most important thing."

We walk over to the tiny stable where a room not much bigger than Percy holds him, and America's most photographed horse, at least on Swans Island, marches out into the daylight, taking big heavy steps, now tears at the grass with his teeth, and runs into the field where the hay is, rolls and rolls. Wesley laughs and laughs, slapping his thigh. "Percy, Percy. Percy, Percy," each time in a different tone, louder, softer. Then he calls me inside. "I've got something for Percy," he says, and under the sacks in the stable, in their own nitrogen heat and that of dung and pure dirt, one of five boxes of apples, probably the bad ones, and sets it down where Percy eats. The horse is at the apple trees themselves, standing tall and rubbing its nose against the branches. Wesley calls and he comes bounding, and from the other direction, into the forest, a larger cat comes thru a thin path in the fields, passes us and goes into the barn. "Yessir," Wesley sings. "Minturn Smythe who owns the world is going to burn it all down, but it'll outlive me," and lights up a Corona cigar.

Percy stands over the box of apples, his nostrils sliding over his jaws while he chaws them, one apple at a time, vaguely the sense of horse-apples, like horsechestnuts, and horseshoe crabs. For Percy stands in the litter of previous meals, shells of lobsters, crabs, and clams, whitened, pinkened in the sun, and beside them an old lobster trap, most of the laths broken off, a perfect carrying basket of eggs, and corn cobs, egg shells, chunks of potato and loose hay, the old culture, using the seaworn centuries afterward on land. "When they first came here," Carl Andersen told me, "they didn't know what to do with the lobsters and crabs, and there were so many of them, they just crushed them and fed them to horses and pigs." He says this with some astonishment and chagrin. Lobsters are what flow between the present-day economy and Mrs. Wentworth's color t.v. and the ferryboat and electric power, and Wesley Gove's world; and so Wesley uses lobsters as in the old days; this time, though, it is the shrinkage from Minturn Smythe's storage bins, the extra claws and backs, and those that are killed. It takes very little to change one world into another, either way: the slow progress of the glaciers, and power blackouts, a few laths knocked out, a sudden flood of cheap lobsters from dragging off the continental shelves. The worlds are separate, but the parts lie around, waiting to be made into one world or another, coherent only when they are used, often burned beyond recognition by the chagrined inhabitants of a later planet when they aren't. Obscurities, forgotten cults.

Wesley is looking for something to show us, "something that would interest your wife." He finds the old postcard of the horse and the ox yoked, Wesley Gove behind them in the seat, and another picture of himself with an accordion. "I used to play with Minturn Smythe when they had dances here. Now my hand's smashed so bad from falling off of Percy I can't do it; one finger's dead and the rest are going." Everything is in Corona cigar boxes: two letters from Dick Westbrook in Vorheesville, New York, who has dedicated a book to Wesley Gove, and would like to buy land on Swans, a note from the children to Percy, a picture of Wesley plowing, 1958 grocery lists, unexplained clippings of car accidents, or maybe what was on the back of them. He is looking for something but can't find it, perhaps it is a picture in the Stonington paper of himself and Marshall Dodge; he thinks someone has stolen it, reaching again and again the section in the paper from where it is torn. Then he finds the accordion. "Just wait," he says. "I'll find something to interest your wife." And we walk back outside, he's carrying the accordion in his left hand, and we call Lindy from the car where she has gone to put Robin to sleep out of the cold, and the three of us walk to the building on the road, the blacksmith shop which Wesley's father ran; there the sun is stronger, beams of it penetrating the sense of a museum, the old anvil standing lopsided, all the tools scattered on the floor, and a stable built halfway into the shop, like an intruder, where Percy is shod. Here in the history of it Wesley's story somehow began, and why he keeps this place, clings so tenaciously, kicking over a plastic jug of Percy's water that has frozen solid, into the sun where it will melt by late afternoon. "It's an embarrassment to Minturn and all of us," Mrs. Wentworth says. She's Minturn's mother-in-law. "You'd think that the people on Swans Island didn't care for each other. Why Minturn's offered to build him a new place every year, and he just won't let him." Mr. Wentworth: "What use is the place. They should burn it to the ground."

Which Wesley recalls with each building. "Yes, this is the only blacksmith shop left on the island, but they're going to set it on fire cause Minturn Smythe owns the world." And it's not even that Wesley believes in farming; he thinks it's a better world coming and hopes that Swans Island won't ever have to go back to farms. It's just this one thing, like

the thing itself, an island once the glacier cuts it off stays
there, and may run electric cables and color t.v. and phone
lines, but even Leon Power, Jr., at 23, wouldn't leave the
island for anything, despite the admission of everyone that
there's nothing to do and no one's getting rich. *Also no one's
paying rent.*

Perhaps Wesley Gove finds what he wants here where the
water jug lies frozen on its side, and the sun, and the Mount
Desert Range solidly set across ocean; here in Vinland or
Norway, not far from New Scotland, I can feel the occult
I was looking for, though it is not visible, just the way the
landscape creeps around here, turning with the road behind
the blacksmith shop, the distance of the forest, the wagon
lying unhitched, the plow, the rakes, the absolute litter, and
the dusty inside of the old mill. Wesley begins to play, and
the music is simply the sun on Swans Island, cold at this
distance we must be, and smoking a Corona, an uninten-
tional pun, the notes collecting slowly in the air cavity,
blown down the steps and thru the trees, the hard metallic
sound of steel, the distance to Scotland, or anyplace, to sheer
inhabitation, Swans Island, here where suddenly nostalgia,
and "time," and the word "old" I have been using as if mind-
lessly, cut finally the fabric of lobster price and return to
the most private of micro-environments. Perhaps he is happy; perhaps he can remember. I can, but I don't know what,
proving again that memory is not our only link to the past.
"The content of landscape is something less than the whole
of its visible constituents. The identity of the landscape is
determined first of all by conspicuousness of form. . . . .
Behind the present forms lie processal associations, previous
or ancestral forms, and almost inscrutable expressions of
time." Carl Sauer.

But the spell is broken. Wesley realizes that Percy has
disappeared around the bend, and goes into a tizzy. When
we came he was trying to get the ancient motor warm for
no other reason, to chase Percy when he went out of sight.
There is no front to the car, but old sacks stuffed into the
ventilator. Once he tried to carry an oil-stove in the back
seat to keep the engine warm, and he set the car on fire. Now
it barely starts, and I am down the road looking in the scrub

bushes and toward the sea for Percy. As I get more and more out of breath, and take in the cold air, I become part of the landscape; I age here as everywhere, and Wesley rushes past me in the sputtering car, cursing like mad. Percy stands at the top of the hill, eating the dead flowers by the roadside. I am not sure why Wesley is so flustered, but he wants no help, and we leave him, and go back into Swans Island Village.

At Clyde Pomroy's (2)

3 P.M., the sea like ice, most of the boats are in, tied to their moorings, the traps piled high atop each other on the wharf, more each day, covered with snow. Fishermen are not fishermen when they are not fishing. They are men. Sitting around. It is not the height of the lobster season anymore, and the men are also scarce, sluggish, keep slim hours, like decapods, and are gone by noon, and even then the sun appears very low in the sky. In the East.

Wesley Bracy is the one man still out at Pomroy's, and Clarence sits idly jamming the pegs in and out of a cribbage set, talking in spurts to one of the Pomroys. The fishermen say that Hawkes is a good egg, but about the other warden they bitch and bitch; on Swans Island they want to lynch him for taking a man out of his boat at sea. I ask Hawkes about it. He says simply: "The law's in this little book here, and I imagine two people can read it differently."

Why hasn't he been here lately?

"There's not much doing in his area this time of year, a few clammers, and some digging for marine worms."

Are wardens supposed to go into other areas to look for violations?

"I imagine that's up the person too. Some people just watch to see that things are going smoothly. Others are out looking for the law."

The conversations switches to a list of what there is to catch in the winter. "Precious thin," says one man. Hawkes mentions quahogs, and this gets Norman Pomroy's attentions.

"I didn't know there was any quahogs around here."

"Sure," says Clarence. "Why, just a couple of years ago a fella came here from outa state and bought up some land in Bar Harbor so he could dig quahogs; he got about four bushels at each low tide, and sold'em to the restaurants. He dug until it wasn't profitable. I suppose he dug 'em until there was too few to make it worth his while."

Laws, wardens, Pomroys, animals, and other laws; state of the winter, this far from what ice age?, or merely an interstadial between inevitable advances of ice? This far from anywhere, from where?, from starving. Everyone is rigging up for shrimp for the first time, as the waters change with sunspot cycles, spans of 13, and 60, and 90 years cast on the Earth, like the shadow of a furnace, or the cold shrimp-bearing wind of the Milky Way. Newfoundland moves south. They abandon the lobsters with November, too few, too cold, and Pomroys itself, the back room filled with colored nets, is taking on the look of a shrimp dealer.

Norman Pomroy is talking about the future of lobsters, and how it seems to be in the dragging for the big fellas, 15, 20 pounders on the continental shelf. "They're doing it in Massachusetts now. You'd think they'd ruin a lot of lobsters dragging them up that way, but a guy who's been going with 'em tells me that it's soft as shit out there, nothing but pure sand." He runs it thru his fingers. "Nothing but pure sand."

A short dark oily man comes in and begins speaking in an agitated voice, something about being late, and netting that broke, and he's looking for another Pomroy who's at Southwest Boat getting his snowmobile soldered. Someone asks where he's from.

"Gloucester. Gloucester, Massachusetts. Not Gloucester, Maine."

"How are things that way?" Norman asks. "I 'magine they're doing well."

"Oh, some of them are, but there's not enough fish for a chowder. The Russians and Pollacks got it all." He asks who I am, and when I tell him I'm doing a study, he snaps back:

"Yeah, and for all your studies in your universities what are you going to do about those foreigners in American

162

waters. Why they're gettin so close you can see 'em out there. Russians. Stealing our fish right from under our noses. They've got nets so fine not even the spawn can get thru. Yeah, a lot of good all your studies while we're being robbed. We pay our taxes so the Japs and British can build ships, then go fish out of our own waters, and sell us back the fish."

Can you buy fish in Gloucester that's imported from your own waters?

"Damned right I can, and 'fore long we're gonna have to do something about it."

"Captain's in," someone shouts. "Captain Bracy." I go down with Clarence and the boy where Wesley Bracy's unloading his boat, a grizzled old fisherman from Cranberry, sputtering about the weather and who the hell am I. But finally he settles down to watch Clarence measure.

"Jee-sus!" he says suddenly. "Know what happened." Very loud, flesh in his chin moving. "The last damn lobster grabbed the measure right outa my hand and gave it a heave overboard."

"No kidding," says Clarence.

"That's right."

"You have a diesel?" Clarence asks, going thru the lobsters rapidly, the boy waiting for the barrels to put them on the scale.

"Yes I do, and it doesn't cost me two dollars a day in gas. I've had her twenty years and she ain't never had a wrench t'her."

The status of materials holds another day, and Bracy rides his boat back out, a little push from Clarence clear of a boat filled with traps. Inside, Pomroy and the net-salesman from Gloucester are yelling at each other, a few minutes later the net-salesman has to make good, and he's hauling all his nets out of the back room grumbling, replacing them. All this time Lindy sits in a stuffed chair, by the heater and the window, nursing Robin to sleep and watching while someone unloads at the town pier, his dog in the boat running back and forth barking. It's no season really, as things are coming in, going out, the big yellow cat asleep in another chair and darkness quietly melting in. It's neither a time of plenty or of little. It's in between and everyone knows it, knows it's becoming another thing, as lobstering changes to shrimping, and the dealers keep the winter business, everyone preparing the Earth to handle new merchandise; from year to year no one knows, quahogs or marine worms, granite or shrimp. But it's the same unending flow, and cold winter is not the winter fifty years ago, but it has that name, and the stove burns the extra wood, the scallop-boats out catching the stew.

Lindy, reading *Life*, and all the big doings in the cities, where the eyes of the nation are, says somehow it's okay being here where the matter is lobsters, special because we can see what's really happening, downhome, where matter, and the Earth originates, while the cities remain a mask or shield. It's not obscured by the media, yet, and we can see, while someone else who's doing it maybe has to film junkies in New York or interview politicos in L.A.

This is *life*, not where it has already happened, there, but where it is happening, which is always *here*. Not a bad lot, nor a good lot, this far from the center, where things which are something else are something else yet again, and by seeing them as lobsters in 1969 we hold to a fix, while America changes.

V

Around the Horn

Sunday, December 21. Cold. Sunny.

A short day. But the lobster dealers are all open:

I stop first at Sewell Alley's; nothing happening, so I stand on the wharf, waiting. Visible from here is Johns Island, at the head of the harbor, a small round clump of trees, and lobster traps and crates thrown haphazardly on its shore beyond the tide. Looking back the other way I see Jasper's pier jutting out, the gasoline pump, the docking area, such a familiar cameo, but I have never seen it; I have always stood inside it.

The wharves of Alley's enclose a small area of sea, at low tide a muddy pool, in it giant oilcans breaking apart, thousands of blue mussels, some open, most of them full, the color of the light from the water, pearl and blue, a stagnation but a fertility, decay but garden.

Now Sewell Alley climbs from his boat with a pail and hands it to the older man who works for him. "I pulled up the last of them," he says, his boat filled with traps, "and this is all there were." In the pail are a couple of layers of white crabs.

"Thank you," he says, looking quite pleased. "Is there a container down in the house?"

"Go look. There just weren't many today, and they're not much eating. Hard as steel."

"Oh yeah?" the old man says. And with almost no gesture he dumps them out of the pail over the wharf and walks away. The workmen are carrying a giant log; they stand it in the water, adjust, and then let it go into a loop of rope which holds it in place to be hammered down into the sea.

165

When they're done I walk over to the edge and look into the water. It's a terrific drop into low tide, the crabs almost not visible, but a few bubbles marking the spot. Motionless, as though smashed on the rocks. Statues.

"They're frozen solid," Sewell says, walking up behind me. Then: "What are you doing here?"

I've been doing a study of lobster fishing, I say. Going around to all the dealers. I've been here before but always when you were out.

"I think you picked the wrong time of year."

[But lobstering is no time of year, is only what is visible on the surface of the moment, a name, and I call the phenomenon lobstering, what is really the life of these people, which is the same, whatever they do, calling it lobstering so as to work backwards to what it is].

*　*　*

From Jasper's I look back at Sewell's. I see one side of the enclosure of lobster sheds, mostly new white wood, and a fire next to where the construction is going on. The large old shed at the end of the wharf, Sunoco emblem, figures visible in their business, moving wood, carrying logs.

At Jasper's, one of the two winter boats is in, Wendell Seavey still out. "And I'm afraid I don't expect him before sunset," Jasper says. "But that's okay because I need the time to go over the books." He opens the ledger and sits down. The only person left to talk to is Emerick Cleaves, 80 year old fisherman who never likes to say much.

"Yes, I'm a lobsterman," he begins. "And the father of two fishermen here, and the grandfather of two more. I've been a lobsterman for fifty winters. But this winter I've got my traps up. And I begin to feel it piling thirty traps."

"Well, I begin to feel it too after thirty traps," Jasper says. "I don't know as you're any different than you ever was since I've known you, Emerick."

"I can tell the difference."

I ask him where he sells his lobsters.

"I sell to whoever I want." It appears he's not going to say any more, but he does. "I sell where I get the most. I've sold up to Stonington. And I've sold in Southwest."

Why do you sell here now?

"I sell here. Don't need no reason." Then: "Junior's a nice guy. So is Emery Levesque, and I've sold to him. You sell too often to a dealer and he thinks he owns a fellow. When I come in, that boat out there, I own every nail in it. And when I sell to Jasper it's because I thought I would. That's all."

Why do you suppose your son goes in one of Jasper's boats?

"I don't know why a man would go in another man's boat."

Ralston does, doesn't he?

"I reckon he does." And no more.

The door opens, first the dog comes in, then a small mild man dressed like a carpenter; talks to Jasper a few moments, after which he decides to stay. Emerick has been standing there quietly; suddenly he snaps a question at me: "You get lost in that tangle?" My beard, he means. I shrug neutrally, and try to change the subject. Emerick, who was your father?, and it was Joshua Cleaves, a carpenter, and Emerick, who was your grandfather?, and it was Jacob Cleaves, a carpenter, "and I guess he went to sea some."

Now the same questions of the new man, beginning with: What do you do?

"I'm a carpenter, have thirty, thirty-five traps down during the summer, haul'm at night, got a whaler, a sixteen foot boat."

Your father?

"Henry, what did my father do?"

"Why everything that Merle Buswell done'd fill a book. He was a handyman, a jack of all trades. I suppose he even went scalloping a bit, but he got seasick."

And your grandfather?

"Grandfather owned his own vessel; he went to the West Indies; isn't that right, Emerick?"

"Your grandfather never owned his own ship. He used to go with Merton on the sloop to Nova Scotia."

"He did? Grandfather Charlie went to Nova Scotia?"

"You were talking about your Grandfather Charlie Lunt?

Why I was talking about Bill Buswell. He went with Merton on the sloop to Nova Scotia."

Jasper gets up from his books and comes inside. They all stand there looking out the window. "No, I don't imagine I'll see hide nor tail of Wendell till after sunset."

Emerick: He's got to stay out and work. His wife's always got a big belly."

Jasper: "I see Robert Torrey's gone out after shrimp today."

Melvin: "Has he caught any yet."

Jasper: "I don't know whether you'd say he has. He brought Lee Tracy twenty-five pounds of picked-out ones yesterday."

Emerick: "That's no fortune."

Melvin: "Here comes a boat."

Emerick: "Floyd Phippen."

Jasper: "I do believe that's Floyd. There's no other boat like that." Chuckle.

Floyd comes in past everyone and draws Jasper into the office, takes a few packs of cigarettes, then says something about how he's going to pay only when Manset Boat ships the right material, and Jasper is full of "That's right, Floyd. I don't blame you, Floyd. I'd do the same thing." But Floyd is angry.

Emerick says, sort of under his breath to Melvin: "I think Floyd left his boat running." Which he did. Then he turns to me and asks where I'm living. I tell him Somesville, and his reaction is instant:

"Pigtown. Hogtown. That's what we used to call the place. When I drove the mail from Bar Harbor, Somesville was the one place they wouldn't let you put your horse under cover, no matter how bad it was raining or snowing."

"You drove the mail?" Melvin asks.

"I've done just about everything."

Jasper, coming out of the office, agrees. "Emerick's done everything there is to do."

"And at eighty, nothing bothers you anymore. You want to know where your last meal's from, and that's all."

Jasper: "I don't think you have to be eighty. I'm not eighty and less's bothering me than was."

We follow Jasper outside to one of the sheds where he pulls out some boxes from Manset Boat, addressed: F. W. STURLOW, c/o FLOYD PHIPPEN. They begin opening them and going thru the merchandise. Melvin Buswell goes back to work, and I stand there with Emerick Cleaves, and each time Jasper opens a box Emerick tells me how much the same thing cost in his day, those nails ten cents a pound, and that rope, but of course it was different rope.

Emerick asks me if I have any children. I say, a son, six months.

"You've got a long way to catch me. My oldest boy's fifty."

Now Jasper calls me and says there's a phone in the shed and if I pick it up I'll find my wife on the other side. Lindy says hello, and could you get some onions on the way home. She forgets it's Sunday, and the store is closed. Emerick Cleaves interrupts:

"Gott's Market open 56 days of the year. My daughter works there every other Sunday, and she's there today."

Melvin returns, and I ask him if he is related to the Lunts on Long Island.

"I've got some relatives on Swans Island."

No, I tell him. I mean the Lunts in Frenchboro.

"I don't know. For all I know I'm related to Floyd Phippen over there."

Jasper has loaded the stuff aboard Floyd's boat, and he's about to pull out, filling her with gasoline. Back in the shed Jasper is saying. "I don't know. I guess I'm just too big-hearted, too much of a fool."

"Floyd does sell you his lobsters when you're short," Emerick reminds him.

"I guess he does. But he's not the type who keeps at it. They're catching lobsters out at Frenchboro, but you ask Floyd, well you heard him, he'll tell you, not much fishing these days, nobody's going out after them. The fishermen that do just don't sell to Floyd. Look at his boat. He hasn't painted it in three years."

A truck pulls up, Fillmore Cleaves hauling a big piece of wood out of it, taking it down to the dock to help rig up his boat for shrimping, which changes the conversation to shrimping. "That's my grandson," Emerick says. Then he calls out, "Hey, do you need an eighty year old man to help you carry that?"

Jasper answers some questions by saying he doesn't have running water in his place, so he can't cook shrimp. Emerick reminds him that they cooked clams here in the old days, and that Sewell Alley dug a well so he could get cooking water. "I know. I know it, Emerick," Jasper says, shaking his head. "But it's more trouble than it's worth."

Is Sewell Alley buying shrimp?, I ask.

"His boat's in, and I imagine if you go over there he'll tell you whether he's buying shrimp or not as well as the next person, because I sure as hell can't tell you about anything going on down there."

*   *   *

"We were friends back in the old days," Sewell says. "I used to lobster for Jasper. But jesus how do you say it! Well, I mean Jasper leaves his books open, and anyone can look in and see what anyone else has caught for the whole week, and if you miss it there, you can always go down to Ronald Gott's store and pick it up. Now that ain't right! When I was first lobstering I went to Jasper because we were friends, we grew up together, but Jasper always had something to say, like that he could catch twice as many lobsters in half as much time, and maybe he could. One man's no judge of another. And I was just beginning. I can't listen to that sort of sarcastic humor all the time, always jabbing at a guy. So I went in with the guy here; at first we were partners; then I bought him out. They used to buy fish here. First year we bought lobsters I was the only guy, but each year it's been more and more. Some of the men fishing here I didn't even know, and some of my best friends don't fish for me. But men like it here because the books are closed, and there's no joking. We do our business here. Jasper and I used to be friends, but I haven't seen the inside of his place in ten years, even though we can walk back and forth just like that."

I ask him what his father did, and it turns out that he had

weirs around Black, Opechee, so I ask him about Buddy.

"We may even be relatives. I know we are in fact. But I don't want him here. I'm sure if you ask him he'll have as strong an opinion about me, and I have no doubt he's as good a man as I am. But I don't want him here. He just pulls, doesn't matter whose trap it is; he don't pick on no one special; he just hauls. I've had the warden out after him, but he's slippery, round the back of islands, and in fog."

Do you think he sells in Stonington because he gets a better price or because he can't sell here?

"A man always sells close to home. Closer the better. At least I do."

Are you going to buy shrimp?

"No, but I'm rigging up for shrimping this year."

It's expensive.

"Yes, it's a gamble. But life's a gamble, isn't it. I mean you wake up in the morning and you take a gamble. You don't know whether the day's going to be what you want it, or on some days you'd just as well stay in bed, but you don't know that."

*   *   *

Sewell leaves for lunch, and I drive around the harbor, past Johns Island, to the other side. From across the harbor Alley and Sturlow sit in the same pool of water, sharing the coast. No action on this side. Poking around, I push open a door, and find myself in a dark smoky room, ten older men sitting around the walls. Emery Levesque looks up. This is the oldest of the lobstering clubs; even when nothing is said it lies closest to the hearth of fishing, the inherited profession. "Do you know where Lee Tracy is?" I ask, to break the deadly silence I've caused. It may all be going on here, but in a hundred years I'll never know.

"Gone home," Emery says. "Be back tomorrow." The rest of them sit there, looking away.

Oh. I thought he might be here because he has a boat out.

"Well, maybe he doesn't know it."

*   *   *

So I complete the grand tour by driving to Pomroy's in Southwest Harbor. No fishermen out, a few hanging around in a card game, Clarence Hawkes watching.

"Twice in a row?" he says to me, meaning that he has seen me at Pomroy's on two consecutive days.

I've been to other places. Have you?

"I just bounce around."

You wouldn't want the men to think that just because you were here yesterday you wouldn't be back today.

"Oh, nothing like that. I just bounce around."

So are the relative positions fixed, and I drive home quite pleased, having forgotten the onions.

VI

At Lee Tracy's

Lee's sitting on a chair against the wall, his book-keeper Geneva Shea behind the desk. Any shrimp today?

"Nothing. Nothing Downeast and nothing here."

Did the shrimpers bring in any groundfish?

"What they did was all covered with gasoline. I couldn't use it."

So what do you do?

"Just what you see me doing now. I sit on my chair and wait. Maybe another month with the colder weather. If not next month, maybe the month after. Nothing to do but wait."

I ask Geneva Shea if she's related to the Sheas on Long Island.

"I imagine so. My husband Burdock's from there."

Why did he move in?

"I made him," she laughs. "That's why."

You didn't like it there?

"They've got nothing. And back then they had less, no electricity, no phones, you had to use lanterns, no doctor; even now they've electricity and phones there's nothing to do there."

Does your husband still fish out there?

"Yes. He knows the grounds. Fishes the same spot as his father."

Would he get his traps cut if he fished in here?

"Well, he tried it and he did. So he went back out there."

Does he know who did it?

"He has a pretty good idea. But otherwise they're all friends, they have an understanding, and he's a selectman here, you know." I step out of the way to let in a big-faced man with glasses.

"Hello, Ira," says Lee.

"Hiya, Lee."

"Here's another Shea. This is my son Ira. He's going shrimping this year."

Are you fishing for Lee?

"No, I'm not. Don't own my own boat, so I'm going with a friend in Bar Harbor, and we're selling in there to his father."

Lee: "What's he giving?"

"15 cents. But that's hearsay."

What are you giving, Lee?

"I pay what they pay to the west'ard. Portland. And that's 13 cents right now."

I ask Ira if he is still lobstering. "Forty pair still down, but they're twelve to fourteen miles offshore. I generally leave'm down till January."

Where do you lobster?

"Well, for one, right here."

Can you go out to Long Island if you want?

His mother laughs. "He does. He can go down there because he's part of the clan. He can go both places."

Is that an advantage?

She thinks about it, then laughs. "It's an advantage if you know the grounds."

Who are you shrimping with?

"My friend is Roger Pinkham the Third, and his father, who they call Roger Junior, is doing the buying."

Lee: "Is he buying the groundfish too?"

"He's buying everything."

I ask Ira what his arrangement is with Roger Pingham.

"I get one-third with expenses taken out, he gets one-third, the same, and the boat gets one-third, that's him."

So it's two-thirds: one-third?

"That's one way of looking at it."

Lee: "I still think it's a pretty good deal. He has the boat and. . . ."

"I don't want to buy a boat anyway. He's got everything, even the fishing nets in case we have to switch over."

Where do you shrimp?

"Where do we tow for shrimp? Over in the bay."

Do you get in trouble with lobstermen?

He laughs. "The Bay is filled with traps. We just gotta get in trouble. But they'll take them up. They're not happy, but Winter Harbor's got its traps up already, and I imagine Bar Harbor, Corea, and Cranberry Isles and the other places will get theirs up before we tow."

What happens if they don't?

"They have to. Otherwise their lines'll get ripped out. We keep in touch on the radio, and when they hear us coming in, they'll pull up."

How about shrimp boats with each other?

"The small ones stay out of the way of the big ones. If they didn't they'd get picked up and pulled along with the shrimp. Otherwise anybody can fish anywhere, but you stay out of where somebody's already fishing. You give him enough room so you don't snarl nets. This year there are going to be thirty boats in a pretty small area."

Do the islands have their own shrimping areas, like lobstering areas?

"I think they're hanging fairly well together, at least so far."

"Well, Lee," says Geneva. "I think I'm going to get me home."

"Nothing else to do, is there?"

She closes the book. I ask Ira how old he is. "Twenty-two." And is he married. They all laugh.

"No, he's not," Geneva says, putting on her coat, "but I'm hoping he'll surprise us one of these days."

"Oh no I won't. It's a bad business. I can't afford it."

One last question. I was just curious if you knew Floyd Phippen out on Long Island. They look at each other with half-smiles, so I add, I mean he gets teased a lot in here and I was wondering if it was true in Frenchboro also.

Geneva answers. "Floyd doesn't conform. He's from away, from outside. He works for himself, for Floyd Phippen and not the community. So he's a little bit on the outside you might say."

Lee: "Floyd gets what he asks for. A gull crippled and the crows'll pick the hell out of them."

175

Geneva: "Say that again so I can hear it."

Lee: "It works both ways. A crow crippled and the gulls'll pick the hell out him. It's a law of nature. It's not something I made up. I saw it. Coming back from Corea we saw this crow crippled. We set right there. Two goddamned gulls just picked at him till he keeled over. He was hurt. They flew into him. We sat on the beach. It was muddy. We couldn't get to him."

Geneva: "I suppose it is a law of nature. Once the crow's crippled he can't fly."

VII

Mount Desert Calls Out Its Liberals

Its cityfolk.

Like one woman who has lived in Bar Harbor for thirty years and thinks, yes, there may be some lobsterfishing left on the backside of the island. She'd know only if she read about it in the *New York Times*, were informed from that distance as thru the grist mill synthesis of chic reading matter.

They hold parties and sing along with the score from *Hair!*, talking about Jews in the city.

Anti-war vigils in Bar Harbor. Vigilant to what? The Bar Harbor Bank and the First National in their pockets. Sponsored by the fascists for their own amusement. No threat locally; the liberals are safely engaged in a new petition to Mr. President.

Nationally oriented means the War in Vietnam, and smog in L.A., and outside help. The six-thirty news is more essential than the action on the wharf, or the role their own employer plays in the corporate structure of Maine.

Debates with snowmobilers. Keep the seacoast clean. No Oil Refinery in Machiasport.

And Christmas carols.

Who are they kidding, who were last on every bandwagon?, and still frown on their children's extracurricular activities. National Parks in America only let the people in to fuck up the land with their decaying gestalts of nothing. If conservation means parks and not human use of terrain, scenic graveyards in farm country, then I'm for the man who stands before the Ozarks and on Black Island, with his gun and no right to and says keep off. Because THAT'S turning in your dollars for silver, and demanding it right now, what lies behind the flimflam of the system. It's not the white liberals that are being hurt, or even the White Panthers, created by cowboy movies and Zen soap operas. It's not enough to be right; you have to live. You have to know what's happening to the core, or in that invisible mirror you will find yourself building it up again from scratch, even on your commune or in your liberated city. Which is why the children of the Weathermen will have to wander in the desert for forty years until their fascist parents, who answered My Lai with My Lai, are dead.

Keeping oil out of Machiasport is a good sentiment, but what about those in the city all winter, living off Alaskan oilfields and the great beds of the Atlantic and Gulf of Mexico, drained into apartment buildings, Indian and Cranberry coal. The Sierra Club woman calls me from New York, can't speak long, been on the phone long distance all night (wherever the hell that is that we're supposed to be). She got my name and number from a poet she met, says they're all coming to Washington County. I went to get the people organized against the refinery there. Les theoreticians from la cité.

Have you ever been to Washington County?

"No. I went to summer camp in Maine once."

Are going to come into Washington County cold, and even expect to see something! Let alone leaflet, organize, picket, announce the Sierra Club program for peace on earth to the local populace. They don't see it because they are playing the other side of the tyrannical coin. But it is just this sort of tender, both ways, that has gotten us to where we are. As witness the Soviet factories. Dirtier even than the American sewers if that's possible. Purpose, production driving the Marxist ape, Sinanthropus, in wild paranoid circles, even as it drives the American eagle, to exterminate the American eagle, for the King, or King of the White House Lawn, or worker as King. It's still that screwed-up dream of getting from nowhere to somewhere on a planet that is round.

Or witness, in the mirror, the Sierra Club publications. Colored books of expensive kodachrome islands and frozen animals, is to make of nature exactly the one thing that can't be used except to sell the books as insipid porn, or to bring summer people trooping in and out of the landscape like Israelis running thru Muslim mosques.

The conservationists in fact serve the cause of the usurers and despoilers by drawing attention away from the total mafioso operation, the U.S.-Russian conspiracy, with petty victories. No Oil in Machiasport. While they drill off Texas and California. And begin quietly on the jetport in the Everglades. Let one redneck say on t.v., "I just can't believe they're going to favor animals over people for too long," and they're drawn like flies.

Pound here: "Pacifists who refuse to examine all causes of war, from natural fitfulness on through the direct economic causes, are simple vermin, whatever their level of consciousness, their awareness or unawareness of the nature of their actions and motivations."

We have lost nature exactly by isolating it, by making it the rigid object of theories and sentiments, by confusing idealism with use, keeping it virgin in lieu of ever having to fuck it properly, a poor troubadour poet toasting nature with a martini, or the patriotic wish not to let anyone touch that woman now that the whole nation has raped her.

There is no solution in stasis; let the motion continue to where it's going; let the blood flow.

The only thing we can do about nature is respond to our own; that is properly to dig our place in it and keep it fertile, to run in its course and be taught thru our lives what we have become.

This is not a snapshot album, glorification of image, waste of dyes and chromatids. Which is nature as sideshow, billboard, and gets the philistines out of their backyards where they weren't doing much anyway, spiritual or earthy, out into the wilderness where they can spread their disease and really mess something up. It is the distraction from home and family which is so dangerous and titillating, stirs people out of the one place where they can do any good, itself. The Sierra Club appeals to nature as a sphere separate of life, to which we go as special, as vacation, vacating, to see exceptional beauty, nature prettier than itself. And so cut nature off and make it an implement of our destruction of ourselves. There is a conscious web of creatures and beings in general on this earth, as well as a web of waste and regeneration, and I am concerned with keeping the bears alive, and keeping their shit in the ground and the berries and fish they eat. But not to eat garbage from campers and pose for Brownie Hawkeyes, which they call our national heritage. God knows we've never had it to give it away.

And nature has never been out there, we in here, unless of course you take everything out of context, a few lines from Longfellow or Wordsworth, cracking apart syntax for a kernel of banal loveliness.

It's rhetoric, propaganda.

Choosing what's beautiful at a whimsical moment, extracting it from the living flow until it dies from inability to suck the wrinkled tit that nourishes it. Sampling nature like delicious wine. He who praises the ugly duckling for its charm usually ends up shooting it or torturing it when he runs out of other things to do.

We have never been able to use nature as a model, we who ARE nature, but the Sierra Club for two thousand years has been trying to sell us a false bill of goods, a travelogue, has been working with Madison Avenue and *Playboy* to pump the economy. Go here! Save this! Desire this!

How do THEY know? Have they ever been there?

I will post a NO TRESSPASSING sign too. PHYSICIAN, HEAL THYSELF!

VIII

The wind drives the rain along the wharf, and the sea comes crashing up onto the stone. The water is dirt-red, drowning the lobsters in mud, so Jasper takes them across the harbor in a little outboard, a string of crates behind him, and ties them up where the salt-blue water remains. It is not enough: money is lost, traps are lost, the day itself opens and closes in darkness, the boats tied to the harbor, and not even they are safe. Trees fall cutting down phone lines and electrical lines, and we fall out of the century: the water-pump fails, the heater kicks off, and the icebox, with its supply of protein, begins to leak across the floor. The roads disappear into the storm, and the soft elemental is thrashed in ribbons onto stone, which is earth, which is wood or glass or pavement, passing at forty and fifty miles an hour thru a world, and thru a business-world where men wait.

"When stars fall or trees make a [strange] noise, all people in the state are afraid and ask, 'Why?' I reply: There is no need to ask why. These are changes of heaven and earth, the transformation of yin and yang, and rare occurrences. It is all right to marvel at them, but wrong to fear them. For there has been no age that has not had the experience of eclipses of the sun and moon, unreasonable rain or wind, or occasional appearance of strange stars. If the ruler is enlightened and the government peaceful, even if all of these things happen at the same time, they would do no harm. If the ruler is unenlightened and the government follows a dangerous course, even if [only] one of them occurs, it would do no good." Hsün Tzu, Third Century B.C.

But when Calvin Coolidge or Richard Nixon is ruler, Warren Harding, or Herbert Hoover, or LBJ, what can the peo-

181

ple do to protect their families, how can they escape the polarization of forces? Bangor Hydroelectric moves slow as a tortoise, as overtime, to repair the lines, and the Insurance Companies wrangle over a few dollars here and there, not paying in the meantime while interest rates go up, and Captain Hook stands over the Boston market squeezing down the price of sea-goods. The state is in danger, and yin opposes yang openly in the streets. These storms over coastal Maine have names, and prices, and the city fears ultimate cut-off from the farm, even as the farm fears both its closeness and distance to the city. It is no longer weather we watch, but human revolution, man is one of the planetary systems, coins. And we feel even when the storm ends, when the roads are clear and the lines are restored, that this is just on more hyperstasis; a manifestation of the heavenly storm has ended, but the storm itself continues, Ming, Mandate of Heaven passing from China into the Western World.

What can man, can one Ameri-man do (root: without the sea)? But inside the lobster shed the old wood stove burns, making the incomplete stone, the black, but giving off heat in our time. Fuel. On the wall a calendar of nudes, square holes cut out of the breasts to include the nipples. What is left for these two fifty year old Americans, Fred Beal and Haskell Rich sitting in their workroom with sandwiches, the radio soft static, the wet red and white of painted lobster buoys drying in the flame? "Gale warnings from Block Island to Eastport." Gale warnings in government and currency, origin of the Dylan line: *You don't need to be a weatherman to know which way the wind blows.*

Lobstering, farming, winter. They sit in their work rooms joining the wood, netting, cleaning the traps, as the farmer on Cranberry or Swans cutting wood all winter for the next two. The women are working in the home; the sea is closed, so the men work in the shed, the barn. The world goes where there is world, and inside the shack, and. . . . . *Everyone who's not right this minute being born is: DYING.* Dylan again.

The wharf is littered from end to end with starfish cleaned out of the traps, reminiscent of the astrals, dead but seeming to come alive in water. And the skeletons of redfish. And

seaweed washed between the cracks.
        a land which is indistinguishable from a water
        a light which is indistinguishable from a sun
        is a daylight,
                        40 photons out of every million falling
into the mechanism of the sea

IX

Dear BZ Copter,

We never fail to listen to you when we are sitting in our sheds watching the jam-ups of fishing boats coming in from a day's work. It gives us pleasure, around the stove at the dealers, to think that not only don't we live in Boston, but we have never been in Boston. The closest we have come to Boston is you, and the six-thirty news.

Every morning coming to work we turn you on. Your signal is loud and clear. That is if we can keep from getting there too quickly. During the ad. In which case we miss you altogether.

Which is a shame.

Just yesterday a car pulled out in front of us on 102 and cost us a full thirty seconds. If only you could have warned us we would have taken an alternate route.

Last week there was a truck parked in front of Sawyer's Market, and it took us five minutes instead of three to make it to the wharf.

And a pedestrian on Clark Point Road today was the last straw. If only we could have had your listing of alternate routes we would have avoided him.

Our hope is that you can take a slight detour around sun-up one of these mornings to Bernard, Maine, and give us a local report, including detours, alternate routes, and heavy traffic to and from the wharfs. At sundown you might give us a description of the harbor, and boats waiting to get in at each dealer. This would much facilitate our hurried schedule and add to the pleasure we have in living here.

Sincerely,
Two Fishermen in Bernard, Maine

Dear Fishermen:
   Where in hell is Bernard, Maine?
   Sincerely,
   BZ Copter

X

At Frank Townsend's

We go there again hoping to find Vance Sawyer again.
"You won't find Vance in there," says Joe Turner, working
on a rowboat. "But his brother Les's down from North
Haven." We go in; Lindy goes thru to the corner and sits
by the Coke machine; I walk up to the front. A man about
the age of and elfin look of Gary Snyder, but hard set eyes,
and a trim straw-red beard, sitting on a chair, looks at me
very carefully. I tell him all about Vance, and he still looks
me over very carefully, says nothing. Then if I can ask him
questions about lobstering? "You can *ask* me anything you
want."

Can I tape it, or should I write it down?

He points to the pad. "Write."

What brings you from North Haven?

"Money."

You selling your lobsters here?

"I sell in Little Deer Isle. Sometimes."

Do you get more money there than in North Haven?

"It depends on how you want to look at it."

How do you look at it?

"I don't know. How do you?"

Well, like how many lobsters you got with you now?

"I got no lobsters."

So you're not really selling on this trip?

"Don't seem as I have anything to sell."

Do you have traps down now?

"I've got some."

Do you do anything else during the winter aside from
lobsters?

"I go scalloping. But I'm waiting for New Year's."

Any reason?

"Well, the way I look at it my scallop license, State of Maine, says 1970, and this ain't 70."

Lindy: "Are they strict?"

"I imagine if you got caught they'd be strict."

So you're going both lobstering and scalloping this winter.

"I'm not going lobstering."

But you still have traps down.

"That's because I haven't taken them up yet."

Do most of the people in North Haven take up their traps?

"There's not much lobstering in North Haven during the winter."

What do the people do?

"A little bit of everything."

What does that include?

"A little bit of everything. Carpenters. Caretakers for estates. I stick to commercial fishing."

What else do you do beside scallop in the winter?

"Shrimping. Stop-twining."

What's that?

"Sardines."

Is it seining?

"It's one type of seining. It's called stop-twining because you stop a cove off to do it in."

Why did you move to North Haven?"

"Many reasons."

Were some of them business?

"All of them were business."

Is it cheaper to live in North Haven?

"It's more expensive."

Then what are the advantages?

"It's an island, and on an island taxes are cheaper. There's not so much competition."

Did you have trouble with your traps getting cut at first?

"They still get cut, but I never caught anybody."

Do you ever sell in North Haven?

"Once in a great while."

You say you're rigging up for scalloping. Do you do that here or there?

187

"Some here. Some there."

Do other people from North Haven come here?

"They go to Rockland?"

Why don't you go to Rockland?

"I know people here. When you know people it's easier to get things done."

How many traps do you have down?

No answer.

Do you not want to say?

"You won't get the truth about traps from any fisherman."

Why do you think that is?

"Because a bunch of fishermen are the damnedst liars. That's why."

But what's a good reason? Like how can it be used against you?

"It can't be used against you. It just ain't nothing a fisherman will tell."

Now Frank comes back in. He was there at the beginning; said, "I better get out. Last time you were here I left and you got a whole lot of good stuff. Men won't talk if I'm around."

Frank, why do you think the price is higher here than in Mount Desert? I've gotten as many answers as people I've asked.

"Well, it's like two goats, wang! together, that's the way the dealers are here, all fighting." He slams two fists together.

I asked them down at the Co-op, and they told me it's because they catch a better lobster here, and I didn't believe it until Hinckley told me he'd pay more for a Stonington lobster.'

"That's right. And I'll tell you what they do. They mix Stonington lobsters in with their others so they'll have more selects and their lobsters'll look better. That's why Hinckley will pay more. But I don't get paid any more for my lobsters in Boston. So I'm getting ten cents less a pound than the dealers in Mount Desert."

Les: "But how much are they giving under the counter, Frank?"

"Nothing under the counter."

"Oh, c'mon now."

"I'm right. I know about these things, you know. I make it my business. It is my business."

As Frank talks many of the men gather around Santa-Claus-Scrooge.

"We all know you're too generous, Frank."

"Not a word of the truth."

Frank: "Everything I say is the truth. 'Course sometimes you don't know what I've said. Once the feds was here, you know the federal government men. They thought I owed them some money. I answered all their questions, not hurried like, just nice and slow, and when they were done, they said, 'You're the damnedest liar I ever saw.' But I told them. It's all the truth. They ended up paying me two thousand dollars. Everything I said was the truth. It's just that it can be taken two ways, two different ways. That's for them to decide."

Is that a skill, Frank?

"I don't know if it is or not."

Les: "You've done all right by it, Frank."

I turn back to Les Sawyer.

Do the traps from North Haven get in the way of anywhere else?

"No," he says, with a very small smile. "Traps from other people get in the way of North Haven."

"That's good lobstering there," Frank throws in. "Vinalhaven. North Haven. Selects there. You can mix those in and make a good batch. Some trashy lobsters too."

Les: "You fish from an outboard near North Haven you get trashy lobsters, but you go way out and you get good ones."

A young lobsterman comes in, looks Les over very carefully. "Hello, Les."

Les looks up at him, and down. "Hello, there."

I feel that Les is somehow trying to tell me something, and I haven't felt the bite yet. However, this is how it ends:

Is your wife from here or North Haven?

"North Haven. She's at home. Where she belongs."

XI

Fish. Fish. Cod. Pollack. Haddock. Hake. Menhaden.
Flounder. A nation's first wheat-field. The farm in the background as long as men can go to sea: Matinicus Island and
Swans Island, Mount Desert and the Cranberries. Inhabitable
as the ocean around them is filled with spawn, with the
young becoming full in schools: hard clams, soft clams, quahogs, mussels, razor clams, sea scallops, shrimp, bloodworms,
sandworms, and the blue clam comes north with the squid
into warm years, found in lobster pots downeast to Stonington. "In 1958 the Central Maine Power Company com-
menced operation of a fossil fuel, steam electric, power station on Cousins Island in Casco Bay." Here the waters of
widely varying temperatures are mixed and transported to
specific sites within the cove, giant rocks like granites and
schists are dropped with cement blocks into the water. A
thermal farm/sun on Monhegan and all the islands these
many years, turn to the sea for cash, for sustenance, the only
hope to support a planet, three/fourths of it lies beneath.
Hatching as the invisible powers of the moon left on the
beach between tides. The flesh clinging to the rocks, and to
old tires and abandoned traps.

Agriculture begins in mariculture, aquaculture. Hunting
begins in scavenging. The sea is first and only and other.
Culture is seashore. Here the turtles and birds lay their
eggs, crabs, mammals, fish, edible shoots, washed up on the
beach; male and female are equally amphibious, access bilat-
eral. Passed over by the seafaring nations, the patrilineal
and matrilineal coming to launch the ships built inland, dis-
persal from continent to continent. Sea becomes luxury,
once each world age, before sea becomes necessity again.
Twice has sea been necessity: birth of human genes in the

starfish, amphibious larvae, carry the ocean, the wet pocket within them onto the land; second time is migration, location and relocation of races, Neanderthal, Cabot, Mongolian and Nadene icefields, ocean is Azilian culture, fishhooks, harpoon bones, salmon runs. Ocean becomes luxury, depot of city's sewage, source of pearls the Spaniards have the Seri Indians dive for and pay them; fishermen on the Cranberries, earning a mouthful for the city in George's Banks, become lobstermen. The market falls out of saltfish, Stanley Fish burns to the ground and is not rebuilt, Lunts and beals open lobsterplaces. The last great field left to man is the ocean, as Kansas runs off into it, iodine and all.

The city of the earth hits the San Francisco coast and rebounds, the communes of New Mexico and Arizona, now returning to Maine and Vermont, the forest passed thru in entering now passed thru again in re-entering, even as Jones Tracy guards the door, and Fred Tracy, and eighty-eight dead rabbits on a stick between them. We've done it in the textile south; the war is over, dragging nature with a net for a prize, slippery female body/eyes in every fish, throwing out her curves, singing, now here, now there. To industry, following. We leave the inner warmed planets, Venus and its country homes, its farms and taverns. We are caught on a cold winter's night in transit to the outer planets of America's fate, the last heavies to be recorded in Ming, Neptune, Uranus, the salts, the gushing back out the sardine factory, currents of eggs washed thru the book of changes, thru the shoals, and lobstermen cutting each other's buoys from the lines and attaching their own; there's no parking lot in New York where you can leave anything in your car; thievery's a recognized business, the Mafia has its own political party, senators and mayors.

For the sea is the book of changes as the sky is the book of changes, thru the shoals, and lobstermen cutting each marks, wind blowing the waters this way and that, out over. A ship sinks and is fair game. A scallop boat tears up a stretch of lobster traps. We pass freely among the objects of our consequences, as floating lands, planetoids, their absolute space, place revealed head-on, wound taut to spring in the sun, is their, our, history, as men among. Island farms and orchards. Monhegan. World-base. Casco Bay. To watch the species grow by the laws of species, fill the ocean, to pursue the species in the ships of men. The laws of society pursue the laws of nature, the free beasts on which the machine runs, and the law is the same from lobster-spore to diesel-boat, shapes cupped easily to assume each other. The hunt. The farm. The horrid hide-and-go-seek of the three pigs. A mark left, says Gerrit, "from microspore to megalith," or Jocelyn, 1670: "From Sagadahoc to Nova Scotia, is called the Duke of York's Province. Here are Pemaquid, Nuscataquid, Montinicus, Mohegan, Capeanawhagen, where Capt. Smith fished for whales; all filled with dwelling houses and stages for fishermen, and have plenty of cattle, arable land and marshes. Nova Scotia was sold by Lord Starling to the French, and is now wholly in their possession."

Do you not see the poisons floating from the inland homes and factories, corpses and logjams of decaying vegetables, bubbling oxygen pots? Do you not see is the soft law of other, touch and deflect? "The softest things in the world overcome the hardest things in the world." *Lao Tzu.* Do you not see a nation under Ming, the individual stars burning at sea, floating in to landings at the points along the coast, is history? is the time of a nation. As James Monroe, 1816, in a journey of the Northern states, comes to Portland, to Stroudwater Bridge, to see a calf of 1,300 weight "at which he expressed great admiration." Do you not see it, the nation in mass, in tons of it, remains, Olson, a one?, an individual sash of consequence. Drunk to the hilt with it, an abundance imagined in tall tales, the endless power of heroes, meaning Jones Tracy, the white man. And Chauncy Somes says: "The blueberries was so thick on Brown's mountain that he got out on the end of the bowsprit and stepped ashore, and when she swung around on the other tack he jumped on the stern and had a firkin full of blueberries."

So we warn Ali about the computer, that it's programmed by a white man, has no voice of its own, Clay versus Marciano, undefeated White man takes on undefeated Black man, three weeks later the White man is killed, which is the real ending of the decade, the punch that is thrown, not acted, the force of the cities working against Jones Tracy and Marciano; the computer must look to the macrocosm, for the momenta, motions, black and white, that move these men.

"Well, Jones went hunting, and in those days they was these wild turkeys, and . . . he only had one bullet and he said they was fifteen of them in the family, and he knew one turkey wouldn't be any good, so he'd have to weigh these shots to hit two turkeys anyway. So, he run along side of a rock. And old Jones said, 'I aimed right for a point on that rock and split the bullet and killed both of those turkeys.' And he said, 'That gun kicked me so,' he said, 'that it kicked me over into the brook,' and he said, 'When I come up the seat of my pants was so full of trout,' he said, 'that it burst off the suspender button and shot a partridge.' "

Which is what we should warn Ali, and Black Panthers everywhere about the computer, and price on the market, and what he's going to do with that one bullet when that's all he has left.

XII

January 1

Harvey Rich and Fred Beal are standing on the wharf outside the bait room, cold choppy sea, none of the boats out. "For Chrissakes, get back to to to . . . . Southwest! Is that where you're from?" Fred says to me as I arrive. Harvey has turned around and is walking back thru the bait room. "Here, here. Harve, look here!" Fred says.

Harvey comes and looks out. "Yeah, he's got a GM in her."

Fred: "He's going to go somewhere with it, wait till he cuts it on to her."

Harvey: "Yeah, she's got a GM, a 471, just what I have, same kind of engine. Exhaust comes out of the side, down there."

Fred: "Yeah, I know that, yeah."

Harvey: "Jeez, they're expensive. Good engine, though. A real workhorse. What's he doing with it?

Fred: "Christ, it's hard to tell. Unless the ferry broke down over Swan's Island. . . ."

Harvey: "Cause that's one of their boats, Beal and Bunker. Yes, I think that's what it is. Cause he went in that terminal. . . . ."

Fred: "And he got those passengers. He came up here, then he went back down there and got one on the other side."

They stand watching the boat for a few minutes; then Fred heads up the ladder to his shed. Are you Harvey Rich? I ask, making sure.

"No, he's Harvey Poor," Fred calls down. "Be careful, Harvey. Be careful, Harvey. Watch it. Watch it." Fred: always like a bird on his perch, calling down, cawing, now, after the final word, going in.

You're going scalloping with Wendell, I guess? I asked him the other day why he wasn't going alone or with some-one in his boat, and he said, 'When you go scalloping, you go with someone who knows how to scallop.'

"Wendell and I are cousins, you know. His grandmother and my grandmother are sisters so I guess that makes us second-cousins, doesn't it?"

Exactly that.

"I've done a little of everything. When I got out of the service, I had rheumatic fever, infected tonsils, couldn't work for a year, so I worked over at Hinckley's boat shop, just so I'd have something to do for a year. I got allergic to the materials they was using. I'm kind of an outdoor fellow. I like the outdoor life, so I figured I'd get me a boat of my own and start fishing again; I like the life."

How do you decide when to go scalloping and when to go lobstering?

"Well, this scalloping is a fill-in sort of thing. I go when I can't go lobstering. But I go lobstering mainly. I go scal-loping every now and then, make a little money, get some-thing to eat, you know what I mean."

Did nobody go out today?

"It's stormy this morning. I imagine they'll be out tomor-row. In New York, though, they're talking about this snow spreading across the Great Lakes, supposed to be down here tomorrow. I suppose there's not much we can do about it, though. We'll see tomorrow."

Were you out at all this week?

"Well, let's see. What is today? Today's Thursday. I was out Tuesday. I was out yesterday, but I come back, I didn't feel good. There was a storm at sea, and it was shifting the traps around. But I stayed out all day Tuesday. Out 30, 35 fathoms where I go, it's shifty, choppy."

Does it hurt financially when you don't go every day?

"You have to let it set now; see, we're fishing off, I'm fishing off in 60, 65 fathoms of water. And the lobsters don't crawl fast out there. You've got to give them, you should give them at least four nights set. Anything less than that, well, you drop down considerably. Of course, it's a different world out there. Their characteristics out there are all dif-

195

ferent. They don't act the way they do on the shore. It's just different altogether. You find, oh bunches of lobsters you know. One place you've got to fish them in a certain way; in another place it's different. I've been chasing them this year. I've read a book, this T. M. Prudden, I believe it was, published on lobsters, this one thing: they didn't think that lobsters migrated, I've got to contradict that, I'm catching lobsters, I'm offshore now about 18 miles, and I'm catching lobsters that these boys have been catching in here on the shoal bottom around the shore, with the V-notch or deflected middle flipper, and they have this yellow band around the claw, right on the joint, so you recognize them, it would be quite easy if you got them in your haul and you weren't looking, and they put that band up over his arm just to identify him, that he's a punched lobster, well I've been catching them 18 miles offshore."

And they couldn't have been banded out there?

"Nobody else is fishing out there, nobody but me. Nobody ever's been fishing out there. It's bottom that you couldn't fish unless you have this modern equipment as we've got today, like styrofoam buoys and floating rope, you couldn't do it. And those lobsters are coming from in here on shore. It's just a school of lobsters that went out over that bottom, and I don't know how far they're going until they stop. But I've been chasing them now for about ten miles. And I'm staying right with them."

I've read the same books. They tagged the lobsters and found that they don't move more than a couple of miles.

"That's a strange thing. I don't know if they're the same lobster they're studying. I was there about twenty-five miles offshore, and I was in depths up to eighty-two fathoms, and I caught lobsters, V-notched lobsters, and lobsters with those yellow bands on them that had to come from in on the shore because no one else fishes out there. I don't know. I think the lobster's a pretty hard old fellow to really understand."

The one study I read was done around Monhegan cause they have a closed season. Maybe it's different there.

"I would think so, 'cause we've got the depths of water. I mean our bottom deepens, our water deepens faster than a lot of places. Monhegan's pretty even bottom. But we can go after them, we can get out there; we're getting in forty, fifty, seventy fathom water. It gives you a pretty good idea of what they're doing, more so than downeast and those places, they can go way off, and they never use more than fifty fathoms warp; fifty fathoms warp you wouldn't be in more than thirty-five fathoms water."

Are you at all worried about the experiments with raising lobsters, like on a farm? That would end the business of catching them.

"I don't think that would be too good. There would be a few'd make something from it, and there'd be a lot of people who suffer from it. I think they should leave the thing just as it is, let Mother Nature take care of it, of that end of it. When you start putting restrictions on yourself, you better be damn sure you know what you're doing. It may be one way this year, next year altogether different. This has been an unusual year. And we're the ones who have to deal with Mother Nature and the elements and all. Like I'm thoroughly convinced that these lobsters came in from the continental shelf. I've never seen lobsters with so many so big; these lobsters must weigh four or five pounds, all the measure will allow. Now where would a lobster that big, where would he hang out all these years, with all these traps so close?, just lookit here at all these buoys, now I can't see why so many of these big lobsters, these four and five pound ones, escaped lobster traps all these years; they'd have to get that big; they only grow about half an inch a year; it would take six or seven years to come up to that five inch measure."

Do you get other things in your traps out there that you wouldn't get in here?

"Well, there's a crab out there; I think they call it a Queen Crab; it resembles a King Crab somewhat. Some have horns on them. They're not much good eating, though, too tough."

I thank Harvey for chatting in the cold, and head up the stairs to see what Fred's doing in his shed. Bending over in the narrow passage, I open the door.

"Come in. Come in."

I just wanted to see what you were doing on a blowy day.

"Just playing around, that's all." He is brushing off a buoy with a cloth. "Just doing something to keep the wolf away from the door."

Are you painting buoys?

"No. I'm just cleaning them. Just starting in cleaning them. That's all. Hey, get over by the stove. Your feet must be cold."

I haven't been outside long enough to get cold.

"Come on. Come on now. You warm up."

You suppose the Swans Island Ferry really broke down?

"That may be. I wouldn't be quoted on it, but it seemed that Beal and Bunker was picking up the passengers."

Maybe the holiday . . .

"And maybe they're a private party. That may be now. That just may be the reason."

Do you ever see any of your relatives out on Swans Island anymore?

"Nah! I haven't got any relatives out there."

Not Kenneth Beal? Annie Beal?

"We ain't got nothing in common. It's two different worlds, here and there's two different worlds."

You still fish out there?

"I fish out there, yeah."

And they don't give you any trouble?

An outraged "Noooo!" "I've fished out there longer than most of them. How can you——I mean I'm fifty years of age, I've fished out there longer than most of their fathers; how can you——you know what I mean, don't you?"

Yeah. Now, who was your grandfather on Swans Island?

"My grandfather on Swans Island? That was Fillmore Beal."

What did he do?

"Do you know Wesley Gove? Well, he was just like Wesley Gove. He was a farmer. You know over by the old quarry wharf? He had a big field there."

Was farming good?

"Oh no no no no. It wasn't good farming. But that's the only things he knew."

What did he raise?

"You mean for crops?"

Yeah.

"Survival. He had potatoes, and he had his oxen, and he

198

hauled wood, and then he'd raise a steer, and perhaps a couple of pigs. He'd live off the land as best as he could. You know these birds down there in the harbor?"

The gulls?

"No. No. No. I mean the ones swimming. They call them dippers, cute little things. Well, back in those days you wouldn't see a one of them, everyone'd shoot them for dinner. Now you see them."

Was there a law passed?

"No, anyone could go out right now and shoot them. But thing's was different then is what I'm saying. It was a different life. There wasn't that much money. You'd catch one of those and throw it in a pot with vegetables and at least you'd have a soup for the night. Get you thru one night."

Was your grandfather born on Swans Island?

"No, my grandfather was born on Burnt Island, right by Isle Au Haut; his father owned it. Then my father, he was born on Marshall's; right now the man that owns that wants a million for it, and he'll get it."

What did your grandfather do on Burnt Island? Fish? Keep weirs?

"He lived there. His father owned it. The whole thing."

What did his father do?

"I don't know. I don't go back that far. I never looked it up."

What's going on at Burnt Island right now?

"I've got an idea Burnt Island is probably worth just as much money as Marshall's. The people from the city; they're coming up and taking over. I don't mean that. I rephrase that. They're looking for a place of solitude. Get away from it all. Now, tell me something. When you were out there on Swans Island, did they tell you about the ship that burned at sea?"

No.

"Well, you'd better learn about these things. They're the tradition of Swans Island. Do you know all about the steamboats?"

No. But then I mostly asked about lobstering.

"Well, you see now Annie's father and Kenneth's father, they never went lobstering, and I know my grandfather never went. And my father went when he had to. The steamers, they were the big thing. Now my grandfather on my mother's side, he was a captain. I think I saw him but once, and I was one year old maybe at the time, and I remember it as if it were yesterday. They had one of those coffins that sat up on a horse, not a real one, you know, those stands made out of wood like they put boats on, and I crawled right up into it and looked at him. He had a mustache, like, like, well, you've got one, but he was clean-shaven otherwise, he had wide sideburns though I think. The trend you fellows are going back to right now, right?"

I guess so.

"Well, you're going back to that trend, aren't you?"

It's less conscious than all that. It just sort of happens. I guess that's what a trend is, though.

"No. No. No. No. It doesn't bother me. I've seen it, and it doesn't bother me. The only thing that, well to be frank, is when you've got hair down over here, down to here. You look at it, and you may see a mouse coming out of it. I don't go for that. But as long as a man keeps it combed and clean."

Well, I've had my beard for six years now, and it's not really as though I think about myself as a person with a beard. When I first grew it, it was my wife's suggestion, and it was before we were married, and then I just sort of got used to it. But it's not something I think about every moment.

"I see what you mean. Well, now, that, like Tiny Tim, that kind of haircut, I don't go for that. I know it costs a lot more money than I make in a year to have his hair fixed that way. But. We aren't *ALL* Tiny Tims now are we? There's a fellow out at Long Island, he wears his hair like that. He looks so much like his mother one time I called him that."

Long Island, really? I wouldn't think of Frenchboro as a place keeping up with the latest styles.

"That's right, he lives there. Now I know he don't go to a hair stylist, but I mean what's the point? Cause now I've got a young fellow growing up. Now he wears his hair *thick*, not long, but thick, and he gets a haircut; he's only thirteen, not old enough to have a beard yet. I don't mind that. But this guy, hair down to here, and chances are he only combs it once a week. When you get into that class, you're classed as a hippie. Now, to me, you're not in the hippie class. The hippies are the people who are always taking over. Like in Nashua, down by Boston. I go down there to see my relatives. Last year I saw the Boston Red Sox play three times, and they lost all three games, but I won money because I bet on Oakland. Do you know those games?"

No, but I was following the Mets all year.

"I like the Mets, in the Series I was rooting for the Mets, you know why, don't you?, because of old Casey. Now I used to live in New York, this one time when I was working on a ship out of New York, that was back in the thirties, they had the Brooklyn Dodgers and the Giants...."

We stand around talking baseball for a half hour, and I go back to the car and get the issue of *Io* with the story of baseball in my life and the picture of me as a kid at bat in the collage at the end. The Ethnoastronomy Issue. He looks it over.

"Now this is astronomy, right? Is it all the stuff about when you're born in a certain month that's the way you are and your life can be predicted?"

Astrology? There's some astrology in it.

"Do you believe that stuff? I mean my wife's interested in it and all, and I think maybe there's something to it."

It would be very hard to explain why, in any way that would be reasonable to you, but I believe it.

"Maybe, you can show me how it works."

I laugh. You want to know the link, don't you? The link between stars and men, just like the trap's the link between the lobster in the sea and the lobster in your boat. Well, I can try to give you some idea of it. But I'm not sure I can really make it acceptable to you.

"That's fine, fine with me. I just want to hear what you have to say. Now have a beer here, won't you. Oh, yes, yes. There. That's good. And I'll have one too. You know in the old days on Swans Island when we had nothing else to do, we'd talk about these things, whether there's life on other planets and whether there's life after death. But you show me."

Well, how to explain. Imagine that this here is an individual. I take the tab off the beer can. And we'll put him right here in the center of the universe. Now I don't care if it's really the center or not. We'll just say that he can see equally in every direction, so this is the center for him. Now the universe is infinite, we don't know how big it is, but it doesn't matter for the sake of argument. It may go on and on in this direction and this direction. And I knock over the can of beer, spilling all over the table and buoys. I pick it up and go on. "That's okay. That's okay," he says. Now no matter how big the universe is, there are only a certain number of directions, right? And I make several pie-shaped sectors with my hands, coming in on the individual. "I get you. I get you." Now it's like at sea. You speak of a North Wind, or a NorthNorthEast wind, that means everything from that direction, or the balance of wind coming from all directions. And however far the wind comes from, as long as it conducts an influence on you, you say it's a North Wind, or a NorthNorthEast wind, and if it doesn't affect you, then it's no wind at all. Now I'm going to assume what you might call a spiritual wind, and its blowing in different forms from all the directions in the universe onto the Earth. Gesturing. I call it a spiritual wind, but its effects are as if it were a genetic wind; it influences things like what type of a person you're going to be. I don't know what it's made up of, and unlike the North Wind, you can't see it or feel it. Let's call it cosmic rays, or cosmic radiation, or just influences. Now the only point I want to make is that when that wind blows from different directions it brings different influences on us.

"How does this come down to the months of the year."

The universe is in motion all the time, like the sea. When we speak about times of the year in the sky, places, it's like speaking about shoals; we can't see them directly, so we describe them by landmarks. Because the universe is in motion, following a regular path; at least each of its bodies are, like the Earth, we need to mark off the different places it passes, so we mark off the shoals, like for schools of fish. But since we can't see them directly, we relate them to stars that we can see. And these stars are the constellations, and they are merely the landmarks for the influences that we're interested in knowing about. Each month of the year, or more exactly, each sign, like I'm Scorpio. You were born in? December, that's Sagittarius, that part of December. Each sign is a different set of influences.

"I want to know how they can predict what's going to happen to me that way."

They can't, anymore than a psychiatrist can predict what you're going to do the next moment by hearing a brief story of your life. And it's not so much the month you're born as the exact moment, right down to the second. Each one is different. It's like the tightening of a spring, if you can imagine the spinning of the heavens as being loose until the moment a person is born, just as a way of looking at things; each second he isn't born turns the spring a little tighter, or the potential spring; then the moment he's born the spring begins to unwind. The exact second is when it begins to happen. Just like you haul at a given second, and that's fate for the lobster, not the whole month in which you haul him.

"So then I have no astrology because I don't know the moment I was born. My mother's dead, my father's dead, the midwife's dead. How do you know yours down to the second?"

I don't really, but the hospital had a picture made for my mother that has the hands of a clock on it showing the minute, or approximately the minute. It doesn't mean you don't have an astrology if you don't know. It just means that the astrology that one makes up for you is less exact. They have to approximate when you were born.

"It's true that way for all the people on Swans Island, say my age. None of them was born in a hospital."

Well, all that says is that the people on Swans Island don't care about astrology.

"They're not too educated, and they were even less educated then."

It's not a matter of that. They just weren't interested. They were interested in other things. Swans Island wasn't as interested in astrology as 17th Century England, where many of their ancestors were; even though they didn't have

203

hospitals there, they always managed to know the time of birth simply because they were interested in astrology.

"What about God? Where does He come into it?"

Don't know. All I can say, as unacceptable as it is, is that astrology says that the individual runs the same course in his life as the universe does in its cycle of existence, and that the two events are somehow the same, and that the variety of people is in some sense equivalent to the variety of motions of stars.

"Now you've asked me a lot of questions, and I want to ask you some. Do you believe in God?"

It depends on what you mean, not to be hedging. All I can say is that I believe more than, say, most of the people I know at school that the universe has elements of deep cause in it. I do believe that things happen for reasons, though we probably couldn't agree on what those are. Whether that would come down to your accepting my belief as God, I don't know. I guess you could say that I believe in teleology, which means that I think when things began that there was an end or a history written in them, that at the beginning things were determined, that nothing is accident. I don't think anybody like a person created them, but is it all that different to say that I think they have meaning from beginning to end?

"I think you believe in God. Now what I want to know is if you believe in life after death?"

These are such impossible questions. I don't believe that when you see a dead man that's the whole story. I think that's only seeing one part of a reality.

"And the soul's the other part?"

Soul's okay.

"Well, do you think the soul goes on?"

I think it can find another form to exist in. Just think of your body. In a very scientific way it goes on too. No part of you is lost. And no part of you has been lost since the beginning of the universe. There are parts of your body that have been stars and stones and plants and lizards and starfish and lobsters, and in a certain sense, you can still experience the real existence of those things if you can only learn to hear the parts of your body that know them. And this isn't just imaginary. The very brain you think with has been a million other things, and in your thinking those things are part of it.

"Now this is something my wife and I were talking about. Do you believe that the soul can come back as some other thing?"

I think it can. I don't think that's the best thing that can happen to it. If we think that the Earth is an important place where certain business of creation is conducted, then I think that those souls who succeed best, call it spiritually, religiously, that they don't have to come back. But those whose work is not complete must come back to Earth and carry it thru in some other form. Then when they have, their existence continues in another body in a completely different sphere of being.

"So then I might have to come back as a blade of grass or a dog or a cat. My wife's always saying she's going to come back as a cat."

Or a lobster for that matter.

"Don't say that. My wife, you know, she didn't want to watch them when they boiled them the other night. They say there's feeling in the lobster, but I don't know if I'm that religious."

A lobster has work to carry out here too, or at least the souls that are lobsters.

"Now what do you say when a person's been religious all their life, never said shit or nothing, like this woman over at Southwest Harbor, and now she's in a mental institute over at Bangor. What kind of a God would do that?"

All you're saying is that you wouldn't do it. But you don't know the whole story. I am sure in some way, if she went insane, that that was the natural consequence of her actions. People don't go insane just for nothing; how do you know the truth of her life anyway? How do you know it wasn't justice that she went insane?

"It was her boy that drove her to it."

That's not good enough. If there's a God, He holds us responsible for our own actions. It's her choice how she wants to be.

"Well, she can't abandon the child. What would you do if

your son got on that way. There'd be nothing you could do. You'd just have to let it drive you crazy."

But it doesn't just happen overnight. If she has a rotten son, then it's been happening all along, and she's had the choice for sixteen years and never made it.

"Well, maybe there's some truth to that. I've worried about these things a lot. It's hard to believe in a God you can't see. But I think there just has to be something. This couldn't have all just happened. I used to talk to a man out on Swans Island about it a lot. He never went to church and we used to kid him about it. One day I was kidding him, and he pointed to a statue on the wall, and he said, 'That's my God. Where's yours.' And I got to thinking about it, and I don't really know where mine is. I can't see him or anything. I don't know whether he does anything or not. We used to talk about it all the time. You have a lot of time to talk winters there. Well, what do you think about this business with the moon. I think it's crazy putting atomic weapons up there. I think we should leave it alone."

I don't think we can leave it alone anymore than we can leave anything else alone. What if I told you to leave lobsters alone; you wouldn't be able to. We don't know what will become of the moon. You couldn't have predicted in 1840 the lobster would have been anything more than cod-bait or cowfeed. You can't tell what the truth is with the moon yet. Maybe we can use it as big field, and have its whole surface be under domes, as wheat and other crops; the Earth is getting awfully crowded and polluted, and that's pure sunlight without an atmosphere on the moon. Maybe it can be used. After all, sunlight is the basis of life; it's what we eat in one form or another. Plants eat it directly; small animals eat plants; the lobster gets it by preying on small animals. Maybe it's up there to take directly on the moon. I don't know if this is what will happen, but it's one possibility.

"What about the atomic bombs on the moon. They could blow any country up just by sending a space-ship in."

There are atomic bombs on Earth. There are some things you can't do anything about. What happens if all the lobsters die off tomorrow?

"Well, don't you think now it's almost like religious to be

able to tell the future. That man in 1930 doing Buck Rodgers, he predicted that we'd go to the moon, just like we have, and that there'd be ray guns."

I hate to say it, but I don't think it was that hard. I think I could have predicted it in 1930. It's been coming for an awfully long time. And I don't know that we have any ray guns yet.

"Do you think maybe somebody read the comic strip and that's where they got the idea from?"

I think it's much more complicated than that. If you imagine one person over here doing a comic strip, and another person over here thinking up ideas, or inventing ray guns, there are a million connections between them, like telephone wires all bunched together, and you can never know if one man got something from another man, or if maybe the comic strip man got it from the inventor. That's what it means to say that something is in the air. There are millions of people, and it's something that none of them know separately, but each of them know in some way, and they're all helping each other in their different ways of knowing to come to it, like a moon-voyage.

"I think we'll probably find life on one of these planets, but it won't be on the moon unless it's underground, like cavemen. I think maybe Mars has the best chance. Are there any others?"

Well, I think Venus has a better chance than Mars, just speaking about Earth-type men. It's larger, warmer; it has an atmosphere, and we don't know anything about what's on it because it's covered with clouds. But if you really want to know what I think, I think every planet's inhabited, though it may take us a long time to find the life even after we're there. I think the sun's inhabited. There's no law as to what form a soul can take, and I think on the sun souls have taken the form of fire. No, I'm not kidding you. You asked me what I believe. You tell me about lobstering. I'm not being other than honest with you about myself.

"How about life outside the universe?"

What do you mean: outside the galaxy, the Solar System?

"Outside the Solar System."

There are a lot of suns. The chances on that basis alone

are great.

"Do you think they will find out in my lifetime?"

Given the machinery they have now, they won't ever find out. It's going to take a change as big as from the handaxe to the rocket ship, maybe larger, to get us to another star. That's what light years are, that even at the speed of light, it would take you so long to get there. The light from the sun takes eight minutes to reach us. We can't get near that. And even if we could, it would take us more than a lifetime to get to most of the stars and back.

"I think we're doing it just step by step. Now the moon is a step. I read where they can launch rocket ships to the stars from the moon, and they're already that close."

Fred, you're talking about step by step like this. I make little finger marks on the table. How long would it take you at that rate to get to Gotts Island, or to China. There are some things you can't even do step by step. I think it's going to be hard just for us to get to anything beyond Mars, even using Mars as a base.

"I'd like to talk about God some more. Do you think He communicates with people, or can influence things? Like one time my wife remembered she might owe this woman something for a church newspaper or social, and she sent her ten dollars, and it turned out the woman was out of money, and you should have seen the note she wrote. My wife thought it was an act of God."

My own feeling is that God is more concerned with creation, and that this is the work of the angels. I mean the angels are always busy making sure we do the right things, whatever we think our reasons for them are. The angels always know more than we do, and if we listen to them, they guide us. I think the important thing is not to stop listening, but to take everything seriously because they are speaking all the time.

"Like I might be your angel right now or you might be mine."

Not "might"—"are!" As long as we are speaking seriously to each other, we are. I am saying things now that you will be able to make use of, and you are saying things that I will make us of, and that is how the angels work thru both of us to both our benefits. And I think that it's important to take things seriously, because everything's serious, at least until we're told otherwise. I mean, unless someone wakes you up two hundred years later and says, Fred, the Earth was all a joke, you shouldn't have believed one minute of it, then I think you should take it seriously. It's a serious business. And I think this is what people mean when they say lobstering's a serious business because lobstering's part of it. The price of lobster is part of it. That's why you have to take it all seriously, and that's religious I think, being able to hear what's happening, to see and decide, which is a good thing about the sea and being a lobsterman.

XIII

Washington County

Giant on the eastern flank of, here the American sun rises, to cross the entire nation in a day and return from the ocean of, year after year. Here the tides are greatest, the moon most powerful in its sweep of 28 feet, dragging the waters of the St. Croix River an inch a minute. Washington County is considered a depressed area of Maine: larger than Delaware and Rhode Island combined and 32,000 people, the poor clam and pick blueberries, dig marine worms and cut pulpwood trees for the nation's presses, St. Regis paper in Passomaquoddy, St. Croix in woodland. Here ten rivers travel 412 miles into the sea. Here news of our existence begins.

Sun. Horsetails and Cat's Tails following the old railroad tracks along the shore. Freight, mail, *Bangor Times*. Cherry-field Post Office, American flag, sun which falls in one place leaves the cold machinery rusting in the shade behind the gas station. Sun as bright on the church clock as the American flag, delivery of by truck right up to the bells ringing out the hours of, here the century passes asleep.

Sun. The bright blackness of an island behind the sun, that can never get out from behind it to be sunny, or is so bright that I cannot tell whether the forests are white birch bark or black stark stands among glacial boulders. Washington County, not as far East yet as Portugal, Cabot, yet lies behind, secondary to the Cranberries, is the process of the East, of the great ship-building nation; here no traffic but the early morning; here the French hung on, and the Indians hung on, and nothing would grow, without wheat or corn or pasture, "bowing down to catch the crumbs that fall from the tables of Ohio and New York [Dr. Holmes];" here the broken coastline of matter, of the East, or Downeast, falls behind even its own shadow to the East: Newfoundland, George's Banks, the weeds flee the wheatfields and go toward the sea. Labrador diploid, hatching pink and white in the spring, fields of blueberries in the summer. Lichen, rock cranberry, and beach pea.

The sun which drags this world for gold drags here not only first but also. The Earth widens to the North along the line of the East and our most imperfect process lies here: the Cabot-ship to return to where it came from by sailing out. As if from sails by sunlight, as if from islands to the fishing grounds of the continental shelf, leaving no family name, not even a rune-carver, but returning to the Mediaeval market of Europe. Enter, and the sun throws off its coating, its coast, the husk it would otherwise carry inland, sets its drag. Here the first fish of daylight are hauled from the teeth of Fundy; here the trees stand on the hill in a blaze of sun, silhouette which precedes body. The old witch, tied with ropes and rags to the basement furniture, rushes free with the tide, her children to drown. The dreamer awakes and precedes East behind the sun.

Tumbleweed of unfinished land. The metal, the underlying principle: black, the arboreal becoming the tundra. Is the quickening of numbers where there is no world. Where the reindeer, set down to populate, and the caribou, return under hoof to the North. The tree-stumps, remains of the pulpwood cutters, their bodies gone to New York to print the *Daily News*, the morning edition returned days later to Machiasport. The mounds of dirt left by the digging of a road. The rocks piled by glacier and farmer. An unfinished surface ecology, an archive. Neither goldrush nor factory, but local gene pocket, those who didn't go to Indiana and Nevada. Beals and Alleys. Left by the War of 1812, defeated invisibly with General Lee, sandy, barren, broken, unfarmed, but two thousand cattle driven across it to New Brunswick in 1827, its ancient orchards burned to the ground by Col. Church, who drove the French out in colonial times, glacial, lowbush, hardpan, made of clay and sand torn from the sea-bottom, still in the glacial, muted; the flowers are blueberry, teaberry, rhodora, and bracken, sundew and pitcher plant. Every number is diminished to mass, a single grey boulder, world which precedes this one is known as mass, whose energy, until then, comes as schools of fish thru the water. Here a world is built on top of another, between itself and another. The neither clams nor crabs nor harvest, but glints of mica and schist, or a brick wall collapsing into utter.

The ice itself has melted and the beds have been brought up upon the shore. Wrapped in the clothing that is not its body, the earth, precolonial, bucks the houses and breaks them, opens the side of a hill, leaving habitation as—old barns crack open and are patched with canvass and black rubber, sack, skinned tires. The roof itself has fallen in, taking all its structures into one hew. Antiques lie in the field with the moraine, hulls of boats and skeletons of farm machinery, skeletons of a sometimes-industrial, of a people who can afford to leave what they could not afford in the first place, even as the new house is built next to the old, and the old is neither repaired nor torn down but kept as a closet or garage, filled with lobster traps and cans, used as history is used, to restore that we will never know which way we go until we go: so the barn crumbles in thru the loft and the house upon its staircase. The body is broken, the nation is, but does not die.

Washington County: the observance that what is in decay can be built back up of its parts, and made to hold a few more years, like a forty-five year old middleweight, can come to sustain the very forces that scatter it, a house built entirely of doors, allow the new generation to step out of, hungry for clean land, even the birds rising to begin again. Bright yellow fungus, marrow passing from the chimney, the dense light in which the occupants awake to the fossil heat of morning, the genetic heat of, an even-spacing force that we neither know nor will know in our time. This is new world—again and again and again. As poor and lethargic as it is. The operation on it which the growth of post-glacial cities cannot change, even the ocean-going vessels of Machiasport and Jonesport. Even from the Fulton Fish Market and the lobster pounds down the coast to Boston, even the streets of the city made out of, the island granite, the granite island; the megalopolis reaches for here with one long arm, grasps and falls short, and the sun rolls over its extended arm, a giant earthmover going Northwest by day and East by night, passing onto all the city streets of Chicago, carrying potatoes to Newfoundland, buying lobsters in Nova Scotia, fish in Rockland, stopping at St. Johns for a drink, to New York and Boston, working against the ice underfoot of this world.

The secret operation is of New World onto world, which we have carried out since Mediaeval, which is not Mediaeval, which is the splitting of a single stone, the spreading of its dusts, is the weight of structure, or superstructure, of infrastructure, where we learn why the economists and sociologists cannot agree on which world men live in, whether they have friends or business partners, whether they spin for the jackpot or merely, day-to-day, ward off the ice, the Crash. They are blind and cannot tell the goods, societas from money, cannot tell the motive of, arm around our fellow man, sit in the smoke-filled shed playing off the blowy day in poker, are blind to the collapse of the barn in the fields, the very weight of us, no other weighable quantity, measure, myth, or market.

So one wants to go inside the body and own it, these beautiful houses, to own a finely carved tower of bedrooms, rimmed with lattice, two-toned in pastels, curved windows, the curtains drawn across. Here psyche sleeps set off from the broadwork, wears the cap of a carpenter, the crown, and wants to be that king, that house. Child sits playing with his buttons, cannot see outside his snowsuit; what is soft as water or light to him is the scenery we try to get a grip on; these worlds, by some magic of identification, become part of us, as the cloth of landscape, trees and houses and town streets, tattooed by machine to our flesh, dressed in it, dancing in it. The left finger breaks with the crow, to cross the forest, to fly over the beach, NorthNorthIce, to fly from the broken body, from the black heap of gleaming rubber, out over the stench of clam-bed, of fishfields hungry to roll with sky, the black wings climbing until they too break, and then fall blue, trees, off into the mirror, is blue, past the barn, past the dust piled, blue, into the field.

XIV

Downeast

1. Corea

And diamonds too she leaves behind. Gleaming on the shore. Fish, billions of them, but too far out and without names, a planet run, run of plenty. The sun gleams in the Atlantic time zone, but doesn't stay there for long, fills it with diamonds, touches the shoals with life, and is gone to the darkness of the West, the Western darkness it always cuts, bisects, measures, and only a few hours are left in the day, the ship at sea.

Now the cold of the ice settles in, the beach frozen, the town empty, the boats lie in the shelter, in the brilliance of it, inactive as gems, utter silence and sparkle and ice. Is invisible around the cove, a building, looking across at it from one piece of land, seems possible to drive around; yet we find our goal always in the middle, in between, located on a tongue of land, a road we cannot find, to the back and forth of it, still find it lying on the other side.

"Corea doesn't even have any place in history. Nobody in the early days was so foolish as to attempt a landing here, where the coast is guarded by submerged ledges, clusters of small offshore islands, a continual tremendous surf, and truly epic fogs. This is the identical stretch against which Champlain warned all mariners in such stringent terms, and all shipping gave it a very wide berth indeed." Louise Dickinson Rich.

No action anywhere, not even footsteps, but a single shed, smoke coming from it, dusty windows and almost invisible in or out, the wind blows against, the heat maintains, ten men, a third of the town, playing poker, this game that lasts two months or two years, a hand of wives or fishing gear, giving the traps three weeks' set before hauling, or sit there in the half-light of it, soaking up what's left; they are living off a hand of nickels and dimes, a few quarters, an ounce of fuel; the stores are closed and the storefronts filled with lobster traps, fishing gear in the roads; they deal silently, half-grumbling, dropping in and out of the game are sons and brothers and brothers-in-law, uncles and nephews, the old man whose shed is king. They deal lobsters; Earl Guptal's hand goes to Lyall Jones and the lobster pound in Hancock; they play for shrimp all winter, jackpot, and then to Cape Cod Tuna in Winter Harbor, summer is cod at, say, 3¢ a pound, Guptal employs some teenagers, and lobstermen who have their traps up, to cut the fillets, and those go to Jonesport.

Harvey Beal, Jr., isn't in the poker game. He's rigging up for shrimping. His nephew Leon Haskins who's buying shrimp gear with him has a hand. Earl Guptal isn't in the game. He's sitting at the stove in his place waiting for Babe Addison and just about sunset to come in from his traps, the only fisherman out. And then in the East again return.

2. Jonesport and Beals Island

Diamonds. Fish without names. Proliferation out of a hidden node. It's not exactly every eleven years, but something like that, something like a long decade, the sunspots, the temperature of the water, the species in the water, highs followed by lows, as the sun alternates decades of scallop abundance, decades of scarcity, and the shrimp run in from the North with the colder waters.

The sun leads lobstermen, clam-diggers, worm-diggers, cod fishermen, shrimpers, man for man, thru a market, an economy based on sun-activity, a water which blooms in the rhythm as well as the impact of sunlight. Suddenly green crabs and moon crabs and rock snails, warm water. Chesapeake animals from the South, come with the sunspots, devour the clams, their natural meat, leaving the clam-digger without. The moon swallows the clams, the clam-digger switches to marine worms and sandworms. The cold water drives the lobster from the bottom into a thin lens of cover; the shrimp boats chase the moon in its down-runs. The fishermen search Corsair and Veach and other canyons for the offshore populations, the offsun current back from, the full pocket.

Here moon is market too, the tidal water filled, breathing with lobster pounds, worth 2¢ on the price; here the rise and fall of the tide brings, gushes with fresh oxygen. At Portland no moon; here the moon rides on the cold waters out of the Bay of Fundy, ripples on the water, a thousand mouths, lungs, opening, churning down the breeze, moon child feeds sun child; tide feeds sunspot; sunspot feeds moon crab; sun feeds clam, round inch by round inch, feeds rock snail, moon feeds on, Beal feeds on, water rushing not to reveal a lunar landscape but moon rushing thru waters to reveal the black earth.

Oil feeds no one's child, sits where the tanker pumps her bilges, suffocating the lobsters in Carver's Pound, crawling out into it, the moon filled, slick, out of breath, the tide withdraws, drowned, beached in midstream, like to the South a panic of whales, here the lobsters panic, oil from Alaska, the great Northern fields and Northwest Passage, out at Machiasport, oil mixes with sun to name the sea's field.

Tidal waters now reveal the full beach of them/ reaped with an ancient hoe, breakage of the fast-growing clam, the thin shell busted, two bushels for every one, and the rotten apples turned over in the bed. No one owns but to the high water mark, beyond that the moon fills the bed of the State of Maine, by Colonial Ordinance passed to the municipalities, 1641, The Great Pond Ordinance:

"Every Inhabitant that is a howse holder shall have free fishing and fowling in any great ponds and Bayes, Covers and Rivers, so farre as the sea ebbes and flows within the presincts of the towne where they dwell, unlesse the freemen of the same Towne or Generall Court have otherwise appropriated them, provided that this shall not be extended to give leave to any man to come upon others proprietie without their leave."

The clambeds are the slums; what Beals Island keeps for its poor people in Jonesport, even as they rip up their own beds for lobster pounds, money in the bank, this the one stable resource; and if a pauper won't do anything else, he is sent to the town beds. Here the diggers from Beals fief have gone into Jonesboro town flats, and the diggers from Jonesport, as they have for years under cover, now in mass, to be arrested, tried in Machias, and appeal to a higher court, for the right to clam in any beds in the State of Maine. They organize; the lobstermen, their knights, go to battle for them in Augusta, the Beals. Albert Alley complains that Jonesboro has one motive: greed, to keep their beds for themselves even as the clams rot in the earth, to join up only with towns that don't have many diggers. "Who does he think put the clams there anyway!" Alley screams to whoever will hear. "Well, it wasn't the people in Jonesboro, I'll tell you that, it was the ocean, the tidal waters, they come in with the tidal waters, and no one owns them because you can't own past the high water mark. Even if you put your boat on a mooring, that's U.S. property. We can't allow it. I'll tell you that. Because we're starving and we just can't starve. And we're going to get the Governor here; somebody's got to do something about it; it can't go on like this. Beals and Jonesport got 109 diggers; Jonesboro's got 16, though that first selectman over there is finding new ones everyday, anyone who doesn't want to work; he's filling the books with them. But they're not clammers; we've been doing this for generations. This is our business. And I'll tell you; our flats won't stand it anymore. And they've closed some of them for pollution. We've got the most clam-diggers. We've got an overabundance. What would happen if Jonesport closed its clambeds to Beals Island; well, Beals got no beds, and it's got the most clam-diggers; so they dig in Jonesport; Roque Bluffs, they dig in Machiasport, but of course they're related to the warden over there. And Jonesboro, they dig Roque Bluffs. Addison digs Harrington, and Harrington digs in Addison. But they're going to keep us out. Well, we'll go to jail. Because those clams there are dying. There aren't enough clam-diggers. Anyone knows that a clam-bed has to be cultivated.

And we're the ones."

We come now, as in a children's story, to the clam-people, in a world where the lobsterman and shrimper is king. And the weirman is priest. The old dragger and trawler magus. The clam-people are families, clannish, move in grandfather old and imbecilic, across the beds, father singing in jail with the redheads, not signing anything and keeping his flock, son no money to go into lobstering, looks like Rickey Nelson standing around in a tee-shirt drinking beer, all the dark-haired children run thru like water, like waking in the middle of night or at dawn to obey the tide, its slight off-rhythm to the 24 hour day, a song, and go when the beach is full, the moon or ocean leaves its crop, the clam people, almost urban in their tacit ghetto, ready to be radicalized by Mao, if only he would come to Beals and bust the regional inheritance and covert landlordism, dark beautiful people, who grow old and lame young, carrying small bushel baskets made from the same forest as lobster-traps, with rubber boots for gear, no boat, and a hoe, break out of the courthouse into the streets of Machias, singing and shouting, pile into cars like the softball team, in a city without blacks, return to the houses along the ocean, the children, nine of them, giggling, or herded along by the mother, home too late from the court for the tide, and the young clam-girls, bewitchingly efficient, run thru the town announcing a meeting on Beals Island tonight, one day to shove it right back up, the moon thru the ass of the lobster back out of history and stand free in Washington County, covered with the meat of it, not having to be in jail to sing it, not having to stand in the tidal waters to be moonlight, the lobsters returning to Veach country, deep under, the tides pouring off the table they have set, the moon itself the moon reveals on Earth, clam-slums of the city, laundry strung frozen on the lines, and the children in the streets playing black rubber ball and coins, and the lobsterman is king on Fifth Avenue. "We've got a problem," Alley screams into the phone at the imaginary man, "and Governor, you're the only one who can solve it."

CHAPTER 5
ECONOMY OF THE SYSTEM

$

Blood in current, embryos swelling to Newfoundland ice (keeping the bathers at Cape Elizabeth and Plum Island out of the glaciermelt: "them's mighty big storage facilities you've got up there!"). Lobsters by the billions, and the whole deflation potential of the Pleistocene, when all the species of the North Atlantic were contained in the letter A. The oil under ice, native salt abundant, and man a germ plasm: a world Schopenhauer felt could not exist, for all its storms and geysers, because its wallet and its heart were made of stone.

The eagle.

Coinstream/claw, creatures of interzone planet, of Europe's shadow West, of Spain's post-Viking Redman.

Oak.

Shelled gold with feet upon the uranium treadle.

New Brunswick laths, forest by forest the Old World's New World/York City. Transcontinental railroad first growth. Penobscot pulp for Hearst and Gannett, and granite, not mahogany anymore, and not chestnut, and no Scottish bands here like at the Michigan football rally. Vinland grapes seed Spain's California scab Mestizo empire. Lettuce a wild leaf over the rocky glacial East.

Twine to weave the diamond cage, downtown Boston, Old Port, Antwerp, antigravity spider, upstream cash gradient, downstream Polynesian sea menstrum. Keeping bees in abandoned bars and deer asses in freezers, soft bottles floating among the reinvested fish eggs.

Hook's dollars at Gott's, for St. Louis beer, for smuggled lobsterfishing maps transcribed from drunk memory, and the path to the crab's soft bed, reappear at First National Bank of Bar Harbor, fishingboat mortgage, secondhand motor, cash for the wharves, Bangor vein, Ellsworth shopping center, crossing of trade waves, winds, highways, abandoned railroad depots, original New England lobster, maple syrup, cod, marble, hake; buy a new old car, drop anchor at Portland, fish market of the Northern colonies, Commercial Street, only 104 miles to the newest fashions and hard rock music of Harvard Square.

The sun in the moss. Wet. Thick grey web of lichen. Past noon.

It is certainly past noon. The day is almost done. We have done nothing, we have waited. Now darkness returns.

Bird pokes at suet hung on the post. Pretty bird. Dark crown marking. Where we have put food something comes to eat its own meal. The string unravels. It is as tight as my muscles. It falls away as the coastline to the shore.

Last night I saw the dance of the squid on t.v., the total species thrown by discrete rays of a dark sun, by their own transsexual hormones, into, shimmering, ass-wagging belly-dancing. Everyone turning on everyone else. Dangling long chic fingers, fluid, boneless, flesh in ounce and muscle, bringing it all here, home, with every wiggle. The community is oblivious to the nature of nature, for this is the nature, and they show inside outside, tugging at the web that joins them as by some x-ray of deep specific telecommunications. They do not even feel themselves being caught and fried for dinner by the crew of the ship. They do not know they are drawn out of the harmony before its climax, crushed in the engines of the spy-ship. The dance is novelty. Each moment, step by step, gaining moment, momentum, is climax, squiddery absolute: not sex in the head, but right there, where it is. If they were molecules they could be no less in control—and no more.

A blanket of life covers them; individuals rush thru it, node, x, transformation, is an ecstacy, flowing orgasm whose release is an implosion—shape. The scientists whose films we are watching believe not in life but in mass, and its unending flesh, cutting away at the total community for specimens, lovers in the heat of, to float them in tanks—and what is the chemical horror of being pulled out of such a dance into stimulus deprivation? But they continue what they have where they are, and what there is light, condition for, and this is all we ever do, we stand alone in the chemical unconscious, crossing the bridge, or does it cross us, or is the crescendo at once and the same?

Aristotle describes the squids of the Mediterranean "with mouths and tentacles facing one another and fitting close together." "A squid imprisoned alone in an aquarium suffers from melancholia, kills itself by devouring its own arms." De Ropp.

And Freud's dance is Jung's dance, and the origin of sexual desire is in the sea. The squids carry the archetypes in colors as blue, as purple as, sepia in, in single tentacles bearing a penis. How can we tell sex from material from shape? We cannot. We do not know what the primal stuff heeds or whence it draws us, but the joy, if that is what it is, of the squid turns red in discharge, its body flush against the momentum, laying out what it has, or everything, getting back what it is, everything.

If history has a mind to it, if p moves q, if . . . . I say that we are becoming full of it, that we are becoming able, not of any glory or even salvation, but that we were always able, and this is all there was, no less than the total blossoming of shape. Mind or mindless, mind is what we have, and surely that which is conscious is larger than the universe, need not *trans*migrate or awake from its many depths/it is always there.

Sugar: name of sap, of woman, sweetening of; it is a deep tunnel coming in at cross, going right thru without coming out, on the tongue. The taste of blood: how could the crew know this, frying the squid, recording the motion of the camera on the body of the world?

My life is neither before me nor after me, is neither matter preceding spirit nor the other way. Damnit . . . . . the arms flowing . . . . . the attraction of beast to beast, red is the color of, and the nuclei of the brilliance of incoming matter, millions of years of them, light years, dancing as planets; the eyes of the squid, as any eyes, are where the head pours into the outside world, blind to all but the unspinning phenom; outside the dance is nothing, except perhaps the crossings and transits of the spheres. It is not Buddhism, dispersed into pre-energy and oversoul. It is not Darwin who operates on the primal plasm with the knife of shape. We need not do away with the squid and grow only the tree of life, for specificity is what it comes to here in its season.

It is history, known otherwise as the historical present. Everywhere we go in great ships and sink our gear to the bottom of it, it is. Everywhere we look we look into Egypt, and Tyrian cities, as history surrounds us, as surely as the rings of Saturn or the speed of light, the squids dance. History will not let us back into matter; it forces us to settle and make a go of it at Monhegan. And James Rosier, chronicler of Weymouth's voyage, 1605, the *Archangel*, must write:

"While we were at shore, our men aboard with a few hooks got about thirty great cods and haddocks, which gave us a taste of the great plenty of fish which we found afterword wheresoever we went upon the coast."

Kittery, Winter Harbor, Stratton's Land, Matinicus, Isles of Shoals. There is no escape from the squids as they surround the men with cameras, and keep to their dance, and fuck as many times as they are able, here where ancestrally they rediscover the mating ground, the spot, where only the singing becomes as loud as the moon they cannot see, the moon they are, and begins to get into their blood, here where they cannot leave, to, or from, surely Squid is S and Quid is Q in Kelly's 'Alphabet of Sacred Animals,' swirt, squirt, swirl, or origin uncertain, as are all origins in prehistoria. Shrimp, or crabs, mussels or scallops, quahogs and horny scalpings: what hope is there for us to escape, even as we flee the harvest, we are brought back, knowing that we never left. Squid is the name of a motion as certain as the motion of a Mercury or Neptune, as the whole earth is engaged in this body of rhythm, dance-floor sea-bottom: and not just a part of the earth and not just inside the earth.

I stand behind you as an animal only, throwing what I have into you from the back of it, pouring it so that hands up signify rain is passing thru me, Reich's rain, and all my questions relent unanswered as the actual moisture of flow. I am marked SQUID, squirt, I have as many arms as I am willing to enter the sphere of, i.e., powers, or centers, dances called Twist, or Frug, or the Monkey, or the Squid. I die off to awake and recall that I am not gone from the Earth, coming as a new generation of squids from the interregnum sleep, reeled back to my partner, who?, in the overall motion of it. It is not that I do not die. It is that history remains, and the nets thrown into the blackness of it reveal how long we can stay alive as a species. Pollution is not what fills the water, but those diabolic lies of breakwater. Precisely what I mean when I say we pretend to know more than we do about everything, thus get into, and think ourselves outside of history; and what we do know keeps pounding to get in, and if you stand up high enough, even on the 6:30 news singing WE SHALL OVERCOME, this is what you will see, unbroken, unending, in the murder of union officials, in the quick enigmatic flashes of bombs; this is the mafia, the boss that rules even the mafia; who knows, evens the President doesn't, no proxy, no forgery, no signature, or doctrine of; power comes from power and the powerful alone march thru the negative capability of their own demise.

The night of the squid is followed by the morning of the moss: the female straining to plant from her own body the embryo squid, ocean sand littered with blood vessels, with the returning tide.

The sun in the moss. Wet. Nature is growth. Thick grey web of lichen. Is thought. Past noon. The shadowy coming of evening.

* * *

Olson, as giant a sun as that, has gone, left, packed his bags in some room in New York, and went out there, regretting nothing, on the heels of energy retained. All week, not knowing he had died, we heard his voice on the tape-recorder in the car, giving us the content, history, from the fish in Georges Banks and the settling of Portland, thru Buffalo and Winnebago, and giant hauls of groundfish gold, diorite stone, angels of the left hand, to that political caucus of

American poetics, running for every vote in the house, even Ginsberg's, the ultimate politicos behind the gown of house rules and night. Telling us how it is you come there, to find that you're capable, and are given a piece, and it's the whole thing, and you're amazed.

So do the dinosaurs live forever, alive even now. Our handwriting reveals us, on our wrist that bracelet of sun-energy, known as economy, passing thru marine worms and hogs, circle whose center at Fort Square would seem to be but is not broken by the death of the species.

The squids awake as though they are, were the same, fight their way from the flesh that surrounds them into the flesh that holds them. Nobody cares whether they were or are before or if it is the same squids, that false sense of abundance; our interest lies in morality, birth, not fertility; the two billion unhatched sea eggs are the endless rainfall of bions from space, the reservoir from which the vital force sucks thru its own tail the living, bios-logical.

He is still talking about Cabot's route in thru, Marco Polo, spending the George Washington dollar bills of a nation where he is no longer, of a world he has left as suddenly as the fish caught by Smith's men, or Smith himself. And by doing has so proved the point, leaving the final fix on us, unbroken, with but a single fishport, his source.

On the Day of Judgement Thomas Jefferson is President of America; whale and buffalo are our beasts of burden. The angel lies to the left hand of creation, stereo, steroid. We are finally going to know something about every kingdom on the foodchain and the history of every enslaved species in chains everywhere, from Kalamazoo to Timbucto: *limits/are what we are/inside of.*

The imago mundi grips the dance, its partner by proportion, ten independent arms surrounding the mouth, the departments of the legislature and offices of the people. Power feeds the mouth: And the body sits, bloody sits in the occult, its veins and arteries gleaming with unconscious use, turning red, shining as a city on a hill. In the end it's all there, and the hands reaching into earth find that they are the roots of a giant tree, fixed like a mask as thoughts flow, winds thru the oak leaves, sunlight simultaneous in the cambial veins. And hands reaching into water feel the colors flowing away like wine, memories, senses. Olson invites everyone to the party, even Whitehead, even Lyndon Baines Johnson, Frank Sinatra, Muhammed Mantle, even Wendell Seavey and the net salesman of Gloucester, even me, the electrical voice going on oblivious to the death of its master in the Tombs. It's as American as cod is, gold was, shrimp is now. Even as the lights go out, and we have too little time left, we don't have too little, and we don't have a hell of a lot either. The interest we seem to collect is fraud. Insurance destroys any sense of wild abundant history. Fish in shoals are in nets only when they flash there, and nothing is paid, not even silence, when they are not. The funeral is reserved for the dead.

The one thing that evolution promises us, *noos* or not, is that we are naked, is that we will be revealed finally as what we are. Or the squid, outside of night and day, "fucking until eternity."

We will find out just how hungry we are, saltfish aside, and for what, where most of our history is locked in moonlight and kernel, Olson frees the germinative moth, discloses the end of the world in the sense that it is knowable.

There are fish, and two thousand, two million years later, we are still here, *and there are fish.*

Economics

It is getting to the season when nothing moves, lobster traps up, shrimp not yet in. Some people dip into Frenchman's Bay for a meal of scallops. The market is still here, but the system detaches from it everyday; the men sit around just not doing anything economic. Consumers don't count in the system.

"Everything's credit," Clyde Pomroy says. "No money, just one thing for another."

"Credit better be good," says an old fisherman lounging in the corner. He reaches into his pocket and holds out: "I've got eight cents and one screw, a few flounders left. I don't know how, but I've got to get over the March hill this year."

And Jasper complains: "Who says we don't give away nothing for free here. I let a man owe me fifty dollars for six months, and another one two hundred dollars for a year. I'm losing; I'm giving away the interest I don't charge. I could feed a whole family on the difference between what's owed and what's paid."

Here is an obvious inequality, though not necessarily an injustice; the economy of the nation changes. But those men sitting on their cold asses, or glad you warmed a spot for me on that bench, are out of the game even though each of them has a hand of cards. Everything costs more than anyone makes, and yet the game goes on, so there is something larger than the economy, or we have mistaken the link between fish and dollar and protein. There is in fact a secret society, too small to be caught in the lobster trap, able to hide beneath the flow of 90% statistics. The true economy is survival, and everything else, including the market, is sacrificed to that.

"I'm just going to sit out this winter," Melvin Lunt says, puffing on his cigar and coughing. "I'll let everyone else lose money shrimping."

"A lot of money is going to be lost too," Clyde Pomroy says. "They've got seventy draggers out of Jonesport, really plastering the bottom there. Even if the shrimp come there are going to be a lot of boats for sale next year. A hell of a lot. No shitting! It takes cash to keep those boats running, and the bank isn't going to pay it. The only people gonna make money are the ones making the winches and diesel engines."

"What's credit now? 8%?"

"8% like hell," Clyde snaps. It's 9%. They're really going into the hole."

Mertic Krentz, a cranky walrus, storms around Pomroy's; the wind took his boat all the way out to Johnson Cove on Big Cranberry; someone called him out there and he went and got it. "Been around the water all my life and still don't tie good enough knots," he grumbles.

"Watcha eating now, Mertic?"

"I got a gallon of scallops from Harold; those things are all meat; they'll last three or four meals."

"On Swans Island all you needed to get thru the winter was deer meat and rum. That'd take you there."

No doubt the individual wonders if there is such a thing as an economy, and the economy doubts the presence of the individual; neither can bear the irrational motives of the other, who seem to have *no* motives when moving between systems.

"It costs me more to keep this place open than I make in a day," Harold says. "You gotta pay lights, wages, heat; you gotta make repairs."

"There's a reason," Hinckley says. "Same reason a man fishes at 80 fathoms on a blowy day when he knows he's gonna lose more money than he makes. It's that the dealer's no good without the fisherman, and the fisherman's no good without a dealer. We're all in this together."

"Economic valuation is a mechanism by which particularized significances of specific resources for individuals and collectivities are *generalized* in terms of their significance to the system as a whole." Talcott Parsons.

When money disappears we create the market, out of wild birds and fish. When there's no money in the market, men sit in the marketplace talking. It's still there.

There is no balance or profit when the scales run right thru the center of the system. What is the history of economic theory but an ancient quantum mechanics, averaging out what cannot exist for any one moment in reality, but flows into its average, and net minus inflation? Behind this is a world, elemental and generative, 92 coins in its currency, and those invented by man; random ceases to be a number, becomes an energy, a transformation. As men live in among quanta, in the money exchange, in the exchange of value, as rightly so the newscaster calls the pouring of gold: here in the temple of South Africa, hoarded in bars, bullion, as a bee makes honeycombs, until the transformation into urine and black blood. Even consciousness is paid for in coin when it happens; the black bear pays for his meal, and man pays, and when it's too much, economy supersedes ecology, and not black shit, but the poison of the whole system flows back into the ocean, every man for himself. There is no economy, but the numbers of the market generate, themselves, a world in which men can be transformed, in which the other becomes possible, as long as it is paid for. What's cash anyway. When in America the dollar is whore and will go to bed with anyone for money?

"I just don't understand people," says Hinckley. "Back when Underwood's was putting up clam chowder, everyone dug their clams. The people from Beals Island and Jonesport went over to the Jonesboro town flats. Now they don't want anyone to dig there. They'd rather let the clams suffocate, rot in the ground. Now Jonesport and Beals Island, they have a class of people that likes to dig clams. Why not let them go cultivate the Jonesboro beds?"

Clyde: "If they can't have it; they don't want anyone else to. You remember old woman Peterson here with that apple orchard, beautiful yellow transparent apples, and big black dogs, whatdaya call them, Merton?"

"Dobermans."

"Well, those apples'd be rotting on the ground, but she'd be damned if she'd let you have one. She called out the dogs."

The economy then is the cash description of the other systems whereby immeasurables become units of the same ilk. Pure metals lie on the market with stars. A comet tearing thru the economy leaves us with: a coin of sorts. As metal on fire approaches a malleable state on which the mint operates. The dollar is stripped away from her in her dance, revealing what he had feared all along, that she was naked, that she has a body, that we desire her, that we have a body, that we cannot control inflation, deflation, cool down or heat up the economy; we cannot even tell the difference between Malthus and Marx, where Chinese peasants are honored for shooting 30,000 sparrows in a winter. And as hard as they try they cannot keep the producer at it; the machine frees the proletariat of the nightly need to dream, all natural hallucinogens drained from his body, a dreamless robot losing value itself creates useless replicas. The enemy cannot see the difference betwen capitalism and communism, between Marco Polo-Luther and Confucius-Mao. And there will be no such machine, for in the madness of production dream seizes all and converts to an earlier material state.

What about the size of it, the numbers in the billions and trillions? The answer, and this is the answer to the astrology of the universe too, is that size counts for nothing; value is born in igneous furnaces, transformed in cities, as the son of the millionaire turns hippie and gives money away, starts a rock band; the leather merchant dies, and his investment buys free meals for the hungry of New York decades later. Why? Unless there is no pure economic motive. . . . .

We hear Harold Pomroy talking now: "..... back when we used to have sole here. The fish hardly moved the fucking scale AND SHE WANTED ME TO CUT IT IN TWO. Why it was no bigger than a cracker!"

Nothing moves the fucking scale because we can't see it, and the beauty or the horror of the system is that we never know where we are. Economics gives the illusion that we can steer this planet thru cosmic storms, comets, depression, but the whole solar system is moving, the whole galaxy, and homo oeconomicus is blind, is squinting to see the numbers which keep changing, which defy their Cartesian history, which threaten to change——IT HARDLY MOVED THE FUCKING SCALE.

At $8 a foot digging an artesian well. "That guy in Jonesport, everything he touched turned to money. He dug sixty feet and the water flooded out, running all over him. Next door Frost's boatshop had to go down to 200 feet."

Economics of the moment: what we want to buy, sweet water, new boat, lobster, haddock, depends not on the sheer comparison between cheaper and more expensive (and certainly not on some alchemical value, for where in the world but Maine can you get a beautiful fish like cusk, which other fishermen throw back in as junk, and for how long were mackerel and haddock returned to the sea?), but on the ostensible health of the whole system (including spiritual). I say we are better off casting our lot with the comet, and perhaps in the end we do just that. Negative marginal productivity and continue to fish.

"No matter what you pay, even if a million dollars per game, *eventually* you ought to come out ahead. This is so because eventually you are bound to get a very long run of heads, in which your winnings, doubled with each head, will mount so astronomically that all your losses will be wiped out. This event will happen no matter what losses have been accumulated. Of course *when* it will happen will depend on how much you pay per game. If you pay a fairly large amount, this may come after the sun has become a ball of ashes; so this knowledge that you cannot possibly lose in the long run has little practical value." Anatole Rapaport: "The Logic of Strategy."

So will all values be turned upside down and all fish run backwards, but too late, too late for America and too late for man. And our present-day coins, which get us by, day by day, is this cash or credit?, and if so, if either, who believes who? Does money stand for no more than IN GOD WE TRUST, meaning *here*, in the sea, meaning the arrival of shrimp with the colder waters in the West, and the hunger and taste of the U.S. Nation. Or, as the Hopi said when asked about this game, we know what to think about a man who puts the name of his gods on his money!

But don't all men?

And isn't his objection really that the money doesn't stand for anything except an archaic false pledge the Western World, America in proxy now, made to the rest of the planet, Monroe Doctrine, or Sioux Land Treaty? And that the frontier is paying for the money not the money for the frontier?

Where else do one's gods belong if not on the money?, and who else should back our money except our gods? So Confucius said also: if in the natural order we trust, then dollar bill is convertor, nitrogen, base. Money is virtue, not profit; an angel leads the just man over the March hill.

And economics without fish is usury, justification for meddling, prostitution, black market. Not even the valuable retains its worth from sunset to sunrise for what happens in the alleyways (in interstellar space). And there is a scale which always balances because you can only see one half of it. The lobsters appear one place at a time, in the sea when they are in the sea, in the trap, the barrel, the boiling pot, or on the dinner plate, and wherever they go they would seem to balance on the visible scale, for they are weighed only against themselves, cash paid to hold the time in between. The point in the center is checked regularly by the local bureau of weights and measures, corrected for due monetary north, but I am not speaking of such balances in which birth control pills are both dangerous and not, and DDT is above and below the safe level for human beings. We know *that* scale; the real weight of the fish hardly moves it. But the Card 11 [a red golden-crowned king sits before an arras, the sword of perception balanced against the haft of physical creation, and that itself balanced by two halves to the scale, which follow it down even into the local lobster wharf, fish market scales]. This card which itself sits in the middle of the deck balancing all the forces of the becoming and returning of matter (not conservation of matter as some would believe, but gateway between incommensurate worlds, insuring that the flow between is invisible, equal, and reconstitutive). Here the lobsters and the shrimp in their generations would seem to weigh unevenly, fluctuating

seasonally, and the pesticides and changing ocean temperatures, of inflation and deflation and migration (or sunspots
playing with the cash register) are seen in different light,
economics revealed as mere surface chemistry. If there is a
real occult it is sociology, the men fulfilling of a deep set of
conditions, silent, agreeing, and if it isn't them, look around
as they may, there is no one else. They know about exchang-
ing lobsters for scallops with cousins, Krentz and Harold
Moody, and giving out a fifth share in a shrimp-boat; they
hold onto their receipts and exchange new lamps for old.
They know it's not lobsters; lobsters are merely the structure of the mystery. It's people who fish each other from
shoals and dig each other out of beds, men and women in
their cata-angelic forms, Somes societas, Cranberry shuttle.
They know there is no content to the system, to the money;
there are only actions, and the markets are sheer visualiza-
tions of a network they embody in their proper motions.
They behave not like bankers but like men who know the
occult is at work; money is feminine, magical, orgiastic;
they sit around in sheds not doing shit for the system, eyeing
the market, for which way it will turn, all the time aware
that the unitary properties of their existence are at stake in
this very room, and will abandon the market in one moment
of revelation that will show them the balance of lobsters and
nature, the real measure that makes a fisherman, which they
pursue more than lobsters themselves: is the balance running right thru America on which every scale even the gold-
en one is hinged, a mirror in which cash and credit have
galactic life, fall as meteors, burning out visibly in the
upper air.

Clyde Pomroy is complaining about two lost bushels of
redfish and some frozen stuff that won't hold out. They are
trying to find the receipts, to tally it out, once and for all,
but they will never do it; it is the attempt to get things off
the books, not that the books will ever be clear, not that the
millenium will come, but the shrimp might to the West any-
day.

"No snow to keep the frost out of the ground," one man
complains, slapping down his cards. "I froze my ass coming
over here, and you know that nothing is going to thaw out

till August. We're living in the damn tundra." These men
know a world when they see one.

Our possibilities lost in ice storm, where meteor showers
crash beyond our visibility, beyond
PHASAL OF THE MOON
What do I see but that the winter never ends. The ice
melts but we are frozen in the reality of it, a slumber which
swallows Buttermilk Brook and returns the warm teeming
waters to our forgotten elders. Black seawater returns from
within Crystal Cove and Squid Cove, drawn by a larger
power thru Bartlett Narrows, leaves an Arctic beach extending beyond the surface of the land: a land bridge like the
Great Northern Sea. The new material joining pieces of
rock is ice, the glacial not the igneous stone. And in ebb tide
the beach is littered by chunks of ice like dolomite crystal,
growing larger in the slapping of the waves, ice geodes, ice
ore in wafers and tits, sticking like glue to the wharf.

And you ask: what is material?

and I tell you: memory. The conditions *remember* winter.
And you ask is there not environment as well as mind? And
I reply that no force has yet been created contingent to the
mind of the Earth.

We remember because we fear the long ascetic boredom,
a death we will remember less yet need more than this life,
flaming and extended between worlds. As we are bound by
the most hidden powers to the production of a universe in
kind: the sheets of ice, the boats of motor, the towns themselves lit in a continuity of switches, flow of ions between
skins, is the tautology and collusion of matter and energy.

We have locked ourselves in a gradient of goods; the hier-
archy sits on the top, mimicking the king: redirective a flow
of commodities, fishes, atoms, thru the house. The lobsterman leaves in the morning, never aware he is walking into

the dawn of an utter and finite world, never aware that he can actually walk out of it, beyond the catch, into the obscure beauty of herself, but unmoors his boat and turns her into the bellum of species.

He does not see that he has remained in the center, with all the taboos and currencies, that he has walked elsewise to the periphery; he does not see the function of his ship, a material converted thru the center, which retains its edges, its hollow, hulk: but on a Cartesian scales, moving across which he hauls up: 545 pounds; as matter flows up from two million feet below, gold into the cauldron, black Xhosa slaves, who are cool under the earth, making the minimum for survival, like a machine, breathing just enough elemental gold to stay alive, to buy a wife, to escape back to the farm.

The lobsters are diverted from their homes into the vast economy, where gold is now their only measure. The scales in the ocean sag; the scales of America balance, luxuriously, upon the shore. The lobsterman cannot cool it; he cannot win by his strategy, merely postpone the decision, as he weighs his cause in lathwood, nylon rope, and an invisible game map, unpredictable and stormy, where the gold lies buried, decapod monster impressed on every coin. He is at Las Vegas everyday, but it is not like Nevada; the waters disguise the roulette wheels; the community fishes in a shape, a shifting flank of territories, the baboon pack in boats, protecting the sanction of society. The deep Atlantic history limits his bet to a gesture against the blind deck.

He cannot get off the scale, the weight and display of his experience. Nor can the child waking from dream, grabbing the bedposts and crying out, in pain and darkness impinging on all his conscious being until the breast is oblivion and sweet flow back thru the gates of an enemy who cannot finally hold him out. The one thing he cannot hold out even thru the long winter is transformation. We are not made of the environment. The environment is made of us.

Red birds fly. Moss and lichen grow on it. The clam-digger's hoe must cut the skin of ice before he can even tap on the frozen sands. The dream is as macabre as that I have stolen the gold, THE WHOLE MATERIAL WORLD, and I want a fortune in ransom for it, a job.

Sun comes to it. Red birds fly. If sun is id, moon is ego, vessel, self, so the text tells us. Hot piss melts snow, the body's retained warmth. The vessel carries a burning rod. A torch. The sun gives fire which the moon takes, earthshine into the crescent bower recalling our racial past, our twice thru the mirror a man dark and birthmark stands before, in the map of his sex, has the body he had, the weight and boiling water of it, melts thru to grass.

It is material, the generatio thru and of, the bricks piggy-back withstand boards wedged between them. You ask if I see anything else within reach. I can only tell you that geo-centricity is yet a power more devastating than the light switch, landing a current which will turn this world inside out. Within reach.

At least we come to it made of this, and melt steel, no world but the world that is changing, priceless, outside the buoy-markers of our outermost set.

We began our trip as passage out of our isolation, having forgotten who we were. We waited and waited here, doing our work, never having anyone over, never breaking the tension, until a plumb thru our position delivered us and we were in the car, packed and going. The best moment was at the beginning, when all the pent-up energy was there held before the brink of anything. We were on the Maine Turnpike, had passed beyond the snowy roads, were coasting at 70, and the sun warm in the car, our personal spring; Lindy and I sang an old rock and roll song along with the radio; Robin fell asleep; Lindy fell asleep; and I shifted into a daylight hockey game, the hectic voice of the radio thru eight Ranger goals until I was the voice, pounding the steering wheel in the frustration-joy. Anything to get outside it. To be the other. To see myself in. Where I am.

This is the clouds, the world that has its top on, cumulus rolling with the hills, and then cirrus above them. Morning is the roof on our heads, daylight, a benign atmosphere, that the influence is never direct, and is always our own. Self, roots in the ground, vegetable gnarled into river, is the old music and the trees on fire, we who have arisen here to meet it more than halfway, on the agreed field of the one, protected by the chains of clouds and angelics. A candle in the wind, a unit of daylight, impinging on us not as heavy objects, but as space escapes from the webwork of a giant clock.

Six hours in the car, the last moments of the game carry us into the city, jagged continuity; note on the door says: "Richard and Lindy, Went Shopping, Back in a Half Hour." We tour the backyard, Robin high in backpack, riding that I am horse, bounce for him, he laughs; we put our giant hoofs thru the snow; we come to the great stone center, boulder beyond which the plants of winter, the dried blood in their heads; I am wearing my woolen cap; Robin pulls on it; I cannot see myself, Lindy part and partner takes ou. photograph. We sit in the car to get warm. Return to our footprints, the dog barking at I cannot see myself. Blind. Hoarse who has lost his voice with a bad winter cold, I am closer to speaking in my own voice now than ever. I have said everything except that there was a real horse at tether in the next yard.

Such is the conversation of the evening with the first friend we have seen in months: TRANSFORMATION, that there is no homeostatic study of culture, ecology all right as an exercise if you like that sort of thing—but the planets our immediate environment; our objective time, making Spengler astrologically correct. We begin with Rodney Collin, the coiled spring of the solar system, sprung loose at the instant of birth so that the planets in their lifelong unwinding set off the glands of the proportions of their weights, the astroendocrine condition of our lives. But what about the link that is TIME, that is absolute in its conjunction with our bodies, the plants as our condition, but no longer because they have us on strings. They surround us and lock our movements in their phases; so powerful are they that they do not have to touch us, for we call time history and history time, and so do them homage. We make them the environment of our world age, called the night sky. How can you believe in astrophysics, which is a stasis even when exploding, and the Tibetan Book of the Dead, which penetrates such outer motions, at the same time? Gerrit says we cannot, not when the skies are in the motion we are in in our proper time and the dead must prepare for death in a knowledge of their bodies, not when the quasars are our unique immortality, happening in Gloucester as Cassiopeia happens in Cassiopeia, as Ousoos is the dawn of the sun. The sky is too important to be left to scientists, as is culture, when our phase is linked thru both to an objective time even the cell grows in from its message. I may pretend to do a reading of ecology and sky physics, but Gerrit shows me that I cannot see that my left hand cannot see what my right hand is doing. Since there is no anthropological time, will I always be a fraud? [I see now in reading any ethnography that the problem is exactly that there is no time, no phasing proper with place; or the time which is distorted onto it is out of time with the account, borrowed from another modulation; the events are isolated from the speed and rhythm of the world in which they occur; the account is false, is ahistorical, and in the deepest sense the Western World is the fastest proper speed of all. Anthropologists mix times hopelessly, and what they mean by ethnohistory is usually no more than the historiography of their own accounts].

So Gerrit has convinced me I am not an anthropologist. We have wine. And later we have tea. The herbal he shows us is Aztec, depicts the habitat of the roots in color codes, blue brooks, red bugs. We are said to be at the beginning of a new age, and the physical requirements of life are changing. Poisons all around us, and we cannot be poisoned, which is why we fear the pure food and drug laws while the rotting carcass surrounds us at every meal. Because everything is a poison, a hallucinogen; there are no pure foods left, no direct leafy sunlight; bios is a body filled in all its parts by the drugs of our history, Chinese gunpowder and DDT, the stony waste of cities and subways; fifty years ago you could buy a fish by any other name from the seas of this planet; now you can't; every fish is chemically altered; the origin of toxicity is everywhere; it has no beginning; it has no safe limits. And we are all in danger, for the food itself is leading us to insanity and a knowledge of insanity, and the stars like children gay without their voices lead us too; we are drugged by everything, hence the false and obsessive fear that some people have toward specific drugs and poisons; it is a world flood, like genes, which cannot be stopped; all poisons are potions. Sleepier and sleepier on just the beans until I can't talk, soaked a few hours, until all my physical powers are dream, and I am very active there, and Gerrit says: "Robin, Robin, is there the spark of an ego there yet, just a spark?" And Robin pounds on the chair and squeals. "Cat, cat, are you a cat? No this can't be a cat. Not the way it's behaving. This must a rabbit." The cat hops after a string tied to itself. We talk so long I am becoming totally hoarse, Tommy Tucker begging for, but there is no real supper, Robin eating the stuffing out of the chair. I stumble sleepily out of the upstairs study, down the flight of the unknown house stairs into, finally, bed; I have heard Harry Smith speaking of string games, all primitives play, geometry in hand, between the fingers, I can feel myself between the fingers of the stars, gently as my flesh, the electromagnetic paths which hold me, which I cannot see myself in the mirror. It's not that I don't take it seriously; it's that I always have.

Morning in a strange house, in a living room not a bedroom, Robin up early, crying because he recognizes nothing. I am hoarse; in the passage of the evening I gave up, and now I know it, my voice. I try to remedy the situation before anyone awakes, fixing a bowl of bouillon soup, a can of lemon juice in hot water, the bouillon the bolster, the citric to cut thru the haze, which is outside too, rising from the snow. Gerrit awakes and comes downstairs, takes the dry leaves of elder and lets them brew, the most local of apothecaries, to give us back our voices so we can go on talking, to drink the power/potion of words. We go to a woman's house on Fort Square; her children are playing Beatles records while she sits in the kitchen—where afterbreakfast coffee goes, instead a six pack of beer, made cold by the dampness behind a curtain. There is a sorrow in this time; Olson has gone from the world of living poets to the noosphere which surrounds anyway, in Gloucester here so strong with his voice, presence, ambience. There is a certain sorrow that we cannot attack the nature of because it is wound into the nature of. The picture window shows the harbor, THE WATER, and on the other side, Gloucester Sea Jackets, the source, which winds its way up along wharves of the Maine coast into Canada, into the sea where men go from which men came wrapped in the garments of another nation, and their birth. Gloucester Sea Jackets: clothing is reminiscent of death. THE WATER. It is the dream you know you are going to have to dream, and finally you go to sleep, this life which is neither the beginning nor the end of a life, sees its shadow across an invisible world and turns back into sleep.

Here in the mirror links of darkness precede the image

even after we begin to look for it. Olson was perfect, no scar on him of trying to escape the strings, grows in fish harbor, a city on a hill, vegetable in the earth, its roots around the whole time and connectedness. The intricacy of the individual, his immortality, is sufficient and prevails. This is the vision of death: the dying man is admitted to the planetarium where he comes and sits by himself; the attendant who admits him stands outside the door beyond visibility; there the dying man sees that the arrangement of the planets at his birth is how they have come to their present and appointed positions, is a room he never leaves because his weight, as solid in liquid, has displaced those heavens, from here to there, and he is privileged, as every man enters anew to see that the same is the self, and that history is indivisible. The nature of the disease is organic to stars, where cancer the crab also climbs in chart of absolute time-motion, absolute still-stealth. The disease is the instructions; the instructions are the biopsy, the written body or the body of light, the light not seen before or after, at the very end remembers everything by remembering nothing. Because it's all there. Whether you know it or not. You know it.

Body is house, where everyone who meets outside it meets. The people cannot see us. Or the photograph of Olson, found among old papers, older than our knowledge of all this, in its yellow previous to light, a man shovelling hay into the North Carolina, into the sun of that hay, into the south of where we are; another is of a child in a mailsack on his father's back, closer to morning than evening, to id to sun, than to spark of ego, moon, closer to the beginning of a horoscope than here in 1970 the women weep the Grecian tragedy. Child in a mailsack is visible the arrangement of awaiting suns, called stars from here, which are the dawn of an era, an immortal one, an individual indivisible, who will remain so, even here in Gloucester and the Trojan sun that has grown in the time of planets, that has grown in America to a full city-world. They weep at the end of the beginning, for the picture frame, gilted gold, is the only picture, and holds a mirror, just as the galaxy in which we live is the only galaxy we see, touches the inner index finger in a chain of command, the stars which control us but never touch us, are themselves held in the place-chain of the stars we do not see, that time is coming both ways. And there is no way outside the era; the suns deliver not to their positions without but to the externalities at the tips, fingers which never have to land because they are always there.

There is only one name for the goddess, and it is the same as the practice of her. Invoke as many gods as you want; be a universalist; call on Odin, Pan, Yahweh, Christ, Agni, Changing Woman; it is still the bedrock sphere of the individual nomen, the one man whose name is marked in the one sky. I oppose then Ginsberg, funeral orator and universalist, to the man who turns all his gods into one, all his neurons into one momentum, as that picture of the hay, the pitchfork in the Carolina sun justifies the appointment of a literary executor, a historian rather than a pantheist. The story is too large for any newspaper or account; its impact on us is direct; there is no story, no political event that can be made popular; there is once again that the history of man is the history of weeds, that one man, silently, displaces the universe, as such, without gunfire or cosmic radiation, but as the energy of his parts—does not divert any of his power to the many, leaves that there is no other account.

The process of the gods is to gather them. Unexotic. To bring them home.

The women weep; the poisons are returned to the system which they threaten but do not poison; this city is his personal history, his body that he puts on in the morning, a complete sphere of dress, so that he doesn't have to put on the other clothing, or go outside to join other than his own entanglement in the causes—Gloucester Sea Jacket worn as Gloucester, *Gloucester Daily Times,* piled as time, blown and unfolded in the streets. Awaking once from the coma, comose, from the comet, to say WONDERFUL, back and forth thru the solar system and history like a glyph in text, a comet into the orbit of its body. 1910 as 1970. Unit as.

We are still alive, and the bands that hold us are supple objective time, fresh snow on the roads, the car uneasy underfoot; almost out of gas we leave the road and get lost in our directions, turn around and come back toward Gloucester, losing 12 miles three times, the weight of 36 miles, the children coming out near dusk to sled on the newly-covered hill, 36 miles of in between, of nowhere. What are we doing here out of place, without a fire to come in to or a sled to carry out to? What are we doing so for out of ourselves? There's no answer now except the warning implicit. Driving is impossible; we give up and go down a series of back roads in low gear, end up at a diner and motel in Saugus, an unknown woman singing over the back of the seat to Robin, a trill voice, he watches the lips, hears the sound, and laughs. Now he rips apart a roll while we order food. My own quarter in the jukebox: Neil Diamond, Holly Holy; the Beatles, Come Together. A child dreaming of the whole world loses the dream, awakes to the whole world, loses that too, but the voice of the song tells it. The Beatles as the food comes; suddenly I fear the liver I have ordered, the poison of my own system I cannot escape, the appetite for certain foods I cannot stop eating, hold you so close that you can feel his disease—before death, meaning all thru life, the body is a hive of visions, call them diseases, what we breed in each other, what we hold as humans, how we make it. The end of one time smashes down on another like granite onto glass, and the snow turns to rain, comes back with the fury of elastic stretched for sixty years thru the somatic cells, until the metabolism snaps, and light returns to its beginning where it is at rest. So what is there for a woman who has given her life to a man but her soul, which is his soul to give, which she carries, disease of which she is the carrier, breeds, into absolute time. The heat of the planet cooled by the liquid of it; for each of these there is a sun-star, from which emerges a star, a creature for whom the water is pure, component of his breath, blood.

Night tossing, strange commercial room, at dawn scrape the elements off the car, frozen rain, the era continues, Lindy's finger bleeding from a razor blade, in the middle of the night unable to find the bathroom light switch, Robin crying until we gather him into daylight and speed.

We are still young. We do not yet have a place, a reputation. We do not know where we are going; suddenly on the snowy road it is clear that, if final, we would have no place to go, and the whole world is outside the temple. Now we come in the daylight to Hampshire, college that has said they want me, I am listed on their calendar for the fall to teach myth, anthropology, and writing; this expectation is woven into our world. I am what I am and whoever will employ me engages in the weight of that myth. I take everything seriously. Know me. Love me. You love mythology if you love me; such is the nature of a life. In comes a man smiling masklike, without how many ears must one man have, and says: "I don't think he's quite what we want." Suddenly our lives broken at this point, written indelibly into the myth here at Hampshire: "I don't think he's quite what we want." The holy book thrown out the window. And the fear that he's everywhere and I will always have to confront him. He was at Michigan, Hampshire, Connecticut. He acts cool; he's phony-hippie or phony-radical or just plain sweet barrel-water liberal. And I think his fear is previous to everything: not that I will expose him as a fraud (which I will), but that surely I have in other worlds, and he will not let it happen again in this one. They are naked officials, having willed that I see them in all their sordidness, soddenness, in their noblesse oblige, fawning after high-priced pseudo-intellectuals to give them a status they lack. Only those who do not know history attempt to create Utopia, which is noplace, and throw good people out the window in their wish to be perfect and pure, a high class operation; "We have been commissioned to select the best faculty in the nation," they say solemnly, as if they could legislate what has been only for brief moments and then by a transforming flash, as if that were an excuse for inhumanity, and finally, as if that inhumanity were justified and purged by the think-tank . . . . . what Black Mountain was better than, for its hay and weeds, its real barns and families, and its knowledge that Carolina needn't be weeded into California, or no place. "The bastards," Nick Dean says. "They're bastards there." Just as I'm home free, about to enter their world, to let in— mythology as the crowbar—light, a real curriculum; the one man, but we have met before, uses his last official act to block me. "He'll set up a free university and subvert the kids from the curriculum," he says. Meaning fear that his curriculum is dead, that Caribbean studies cannot be transported to New England, but that as I predict, all will be revealed as New England studies here in New England, where it is. "He'll confuse the kids," he says, meaning *they* will and I will expose it. He thinks he is home free, not realizing that Hampshire, thru its last inhuman act, had handed me its soul blindly and on a silver platter. They reject the very nature of the myth they cannot escape. They are counting on Utopia and Olson revealed that nonsense. "The kids are great, but the faculty's out of it," meaning don't go there—academic conservatives and pious house radicals and programs for social reform support each other like crutches. Why me? Why give me the soul?

But we are in the period between, and no job, no place to go, I find myself falling asleep at my father's on the living room floor while time—the stasis—is at question again: they cannot decide in Los Angeles whether the goal was scored before or after, and not only is the game in doubt, but the nature of the game is threatened, the bound time from which we would only seem to be released by victory or defeat. I awake to angry players buzzing around on the T.V. set, twenty minutes later the game still undecided. Why don't the Rangers admit it; they played a shitty game; and go home. Why don't I give up.

We meet Chuck in New York the next morning, drive right into downtown Broadway traffic, and on 34th Street we are stalled indefinitely. Chuck is pointing left and right; every face he points to is ugly or angry. "They have reason to be angry," he says. "But they're running into each other. There's no retribution. It's near the end of the world. We just don't have that much time." It is the heat of the time upon us, not something extra, or something we blundered into, like a traffic jam or a fraudulent college. Chuck says: "It's no longer between those who know and those who don't. Everyone knows it's happening. It's between those who think something can be done about it and those who know it can't." To which my addition is: It's between those who think it has yet to happen and those who know it has already happened. We are living in the darkest West, before utter darkness, and the birth, Kelly says, of a radically different order of things. In these days, and my paranoia, I see the face of the devil everywhere, Ahriman cleaning up; the angry dogs are grinding the shit back into origin, original, from where another comes.

We are in the camera store, and the man who has raised the price two dollars has just raised it another eight on checking again. "But you already raised the price once!" I say.

"I? I? *I* didn't do anything. It's not my fault. The company did it. The company re-evaluated you. Olden camera re-evaluated the German mark. We have the choice of customers, the pick of the crop, and we find that you're not quite what we want. It's a personality thing. Yours was found wanting. We can back it up with substantive data, though. We have economic papers from Germany indicating the new prices. We can PROVE it. You might have been subversive. Hampshire College re-evaluated mythology, re-evaluated the role of mythology in the curriculum. You were found to be mythological. We decided to use a more serious subject. It's not our fault. We did the best we could. It was an honest difference of opinion. If you check back you can see we never exactly promised in just so many words you could have it at that price. It was written on paper, but that was a month ago. We said we would hire you, but we meant informally. You were naive to believe us. Business is business. Why, we've just flown out to the Coast to get someone to take your place. We always support the customer. Sorry we couldn't do better by you. Maybe next time."

"That's right," Chuck says. "It's the company's fault. You didn't do anything. You're a good Christian. It all comes from up there. You're not responsible for anything. It's all God."

"They're good guys, the deans," I say. "Deep down they support me."

"It's no good for them to claim they're on the right side. They've got to win."

"We did not prevail. . . . ." But the world age goes on. And this is a new world age in which motive doesn't count; you've got to win. Including soldiers wearing peace emblems around their necks while they pull the triggers on Vietcong. Deans wearing peace emblems, grooving; they're on the right side; they just never win when it counts.

They think that myth is one thing and truth is another, but there you can see in my own causal mythology I bind, I prove the two were never anything but one. And the deception is what they hide behind statements like: "These fine gentlemen and we have an honest disagreement." That's a nice little jig. An honest disagreement about appraisal. We know what to think of someone who claims to be starting the best hockey team in the business, and in Boston no less, and leaves off Bobby Orr. That man's got prejudices. He'd rather pay some old-timer twenty thousand to meddle in Joseph Campbell and play games with a computer, or bring some bitch in with her facts to gloss over that it's language at the root of it. This is the world age where you've got to have the goods, and when you take the ice it's going to tell.

Ringing in my ears: "I? I? What did *I* do?" Letter postmarked February 6, three days stale when it gets here: "The forces of evil have prevailed." I stand there. "Well, have you brought any lobsters?" he says. That's nervous chatter and we both know it. I carry the myth. I claim no more and no less. I—physical. In objective time. It's not enough to be a poet; you have to be a man. You have to use people well. End of an era. "Richard, you're a victim!" A victim? I bring it on myself. Part of my myth is sabotage; I operate in the underworld, the underground, psyche's child; I strike out when I am about to make the team, this moon static even in high school, interference of one orb with another in my chart.

You allow yourself to be a victim. You sabotage yourself. But part of your causal mythology is to come to the meaning of that in the end. There is no other way.

Back at my father's. Falling asleep again on the living room floor, and the conversation as I fall into half-sleep is of some rock festival in Montreal; the words are like dark cows that will not be born; I hear them in another world but I am asleep. I see that forms precede words. I see the trees without language, dark and restless, absolute. The forebears of oak and elm. I lie in a world that has not been born, whose language is stormy and cloudy, atmospheric. I awake to find myself between worlds, on the telephone the

kids are sneaking back and forth across the border; you
can't hold a rock concert in Montreal someone is saying;
everything'll be held up while they search for drugs at the
border, and a Wall Street pig is talking about money, how
he wants to make a strictly financial investment in a rock
festival in Montreal and wants to know if it is a good propo-
sition, back and forth across the border, the unnamed Neanderthal specters of pre-language; I am not yet born; I can
awake in any world. I hear them asking if they should invest. The shadows on the caves, the bears; there is nothing.
Nothing has begun. Should we invest in a house of consciousness?

Of course. Invest in me!

Let me be born!

I walk into a house and it is blown apart in the shadows
of leaves, the moonlight.

Let me be born!

I try to speak but I am hoarse.

I am in a silent dream, and the moon, I am held in one
position by it; I stand there, hung.

Let me be born!

I awake, and they are gone, my parents, the impressario
on the phone; the whole rock festival has moved out. The
T.V. is left on. I am too tired to turn it off. I fall asleep,
over an hour later awake to Sherlock Holmes and music
boxes; he remembers the tune; the key leads him to Samuel
Johnson's house, the plates of the Bank of England, the irrevocable elms and oaks and blackthorns, the appletrees that
lie at the beginning of our logos and economy. I fall asleep:
voice from the Everly Brothers: only trouble is, gee whiz,
I'm dreaming my life away. The whole planet a dream; why
do I live here?; why do we dream while Rome burns?; why
do our precious cosmic resources dissolve in karma and wash
up smoky on the planet's shore? Want me! Let me be born!

I awake again; nobody has been in the room; nobody has
turned the T.V. set off; I awake to a Swedish girl trying to
seduce her professor, the late movie. He refuses to hug her.
She falls into his arms. He says I can resist you. She slides
against his body, rolls around him, on his hardon, draws him
under her onto the couch, into her body, biopsy writes the

250

poem——No, I cannot resist you. I was wrong.

She destroys his books, his photographic equipment. The only chemical left is sperm. The pictures will remain undeveloped maybe 25,000 years more; we do not have a hand for it; the only chemical we can tolerate is not poisonous and comes from within; the body fills with spines to release it; there is no timer, no measure; we need not pour from a spout; we are the system, the imago, delivery and all. Come, come, come now, there is no picture of it you will ever see, no sex in the head, no porn.

I cannot resist you. Naked in the mirror. Upstairs in the house. After all these days, years, see myself. I cannot resist you, living in my time.

I do not know whether I was just asleep and have awakened with a start, struggled upstairs, or whether I am in a trance from penetrating the sleep. I have never been able to look at myself like this, this long and hard. I am not too much or too little; the eyes are dark on themselves, watch themselves watching themselves; the features are large. I am looking at a race of them, a sexual being. His eyes are on me watching him. I have surprised him in this house which is not my own but not his own. We are irresistible. I have the words; he has the form; we meet. And I think I have hated him all these years, for being, for being told: You're not quite what we want. For being told: a poet is not enough; you have to be a man. I am a man. I am what you see in me.

The old joke returns. I say to Lindy: "You never would have married someone good-looking."

She says to me: "I never would have married someone not good-looking."

I am stumbling thru mirrors. I want to be born.

Why do they keep asking me questions, as if in a million years they will settle it once and for all, know whether I am good or evil. When they have found out, maybe they will tell me: angel or demon, curse or salvation. I will be my own salvation. There are no universals and there is one God. Know me: is the law of anyman. I am the dawning of an era, utterly unique, surely immortal. I want to be mad. I want to teach you history; the stars are my objective time. I am the delivery of the whole thing. I stand here to be taken. Robin says: DaDaDaDa, and smiles, and I say back to him: DaDaDaDa, back and forth, we exchange dark cows. We don't have to talk about anything. We can exchange these words all day. Because I want to talk to you more than anyone else.

Let me be born.

Moving at a speed close to light, intercepting a school of energy, the wingboards are opened, the doors, 100 feet across at the mouth, swallowing that energy, squirming, whole.

Mingo: ghost ship, motley crew, is made up of men forgotten by other ships, young boys, prisoners of sardine boats and the 1920's, with a Mediaeval assortment of bracts and winches, pulleys and nets, to do the hangman's operation upon the sea.

These are the Pittsburgh Pirates, for whom the secret name of Pittsburgh is MELLON when exercised in Cranberry waters. Look at whom they have dredged up from the graveyard of minor league managers to captain the *Mingo*: Floyd Phippen, of Frenchboro, how in America the impressario hires the black sheep to do his dirty work for him. Not that dirty work is dirty. Sometimes it's the only thing that cleans the system, from the bottom up.

The badmen are turned loose on the seas, the linebackers, the pirates. Do not mistake this. We are all pirates, Cranberry Island Pirates. The nets are pulled into vehicle, in them is harvest, shrimp-meat, caryopsis of grain, cooked for six minutes in the ship's ovens and alembics while the nets make a second pass. They miss nothing. Flounder and cod, great gods of the sea, are dragged up also, pulled from the mass, their ancient bodies, and thrown down below, corpses into the dungeon to rot.

"The *Mingo* just lets her cod sit in bilgewater," says Enoch, an old cod-buyer. "One trip her shrimp was so bad no one'd buy it. All they'd have to do is start up the pumps."

Why don't they?

"Maybe they're just a bit lazy. I'll say one thing. When

you're fishing for four or five days no ice on the fish ain't good."

They sit in three separate mounds in a corner of Lee Tracy's backroom, long angular cod and two loose heaps of the flatfish flounder. The ice that was shovelled onto them has evaporated in the steam and turned to snow. "I like fresh fish," says one man, "but I wouldn't touch these. God knows how long they set aboard the ship. But we send 'em to Jonesport, they cut off the fillets and salt 'em. Once they've been in salt you can't tell the difference."

A ROOM CAN'T BE COLD AND HOT AT THE SAME TIME, says Fred Beal,

but the giant oven has been turned on and is releasing its steam, covering the cod and flounder in a rich mist. Three sacks of salt are poured into the water, and the room is filled with so much steam we can only smell where we are. I see it settling on the snow and refreezing, the fossil cod caked on, and pouring off in rivulets across the floor. Cranberry Islands. Cod Islands.

Here in the tropics from the West, the red shrimp water, the pink scum, and the snows of the East meet at the pluvial divide. And in the sun's cycles of waters and climates, the Gulf of Maine is joined to Chesapeake Bay as blood vessels along a flank of nerves. The men rig up their lobster boats for an arrival they can surely expect, pure red cash, dollar bills and loose change dredged out of sun-shadow, and the sun's appearance in our economy. Yes, all commerce begins in pure coin, pure value, creation itself.

The yellow river of gold of sun flows into shrimp waters, migration only in that eggs hatch further and further to the North, turning tundra into gold rush, the bursts on the sun's surface reversing, flow back into the steaming retort of Lee Tracy, or lifted from the Moon's wingboards, carried ship-back, camelback elsewhere, converted at night when the ship is quiet and at dock, and the crew has a drink in Southwest Harbor, and the planet rests at Southwest Boat.

A redheaded man with bell-bottom pants turns the shrimp with an oar, the solution growing pinker and pinker, less water, more aqua, more syrup, regia, tiny black eyestalks in a single character of change, all their legs and antennae flowing forward in death-mask mime of the body.

Scavengers and starfish throw off their limbs, growing new ones, taking into their mass from the pool of outer species: prawns, crevettes, Chinese and chelae, as the greater portion of the world's population lies beyond the *Mingo*, beyond America, as it once stood outside the gate of Great Cranberry and Mellon City, waiting to enter. Now they are bones. The pirate ship follows Atlantis to the scrap heap, the stock market crash is next, its gold dropping to the bottom: "caught in its folds were three identical Roman amphoras. They were intact. Full of mud, they weighed over a hundred pounds apiece." Throckmorton, "The Unharvested Sea."

From the bottom arises a new market, Earth's archipelago, wombic changes, of consciousness, prawns ourselves. I am speaking of remarkable regenerative powers, those usually associated with the sun.

VI

At Jasper Merchant's (7)

Stormy sea. No one out fishing. Merton Hinckley marshalls the bait truck in, shouting instructions as it tries to find the driveway. Jasper, who is inside discussing South African lobsters with someone from the Navy, comes running out to a knock on the door. "I've got two meetings this morning," he says. "One of them has happened and one of them I'm not looking forward to, but here it is." A young husky man stands there half-smiling. "No sir," says Jasper. "I'm not glad to see you. You've come with a truck full of redfish, and I've got only four men going, and I'll bet that's more than all the rest of the places together."

Merton Hinckley is there, his little dog riding on his shoulders. "I've got an order up the harbor too."

"Up there? What could he be ordering? How many fishermen does he have? One and a half?"

"Two," Merton replies.

"Two," Jasper scoffs.

Now don't tease Sewell, I say.

"Tease him? I'll tease him right out of business."

Fred has come downstairs from his shed where he's been painting buoys and surveys the situation. "You've got to be organized," he says. "Without Merton Hinckley we'd never get our bait."

"I don't need redfish now," Jasper argues.

"Bargain prices," shouts the truckdriver, and he opens the hatch, sets the mass past inertia with a kick of his foot, spilling skeletons down into the baskets, single racks popping and scattering all over while Fred hops around spearing them with a pitchfork and flinging them into the bait barrel. Jasper stands there, more or less nonplussed, watching the unending flow for which he will have to pay in cash.

The truckdriver's name is Bucky. He's perched on the side of the truck, half-whistling, half-cursing. "Bastard is sitting on his ass back there," he says to Merton. "And I've got to go to Boston yet today. Shit! Shit! What am I doing here?" He shakes his head a number of times.

"He wouldn't take it himself, would he?" Merton says.

"That's okay," Bucky snaps, getting up to help the fish down the chute with a shovel. "My day'll come. My day'll come." And perhaps that's what they all say, because it's the one thing that's finally true.

Fred is pausing, watching a family of ducks, sort of out of the corner of his eye. "That would make a fine dinner now, wouldn't it?" he asks. He grabs up a piece of snow and throws it at the water. "Bang Bang now. Bang Bang. See. You can't even scare these birds anymore. They know the law says you can't shoot them."

The fish are spilling all over the place, and more men are helping, picking up one here, one there, and throwing them into the baskets and barrels. Jasper has gone to get the salt. Buck is still cursing, in between refrains of "Bargain prices! Bargain prices!" as he shovels it on out, standing high up in the truck, symbol of the future.

Two rowboats filled with men pull up down below at the wharf. They are rigging for shrimping like thousands of ants carrying food away for the winter, all over the place with wood, saws, nets spread across the floor, and men, women, and children, drones, weaving white threads into the broken yellow.

Jasper, I ask, do you consider the wharf private property, or don't you mind all these people working here?

"It's first come first serve."

Even if they're not selling to you?

"I know what you mean. The rest of the country's like that. But we don't have to be that way. Yet. If I have enough money for my little corner I'm not going to try to squeeze out every penny where I can get it. But, I'll tell you, they're forcing it on us. They're making taxes and insurance rates so high that we're going to have to. And I believe that's what they want. Then it will all be the same everywhere. Private property. But until then it's first come first serve. The wharf's there. Whoever wants and needs to can use it."

Fred is staring down into the water. Now he turns to me. "Do you think we're polluting our waters?" he asks. And then begins to answer. "Now I don't think throwing fish overboard hurts because that's just food for the gulls. The ocean eats that. It's the oil the ocean doesn't eat, and that's just what pours out of the sardine factory."

The rest you know.

VII

Displaced Note

We sit in the living room with our tea, saying nothing, nor able to gauge. Orange cat licks charcoal cat. And white cat lies upsidedown on the heavens, rolling on the rug. Relaxation is proprio, receptive of position. We are tense, uptight. These creatures, light as snowflakes, medicines, do not see our world, fill our world, whom we have had beside us so long the markings on their coats and underbellies are like the emblems of our house. Making a home as birds do on our roof.

We have no home, no proper field-study. I call it Maine as a whole, but we lack the fuel for such a voyage. We are displaced. It is too late to go back to the beginning, to 1915 or 1910, to New York, or 26,000 years before that. Our youth is over, exhausted by the paleness and distance of the outer planets. The days pass. The first is rain and the second is snow, and freezes it; the third and fourth likewise.

On the fifth day nothing happens. I don't go to the lobster sheds. We don't leave our house all day. The snow falls. A few years ago there were over a hundred things we might have done. Even in the fall there were a dozen. Now there are two or three, like the knuckles of our hands.

We pile into the car and drive into Bar Harbor to buy groceries. The town is deserted. The bookstore is closed. The stationery store is days behind on its newspapers. We simply buy the groceries in the bright variety of the A & P and head home, the same ten miles back. We would have stopped at the library if Robin hadn't been asleep, a peaceful smile on his face, as he too drops out of/into the playing-ring, where it all goes on, clutching a toy to his snowsuit.

We don't pass a car either way, coming back along our own tire tracks in the snow.

On the tenth day a couple drives seven hours from Northboro, Mass., to get out of some of their own urban hassles, arrive in time for corned beef and cabbage, to sit on their unhatched eggs and yarns thru a whole day of snow, driven as irresistibly to the country as they will be back to the city, nothing changing, finally quarrelling, leave first thing Monday morning and return.

The snow light on the branches, crashing as the winds bring it to earth, footprints in which the cats wade, a frozen ocean, the road to it cut off, and a red fox seen passing thru the forest, stops and looks over his shoulder at us, returns to an earlier age.

And we are writing letters of inquiry everyday. When this ends there is no place to go. Everyday the mailman comes and goes before we even awake and I troop out in bathrobe and slippers, thru the snow, so that if there is nothing I can at least return, in my footprints, to the warm of the house.

If the snow keeps falling more than one red fox will come, closer and closer, until they travel freely over the buried roof.

Dreams of returning to Amherst are in their death throes, leaving a clenched undirected anger. I don't have the energy to go to the wharf. The outer planets, moving so slowly, rule. I don't have the energy to be myself anymore.

We look for diversion in Bar Harbor, and go with Father Gower to visit his father. Old Earl Gower is at peace on the outermost planet of all, has painted himself into his room, one giant vision of a landscape on all four walls, like eyes, looking in, borrowed from a picture postcard of Idaho, dislocated, but the mountains are rounded and made *des mounts deserts,* and a cabin not in the original is put on a point of land, where Earl imagines he lives, although he can never enter it and it is always inside his house.

We have some tea there and then leave, go back to our own brooding silence. How displaced, jobless can we ever be, from house to house, Ledgelawn to School Street, to visit Bar Harbor like this, and watch the small town thugs play on the street at night, selling hard drugs and porn, the only hotspot in the whole winter, but radioactive and offcenter as a hanging wire. Or Earl Gower playing his mandolin, the memory of it, in the carpenter's shop, his son balancing a door on its hinges, poised enough to spend hours on this one measurement without bolting. Hampshire was an image, like Idaho; we have no patience for anything else. And where its twists around him he makes the bathroom door stop on a dime, even with all that vertical displaced weight, a craft of measure and topos, he takes his place among tools. He borrows his elegant windows from houses that have fallen; he knows the locale so well, from fifty years of dormant observation, he can pick the single appropriate item from the single house. His craft is one.

VIII

At Jasper's (8)

No business, but, as Smokey Robinson says "if time was money, I'd be a millionaire." Radio on in the background, a crowd anyway. Francis Hutchings is giving directions on where to find the best scallops; Harvey Sturlow and Aubrey Fowler are sitting on the chairs, an unnamed old-timer on the barrel, can't go lobstering anymore, his heart is bad. Time to burn talking about fish, the sea rough. Harvey Rich comes in and stands by the door. "I went out, got no farther than the end of the harbor, and I came right back. It is bitter. You know I've been looking at my records for February, and four or five is a damn good average."

"You've been catching big ones," someone offers.

"They're the same ones from inshore. I follow them out so far and then lose them. I wish I knew where they went." He stands around silently for a second, then says, "I'm going to go finish those two traps and get me some supper," and is gone again.

Jasper walks around the shelves marking down inflation while the men shake their heads, crossing out 10¢ and writing in 31¢. "That's a good one," Francis Hutchings whistles. Gloves go up from $2.00 and $2.50 to $2.50 and $3.00. Suddenly Aubrey Fowler starts talking.

"They're getting some shrimp over at Northeast; yes they are. David Sprague and Sewell Alley, they don't care if it's storming so they can't see two feet in front of them. They're out there getting $400 a day, and I don't blame them. They are at it something fierce. Yesterday he wasn't going to go out, but Sewell, he doesn't care, and David Sprague isn't going to let him go alone, so he goes out there too, 950 pounds. It's those Mississippi nets that are catching everything. No one else's doing nothing. Now Robert Johnson over at Bar Harbor, he puts one on. They're just better. They bloom up, got lots of twine in the top. The other ones you can't tell the top from the bottom; they got lots of orange floating stuff. These are all nyack."

While he's talking Fred Beal has come in and sat down; as soon as Aubrey finishes he begins:

"How about those two small boats standing up to the dragger. He tried to make them move over, they wouldn't budge, he went right on thru them; you hear Donald on the radio? He was madder than hell."

Aubrey: "First time I ever heard of an overtaking boat having the right of way."

Fred: "What a temper that Donald has. He's gonna get sunk one of these days. That was a big boat, a dragger from Stinson, 85 foot."

Aubrey: "Linwood Peabody was the captain, wasn't he?"

Fred: "A downhomer. Raymond Smith from Jonesport got on the phone and said, 'Somebody better call Linwood's wife, he's gonna get himself beat up,' and she called back and told him to be a good boy. Was he burned up. And that Donald, he says, 'Just because you got a big boat doesn't mean you're pushing me out of the way,' he's gonna get sunk."

I ask Aubrey to explain and he says that two boats from Winter Harbor got there first, but a big converted sardine-boat simply overtook them, went right between when they wouldn't give way. "They were there first, but you can't fight those big boats; they go after their bread and butter."

Why do you suppose Sewell Alley is doing so well? What makes a good shrimper?

"I imagine those Mississippi nets help. Then he's up early, gets the first tow in the morning, and the last one at night. I'm not sure why it's better then, but it seems to be. Maybe at night they sag down to where they can catch them, but they can't catch them when they're up high."

Do the big boats not get out first in the morning?

"The big boats aren't so fierce. A man's giving 40% to Stinson he's not likely to go out of his way eaxctly. And the *Mingo*, they might as well sink her, she won't even get her net wet. The other day Floyd was about to go out and suddenly he turns around and says, there are too many boats on the outside. That Floyd has too many excuses. But I tell you Sewell is something fierce. And did you see those Stove boys over in Northeast, can they drink."

Fred: "Are they related now?"

Aubrey: "No. One's a little darker than the other. They might as well be related when you see'm drinking together."

Fred: "Alden Stove, he's a black sheep, isn't he? They had him before they was married."

Aubrey: "He's Alston's son, the one that was drowned."

Why does Sewell Alley take his shrimp over to Northeast when he lives right here by his lobster place in Bernard?, I ask Aubrey. He explains that Northeast is just around the corner from Frenchman's Bay, where they're fishing. "He saves an hour not bringing them all the way over to Lee Tracy in Bass Harbor, and he can leave his boat right there. When he's done he's done. And David Sprague buys the shrimp there; he has a dock tied up and some men doing it for him; they cook the shrimp right there, and Lee sends me over in a truck to get them. And I tell you, it is cold there where they cook the shrimp, but they don't seem to mind. I'm surprised the oven even goes. But that David Sprague is tough. They won't even put up plywood. The other day he ran out of trays for cooking the shrimp, I brought them over in the truck, he said just throw them down, it was ten below down by the water, one of them hit him right in the mouth, he just went right on going, he is tough. But I tell you, he's getting taken there the help he has."

"Taylor and that Smith kid, isn't it?" Francis Hutchings asks.

"That's Leslie Smith; he's got no brights at all. You have to wake him up in the morning and point him where he's going. And Taylor can't read the scales. They've got Dudley there too, and you know how much he wants to work, he runs everytime he sees the truck. He had nine thousand pounds weighed out there the other day, and we take them and count 6771, and David Sprague is compaining to us. He says there's too much shrinkage. Well, that's 24¢ on the hundred. That's not shrinkage. That's carelessness." Everyone is laughing. Lobsters die and that's shrinkage there, but who ever heard of shrimp shrinking. "I'll tell you how it happens too. They don't weigh every tray; they just take the weight of the first one and multiply. Well, you leave it to a fisherman to get a little extra. I don't know what they do, but I'm sure it's something. They fluff it up, I bet. When the shrimp's froze it's colder than a bastard, it piles up just like straw. And then he counts 7 pounds a rack. I was watching him do that and I put one on just to see; it was eight and a quarter."

Jasper: "It's no job at all to weigh everything. Bet it wouldn't take fifteen minutes. He'll learn to if he's in the business long enough."

Aubrey: "He won't be in the business too long losing $900 a day. He's just taking too much for granted. You can't take nothing for granted, not in this business. Why Gary Moody and Russell Stove, they got a way to make it look thicker in the tray, and those trays are not going to weigh seven pounds all winter. And Lee says, 'let 'em set between cookings, let 'em drain.' But they don't."

Why don't you tell them?

"The less I have to say over there the better."

Fred: "That Lee, you don't get nothing by him."

"Nor Emery Levesque. They're all in it together, I tell you, Emery Levesque and Hook and Lee Tracy, I've been noticing them long distance calls to Boston. And that Emery, you don't get anything by him either. He puts his hat on sideways, unzips his jacket, and stands there with his hands on his hips, he is stubborn, he knows what's in his head and you aren't going to change his mind. Old Emery is stronger than hell too. I saw him lift a thing of flounder, no one else would try it, almost pulled two other men thru the floor. They're all working together, though; it's Kresky going to get left out, while he's off skiing somewhere. He wasn't too happy when he got back and saw that Hertz Rent-A-Truck there. But Emery, he got the truck for Lee. He talked to Hook. There are a lot of phone calls back and forth. It's Kresky's fault, though. He let them run out of shooks. Hook would have been burned up to know we had the shrimp and no boxes to ship them in while Kresky's off skiing."

Fred: "You seen Robert? How's his hand?"

Jasper: "He mashed it pretty good. He was in here this morning, had it wrapped close to his chest like this, wasn't going to take a chance on hitting it; but he went out."

Harvey Sturlow: "He was carrying a battery when he fell, wasn't he? That's how he done it."

Aubrey: "Fell right on the hand, crushed two fingers. You should see that man's hands, though. He froze them once rowing ashore and they've never been the same. He'll lose feeling in them and not know the difference. He was in the other day, and I say, 'Robert, what's wrong with your hands?' They were yellow as an oriental. Well, he puts them in the boiler, right in the hot water getting ready for shrimp, and they turn purple around the wrist, they come back to life. But I tell you, when he walked in they were just as colorless as that door. Jesus dying Christ." Aubrey is really going. He's talking in another conversation in the other direction about someone else, and he's saying, "Christ is he fat. He blowed up fatter than a pig."

Is this the first winter you worked for Lee Tracy? I ask Aubrey.

"Yes. Last winter I worked for the Park, got so anxious I set my traps the 18th of March. Harry Smith gave me hell for not waiting for the full moon. I was a full week early."

Why the full moon?

"There's most always a storm before the full moon."

How long did you work for the park?

"Just last year. Before that I went trawling or fishing. For hake during the war. This place was humming with trawls then. I went fishing for Underwood, so now I can draw unemployment. That's more profitable than setting traps out there."

Francis Hutchings: "When he was nine years old he baited trawls for me."

Aubrey: "That's right. No one goes haking now. There's no market. They're not readily freezable, so they can't be used for fishsticks. They're what you call a watery fish. They're like a sponge, got water between the scales. Away from here they call 'em trashfish. Years ago they used to salt 'em and take 'em in coasters to the West Indies. I guess those people needed salt in their diet, otherwise the sun'd take it out of them they'd be so thirsty all the time. Now they must use something other than salfish."

Phone rings. Jasper answers it. "Aubrey, it's for you?"

"Is it Lee?"

"No, your wife."

"Same thing."

He says two words on the phone, then hangs up. "Lee called home, wants me there. I knew it was coming. You can see cross the harbor a boat's in there, Ira Shea. Say, Jasper, you got some gloves." He throws him a pair. "You let shrimp get on those gloves, well, you may talk about lobster bait, but Jesus O Christ are they ripe." Aubrey rushes out and we all sit quietly for a time.

"He's quite a talker," Harvey Sturlow says.

"Been that way since he was nine," adds Francis Hutchings.

"I used to think it was just talk," Jasper says. "After a while I realized he likes to talk, but he's usually got something."

Things quiet down, so I leave and go over to Lee's. Ira Shea has unloaded, and his partner, Emery Levesque, Jr., the boy, is watching his father cut fillets out of the flounder. So are five other men. Emery Levesque has charisma. Observe. Here he is running the show in another man's establishment. "Just helping out," he would say.

So if time was money they'd all be millionaires, standing around, watching the Man show how it's done. "Who are they?" I ask Lee, concerning two young-looking men with torn boots and pants legs, teasing and slapping away at each other.

"Got the flu today. Brain won't work. Can't talk," Lee says. He means it, knocking against his head with the pencil, can't figure out numbers. I leave him and go back and ask the boys.

One with curly hair and woolen cap is Billy LaFleur, goes lobstering during the summer, his father's a mason. "Do you own your own boat."

He nods. "The leaky teaky, they call it," says the other, leaning into him with his shoulder. His name is Lucky Farrell, only 25 traps he got from his father.

You building more?

"I lose as many as I build."

You sell to Emery Levesque too?

"It's a family affair. My father did and his father did."

Did he help you with your boat? The dealer?

"No. He helped me with gear."

Do you own your own boat?

"The bank does."

Do you do anything besides lobsters?

"Drive truck and collect unemployment."

Lloyd Chambers is in with his boat, and the group disperses to go look at the haul. Aubrey shows up, having put down a nice lunch in the meantime, and he and Emery work the pulleys, haul the shrimp out of the bin in cloth barrels up to the wharf and onto the scale. "Not going to make a fortune on this much shrimp," Aubrey calls down. But the net is torn and he had to come in early. Emery is businesslike, efficient and silent; his eyes and Lee's, nothing could get by, every shrimp picked off the wharf, every starfish tossed back into the sea, all eyes on the scale. The men give Emery Levesque a radius when he works, when he cuts a fish, works the pulleys, even at Lee's place, even his son. Inside they're getting the ovens ready. One man holds up a shrimp. "Hey, it's got a window in it," he calls out. "You can see right thru." He knocks on it with his fingers, then tosses it in with the rest. "Fantastic things."

While sorting they toss out a big fish, with horns, still breathing, heavily, its large oval eyes set onto its head. "A horndog we call it." Pulled from the mass of shrimp where it was swept from a different direction into the same net, its body going, to recall its environment, and why it is dying, and what it is. I don't know why I brought it home, and all the starfish. It should be alive in the ocean or dead waiting to be eaten, and if it's scrap, junkfish, then I should have left it on the floor. But a live fish swimming in a kitchen pot, or is it dead and are those mere tropisms of the body's remainder, its sides heaving even after the cats have eaten half of it? Why didn't I leave things as they were?

And this discrepancy ends the day.

IX

LETTER

To Fred Haddock
Department of Radio Astronomy
University of Michigan

..... My work in Maine is going well, and if one is going
to live in a place where something is happening (historical-
ly, dynamically economically, sociologically), then here is as
good a place to grow roots if any. Yes, the country is happening in all of its parts, and one needn't be in the cities to
see our people and their work. At the resource base the focus
begins, and this is true even of the astronomer's telescope;
Earth is point prime, point biological whole. Thus, our idea
of making at least a two year commitment to the state is our
commitment to the roots and letting them grow, rather than
stealing a few fish and running. And to where? With Hampshire I was interested in the process of teaching, all of which
is to say I wanted to talk to people about what we all know
anyway, the emotion and relaxation of that, the dance. Here
I am interested in land and history, the doings around me,
and the construction of an objective system.

..... Perhaps you know of Charles Olson's death. Right
to the end he wrote. That the nature of the disease, the process affecting him to the death remains in the causal mythology of his life. Antientropy here, if you will have it. Life
is energy; myth is physics. History of the Maine Coast of
antimatter. History of Charles Olson/mark of the electron/
neutrino. Path. Ousoos Zeus. One man who works to dis-
place the universe. At Stonehenge a stone.

Just recently have been doing a different reading of astrology, getting out of the glandular weight-water relationship of man and the planets, or out of the long body of the Solar System into another biology of it. It seems now that the heart of the matter is a relationship (a relativity?) between the times of the planets, objective time, and the time of man, biological time. Planets *inter alia,* man *inter alios;* not quite —this is making it into language. I wanted that *inter,* but not exclusive of the *intra* in it, and the reflexive *se,* (*inter se,* among themselves). Between the moments of birth and death is a fixed immortality, a flash in the biological pan, that itself is never destroyed; and the only out-of-biological time with which to write this is big sky time. Not to rob the stars of their biology, but to give them a new fix on biology itself; *objective time.*

I tell you this realizing that you are far afield from such literature, but as a part of a tradition of talking we have had and that has been helpful and useful to us both. This astrology predates the astrophysical cosmology which also, in trying to find its time and topology, draws the relationship between "biology and temporal human" and "stars as pure time" to yoke them and so plow our field.

X

Davey Sprague's wharf is an old barge tied brazenly to the town pier, the scales and ovens floating on it, a hood over its head on one end protecting the books. A mass of blatant and uncouth structure, four sides to it, its thickness afloat. Or an ark which was a granite wharf once, back in the Old Stone Age, chunks of paving stone unloaded from Swans and tributary quarries for the cities. It bore that weight for years, until the rock business went bad, then sunk into the middle of the harbor until Davey Sprague paid its old owner $100 to raise it up; he rode it bareback into shore, and lassoed it to what was there. Afloat again, 1970. Red shrimp.

At Davey Sprague's the men are said to be fierce, as fierce for beer as shrimp, and some nice bottles of whiskey to burn off the cold while they work on their nets. Elsewise Northeast Harbor, the spinster, is silent as a tomb. Yet the gulls know where the action is, who's throwing the party, and are drawn to it by the party lights, bright shrimp, fresh-cooked, floating in amongst cakes of ice.

"Davey Sprague, he wants to be king fisherman," Aubrey says. "But he can't be dealer and fisherman both. In the end it's coming down to dollars and cents."

The gulls are all around the barge, and great puffs of steam shoot from the ovens. The men work from sea to land, from hand to mouth, nets full of shrimp emptied into trays, the trays weighed and tipped into the ovens, the ovens tended by men in heavy coats, sentinels beside each one.

Davy Sprague is on the boat that's just come in: a small chunky man, some leftover whiskers, the quixotic face of Coyote, so that when I tell him I hear he's doing real well he smiles like Billy the Kid and says, "Aw well, there's lots of talk. Talk don't mean nothing."

Is it good to get out early shrimping and make the first run?

"The early bird gets the worm I've heard say."

Ray Cunningham is working the gas pump, chattering away. "Not every early bird, huh Davey, not every early bird gets that worm."

Gary Moody and Basil Travis roar in and begin gaily tossing up trays of shrimp. "Hold it now. Hold on," says Leslie Smith, the boy on the scales. "I can't do all this at once." They give him another volley and then sit down, impatiently grinning at each other. Basil Travis, young man, big woolen cap, golden beard, sitting on his ass on a crate, begins tossing single shrimp up out of the boat at Leslie, who is brushing them out of his face. "Hey now, I've gotta see the scale." He writes down the amount and passes the tray on to Philip Taylor who tends the oven. Davey Sprague prowls by. "Hey, that's not, hey, what is—," he interrupts suddenly and gets the tray back on the scale, snatched right from the jaws of the hot water. He adjusts weights while Leslie, tall and gaunt, stumbles back, with a silly smile. "They're cold, stiff," he says. "These weights." He tries to massage some life into them. "Get me some oil," he calls out. Leslie brings it. Generously he spatters it all over the top of the scale, pouring freely. "Watch the shrimp!" Philip calls out as the oil drips. Basil chuckles.

Aubrey's words are recalled to me. "You watch and see. They'll try and confuse the boy, make him so he don't know what he's doing. Those fishermen are smart, and they don't miss a thing. Now you need a Lee Tracy or Emery Levesque on the scales. Those men are masters. I'll tell you: when Lee's not there, Emery always arrives for the weighing. It's a regular thing. It's very easy to read the wrong amount. If you're gonna do anything you've gotta begin with knowing how much things weigh."

How's the shrimp business?, I ask.

"Catching a lot, but the shrinkage is something awful. You've never seen anything shrink like these shrimp."

Are you going to buy here next year?

"That's something I'm afraid you're gonna have to ask the town of Mount Desert. I don't reckon as they want me

272

here messing up their pretty harbor, making some money for my living, working, while they're not."

Is the whole town against it?

"The Harbor Committee is. They figure we're tied to the town wharf and they can tell us to leave. And I guess they can. I guess they can. Now out there in the center of the harbor where I buy lobsters they can't touch me. That's no man's country. But I raised this barge from the bottom, and put my money into it, and now I'm beginning to make something, and they're a bit jealous."

"Acting like a bunch of children," Leslie Smith says. "If they can't have it,. well, then no one else can. You know what my wife's father said? He said that if he wanted he could come down here and tie up a houseboat if they're going to allow this, and his wife said to him, now ain't that silly, ain't that just like a child, everyone knows you're not coming down here with a houseboat, so why talk that way?"

Who's your wife's father?, I ask.

"He's on the Harbor Committee, runs the upholstery store here in town."

* * *

Davey Sprague goes home, more boats come in, the party gets rowdy, the birds cluster around the fire, the whiskey burning, so that the men drop more and more shrimp overboard, and the birds clean it up. The system is loose; the left hand always knows that the right hand, that the left hand knows what it is doing. Virgil and Frankie are popping their shrimp in their mouths like peanuts, tossing the heads away as they bite them off, ducks battle gulls, whistlers diving to clean the bottom, gulls displacing each other from post to post, for postion, and in his boat Alden Stove throws the last beer can over and says to Russell Stove, "We can't mend this fucking net tonight. Let's at least get last call at Kelly's."

"Have some shrimp," Leslie says to me.

I don't want to add to the shrinkage, I say.

"Shrinkage!" howls Leslie. "This is penny ante."

And an oil slick as wide as the ring around the moon,

around the barge, as it gets dark, as the moon gets brighter, as the ducks trying to walk across the ice fall thru, and the men sit by the ovens roaring at the slapstick, as the sky darkens and the stars appear, more shrimp, more cans of beer. A thin ice forming on the very wood.

XI

Fred sits in his shed, hammering the curved laths into a brand new trap. Into the base of the wood he burns his number and initials.

Is one trap the same as aonther, or do you have something special about certain traps? I ask him.

"Nah. Nah. Traps are all the same."

You don't know of anyone testing one trap against another just to see which one's doing better?

"Nah. Nothing like that. Well now once I gave Frankie Seavey a head when he needed one, and from then on that was always Fred's trap, and he'd tell me about it. When the children were young I used to set aside one trap for each of them, and everything from that trap would go for them. Lots of the men do that."

From down below Clarence Hawkes looks up and sees us in the window, then his footsteps on the stairs. "No! No!" Fred cries out. "Don't let him in," and jumps up as though to block the door. "Throw him out. Throw him out. Throw the bum out." Hawkes gets in sort of sideways.

What are you doing this time of year? I ask him.

"Oh, no more than I can help. Got a few worm-diggers, clam-diggers, checking the licensing on shrimp-boats."

Do you ever get shrimp-boats that have hauled up lobsters in the nets and don't throw them back?

"Oh yeah. We get them. But it's just carelessness. I don't think any lobsterman sees any point in that. They're getting smarter on things. Usually I just tell them rather strongly that I think that shouldn't happen and usually it doesn't again. At least I've never had to take anyone in on it."

Fred: "Now I think we've all taken short lobsters home in the old days and eaten them. But what's the point anymore.

If I ate a short lobster, sure enough someone'd come in the way people are always dropping in these days. And anyhow the fishermen have gotten wise to what their living is. I don't have any other livelihood I can go to if I lose my lobster license. So it just ain't worth it, to go playing with my living."

Clarence: "Now I don't find I have any trouble with the regular fisherman, the one who goes for a living. But it's the part-time ones, the ones who go from a skiff and outboard. They get careless. You can tell walking down to a wharf just who it is who's going to have shorts. His gear's run down, he's not tending to his equipment; there are no numbers on his traps; he's just careless."

Fred: "And how long does it take to mark a trap? There. It's done."

Clarence: "If a man's lazy, he's lazy. He leaves his traps out untended during the winter and lets the weather get at them. When there are both hard and soft shells he tries to squeeze the measure on the hard ones to get a few more in."

Fred: "Myron just left his out there, and he keeps saying he's waiting for the low water slack to get them, but it never seems to get quite low enough before it's getting high again."

Clarence: "You mind if I ask you a personal question?"

Fred: "Go right ahead."

Clarence: "Well, I've often wondered if, now, I'm just talking, I've wondered if it bothered a fisherman not to have any security. I mean you think they'd want to give part of their income to the Association for a pension?"

Fred: "You'd never get fishermen to agree with a thing like that. Of course I'm already getting disability; some other fellows might feel differently about it. I think, though, they'd rather set up their own savings plans."

Clarence: "What do you think about fishing in the winter?"

Fred: "I don't think they're making a cent. What they're getting from the lobsters, why they're taking it right back out of their gear. I ain't pushing. As long as I know where the next meal's coming from. Boy, you take it out of your health going now. I'd rather save it for later when it counts."

Why do people go now then?

Fred: "They kid themselves they're making money. Just like on the shrimping. But they forget how much money they put into it or how much they have to pay later."

Clarence: "I hear things are getting crowded over in Frenchman's Bay."

Fred: "You should have heard Donald Batman when Linwood Peabody tried to run him off. 'Goddamn your soul,' he says. That big boat could have tore his head off. And Roland Butler said, 'That's the first time I ever heard of the overtaking boat having the right of way.'"

Clarence: "What effect do you think the shrimping is having on the lobster population? Is it driving them away?"

Fred: "Just the opposite. Before this year the traps used to come up filled with shrimp. No lobsters. But an awful shlug of shrimp. The lobsters were eating the shrimp and staying away from the traps. Now they've got to eat the bait; they've got to go into the traps. Yesterday I got 51 pounds; last year it would have been 10 and a trapful of shrimp. Or small lobsters. Shorts. I used to get plenty of snappers. They'd keep the big ones away like the two groups of lobsters was mutually exclusive. One wouldn't go where the other was. That's why I leave a longer haul this time of year. The short ones come in first; then they leave; they're driven out by the big ones. And *they stay*. The longer the set the better the fishing, and not many snappers."

Clarence: "One thing that's always amazed me about you lobstermen, I mean as someone who hasn't grown up on the sea like you fellas, is that you spend all this time building traps. I mean isn't there some easier way? Couldn't they manufacture something? They seem to do so well on other parts of gear."

Fred: "Well, it's not that we haven't tried different traps. But these are the only ones that work. Harry Smith had some iron traps for a while, but they were taboo. He tried out a Canadian round one, and caught just one lobster in it. I'll tell you, though. It's a good year, and when it's a good year for lobsters, people aren't going to spend their time experimenting with traps. Now just a few years ago Haskell over there built the perfect trap. They go in one way and they can't get out. He tried it several different ways, the first time with fiberglass, then he replaced that with wood and had these leather slats, just like fingers, that caught when the lobster tried to go back out. Carl, out on Swans, made a little diamond shape in the center and he had his two heads at the ends coming the both of them into the diamond; so they couldn't get thru once they got in. Well, it did okay, but he was using so much twine and it was taking so much time to make them that he gave it up. It cost too much, a whole ball of twine for a trap. And you know they've tried square traps and couldn't get a lobster with them. And they've tried wire instead of laths, but a lobster or crab'll pinch two wires together; they've got a terrific bite, those crabs you know. Now let me ask you a question. Why do they stay in there in the first place? Why when they can go in and out just like children if they wanted? And when one bar is busted they can all vacate the trap. Yet they're in there when you come. There must be something about the trap."

Clarence: "There just must be. The lobster's a smart baby; he can see those holes leading back out just as sure as he can see them leading in."

Fred: "It may be when his back hits something that doesn't give he backs out; something's keeping him from leaving that trap. Or maybe he makes it his home; there's plenty of food, and he's contented in there. He doesn't want to leave."

Clarence: "Let me ask another question? If it's true that the trap will only draw the lobster when the bait's deteriorated, why not put in bait that's a little gone already?"

Fred laughs. "I'd say that stuff Jasper's got in there is more than a little gone. But I think the lobster has to wait there and watch it for a time. He doesn't go in it right away; he just sort of stakes it out. He must sense that it's deteriorating. You put down a trap, and there'll be eight or ten of them around it, crawling on top of it, but if they think something's wrong they won't go in. Sometimes you don't know what it is. Certain traps they've just figured out to ignore. Something about them must tell'm to stay away."

Clarence: "Now is it true that the tailer fishes better than the main trap."

Fred: "Well it certainly is true, and I'd say it's the vibration of the rope on the main trap; the tailer doesn't move around as much."

Now footsteps; we turn around and Harvey Rich comes in.

Fred: "Here he is: Harvey Poor."

Harvey: "I don't know what it is, but every year the first week of February they decline."

Fred: "We were just talking about fishing out where you are. How much does that rope cost you, Harve?"

"Fred, I don't think I ever figured it out."

"Wouldn't you say that they was costing you about $30 a pair?"

"It'd run pretty close to that."

Clarence: "That's a lot of rope."

Fred: "We were talking about that perfect trap you made. What was it you had on it at first?"

"Plexiglass."

"Yeah. Yeah. That's what it was."

"And it never caught a thing. Harry Smith and I tried it out one time in the lobster car and we saw what was happening. It was okay, they were coming to it, until the fuzz in their claws, just that little bit, touched against it. Before you know it they had all formed a big circle around it and none of them would go closer than that. I'll tell you: we also tried out a regular trap, put bait in it, seven or eight lobsters went in. All of a sudden they must have figured something out because all those lobsters that were trying to get in they backed away, and there was a circle around it so wide with just those seven or eight in it. Now you know Harry Smith, the way he waits a long time before he says anything. Well, he's setting, and he's figuring, and then he says real thoughtful: 'They got some way of communicating. They know there's no way to get out of the trap. The ones inside told 'em.' But I tell you, that lobster's a strange critter; you'll see'm laying all over the trap but none going in. Otherwise you'd catch'm all in one night. Now last fall there was, and I mean, good fishing. I'm gonna say two to four pound lobsters, and 70 to 80% of them females. Now how many years does it take them to become legal size?

Clarence: "Seven years they say."

"Where were they all that time?"

Fred: "I think they're from the continental shelf. All that dragging out there's stirred them up. Like when you go deer hunting; after a while you've been harrassing them one place they'll go somewhere else. These lobsters are getting the hell out of there."

Harvey: "That's what I think. They can't tell me they're just hiding there in the mud all these years. They've got to come out and eat, and that's when they catch'm; these lobsters're from away."

Fred: "Leon Pettegrow, Jr., well, you know he's got a hundred, say 125 traps out, all summer long in one place, nothing; come fall and all of a sudden he's whaling them hard. These lobsters there was just not crawling. Then suddenly they go. It must be a calling they got, like birds."

Harvey: "I just don't know how come those three and four pounders escaped year after year unless their breeding grounds, they must be where we can't get at them."

Fred: "The continental shelf I tell you."

Harvey takes a step over toward the radio which has been on all the time. "I think that's the weather coming on now, Fred. Let me hear." Fred turns it up. "Got to know whether I'm going out tomorrow." He hunches forward, his hand on his chin. Silly music introduces us; then the announcer comes on laughing like a hyena.

—Yessir, flowers, I mean showers tonight, ho ho flowers, you thought it was an early spring. And the wind buhbuh-buhbuh is from the Northeast, right by Grandma's house isn't it, flowers, my my!—

"Boston?" Harvey says, looking up ever so slightly at Fred.

"Yessir."

XII

From a Letter

"The sensation of growing older has been very strong lately with incredibly vivid memories of childhood (preadolescence) pouring in. Been thinking a lot about memory, it strikes me as such a strange thing. To remember something. Ideas of memory being infinite. (And macrobiotics: The Book of Judgement: memory is imagination)." C.M. in Ann Arbor.

Or memory is the key into history, what we fail to call history thinking always that it is something else than what happens, something from outside the planet placed on it or in it. The only history is a Whig history. This is not only to be desired; it is unavoidable. A causal mythology in which our own place among the gods of memory is assured. Not that it happens because we are there. Because it happens we *are* there. The vivid memories of childhood pouring in.

To be problematic is to look back and pretend to see all sides and angles, how no one was right and no one was wrong. But history, like memory, is a force, a thrust into and thru the present made up of everything in its own time, as it is magnetized by the event to be part of it. The problematic interpretation is just that: interpretation; it makes it appear that it could have happened in many different ways, pulling the events out of time. I am saying that memory is the clear passage of a body thru the concomitants and assignations; no single photograph of a fight will show why the punch landed. There is no such moment of impact.

Did you ever read one of those introductory psych. textbooks on memory? After a while you begin to think of your head as an electrical station; your memory becomes something other than you know it to be; you stand outside knowledge of the synapses, which is proof enough that you can outrun them, that you have a right to be there. So it's not just problematic. Memory is imagination. I agree.

Brakhage always said there is no memory. Do you see this in his films? How it is all happening now. Memory would seem to be chemical, Proustian, two days exposed at different instants in the same place. But this disregards the motion of the film thru its rhythms—a continuous conjunction of active living superior bodies; the astrologers call it lunation birthday; he and Kelly have called it *fire of waters*. The moon pursues and overtakes the sun again and again, as memory overtakes its content, and passes it into form, materia, old moon into new moon into old moon. We are born at a cosmic moment, intertwixt, inter bella. There is no halt in memory. We are born into the action we remember/we become.

I too have been playing my memory lately, trying to squirm thru its holes, to get into it and outside of it, to locate its body, its source-streams, isolate its feedings, a hopeless exercise but a beautiful music. I have been imagining how many times, trines thru the mirror, twice, thrice, or the sheer sum of what I give ground to, space in my head.

Does the dream materia come from only the storage-memory of this life? (only?, and what's *this* life?). The imagination has no beginning, and for that reason: nor do we.

We are born into a world we already encompass. Vivid memories of childhood. Always the historic present. Always everyone is alive now.

Are instincts memories? What is genetic history? What does Jung mean by race? by racial memory? What does Freud mean by civilization? Is not the environment of civilization the civilization itself? Is this not somehow what Ferenczi means when he says we contain the Atlantic or any ocean, imago mundi passed from seed to cell, from seaworm to landworm, always twisted and reborn at the angle of life, threaded from embryo to panoply of brains and nerves, and this is the accurate topos of world. Geo-lines from the topography, oceanography wind thru us without a break. We inherit everything, including locale. We pass thru starfish and frog and dark unconscious soma in becoming men, and can turn it into sense by forgetting size and making all origins the same. There is no measure for memory or experience; all channels, at the moment they pour into sense, whatever their sources, in cold distant waters or hot upon-us suns, become mythological, and human, and this is Olson's *human universe,* electrical as the center from which all colored images and transformed glyphs pass into the text of the city, the home of man. Astrology which can bring us in here too is the only system for understanding why we can't get out. To hell with what we remember or think we remember. We make it anyway, despite.

And what does psychosomatic mean? We know the psychological disease as trauma, the somatic disease as environment, infection. Where do environment and memory intersect, fuse? What about the memory of the cells, which we never know as content, psyche, only as soma, its message in DNA, flesh code, that the body is restored utterly every month or two, and not one cell is again the same? There is no memory; there is only message, to keep the imago, to replace it with itself which is not to replace it at all. It is a wonder that we remember anything. It is a wonder that we don't and still get by. Metabolic time changes, and as it does the message loses its hold on that one piece of material, the body tumbles back into the forgotten memory which precedes it; once the cells forget it can no longer be made, and can only grow wildly without respect for proportion or parts, as the cancer, disease of communication between all parts and their origins breaking down. When memory ends does the individual end too? Does history end? When the body forgets everything, is it that it never happened?, or just the opposite, that it did and is immortal, and can never be changed.

All energies are chemically present, in orgasm speak their memories and are recalled. It is Reich alone who never questioned the vast bioelectric explosion that the human body is, and how, when reduced to their operative size, all universes cross there and are realized whole. He wastes his time who looks at quasar-creatures marvelling at their energy to fill a universe without realizing the actual daily displacement of the same energy by man, equal as well to the whole universe, equal to a memory that is always as large as ONE, no matter in how many parts. [Nor do quasars escape that their memory is mere continuation, body of their fire].

Yesterday an old rock and roll song on the car radio and I let it go full blast: I'M A-WALKING IN THE RAIN. I let it in where it filled me with immense memories, so many I could not find them all, heads and tails, and became merely their transformer. The whole world shook; then and now throbbed in between the throbs of each other, in one body, in mine. This perception about the memory: It didn't happen then. I only thought so then. The song never had that power. It is memory itself. It is me. It is happening now.

After dinner I go back to it, all the old records, bursting as the day itself, an incredible spring rain in February, foggy and warm, the streams heavy with mud. LOOK AT YOU. LOOK AT ME. SEE THE WAY WE GLOW. I think I began writing because I was so frustrated I couldn't dance to the music I had to do something to it, thru it, thru me, HAD TO dance to it. And there was no way I could have known then the thing that was happening to me, which these songs fill me with now, the power to set off a simultaneous flow of words and visions; lying on the bed isn't the house incredible, the fullness of this lit room, how different it is than what would otherwise be here. With a dot per house the topographic map shows nothing. The real topos will show at every house deep isobaric twists and land-world breaks, shelves and twists of existence, displacement.

Then: I always thought of memories in terms of the beginning of a life. Now I see they are at all times all things. At the end of a life we have not the memories but the connectedness; the separate fires burn as a unity, unicell. Hearing of Olson's last days, hearing the last poems: how he reached out and held the whole thing without a single precious memory except the roots and bark which are the exact physicum anyway, the visible memory of a tree. Psychology and botany are but one sunfield, one stubborn growth-happy photosynthetic mass. I mean the brain, the structure of memory. It does not have to grow like a medulla. It can grow like a tree.

Don't we love to run in the forest, in ourselves. The Jungian oaks are Freudian elms are Reichian appletrees. The textbook on memory returns to, is a key to the local roots and berries and cambia. The forest is made up of neurons, songs, and the sun is memory, the closest unicell king to whom we can identify what we are, that the one needs no other.

I had been thinking too much of childhood and adolescence as memories, vivid in their distance. Suddenly, with the songs and a cup of dandelion wine, I saw how life itself is an immortality. We *do* die. I know that. Yet memory is at the end as well as at the beginning, and in Olson's last poems so many vegetables and roots, so much connectedness, the beginning and end claw around each other, all the memories are part of a giant tree, gripping the whole of life—even when the very tower of it is beginning to fall, to forget, it holds and is as strong as ever.

You write about Ecology also, and want to know what to do about what is being done to the world. "Am very torn between being political and not being political. That is, the immensity of the repression in this country and the immensity of the interrelationships between big business and the war and racism. God, it's so incredible." C.M.

Yet Ecology is not a simple political issue. It's just one, the newest, going account of man-history. It is political in the sense that it is politics-making. But it cannot be politicized. Legislation is not consciousness, cannot change how we live.

The condition is the planet's memory of itself, literally the house we've been building, and if some of the shit should appear for real, like in the living system itself, rather than as issues or causes, we shouldn't be surprised. It's not just in Vietnam and Washington and Biafra that it's happening. It's happening in your backyard and in your head and is the condition of the Earth. So any action you take should be local, literal; consciousness only operates locally, only exists locally, and when torn away from locale makes no sense or truth but merely utters clichés and propaganda. Our cause is to be conscious, not to have an issue. If you abandon locale you abandon where you are a individual, and place yourself

285

where you must become a number. This is why the University will allow you to be radical and activist, as long as you don't become conscious, as long as you don't develop spiritual resources. They can handle demonstrations, but they fear the inner power which clings to the ground as weeds and follows men wherever they are able to go.

So our conditions have become literal in the oceans and interior waterways. And this is one fire you can't fight with fire, and if you try it'll just be twice as hot, twice as barren afterwards. Don't try to be political. You *are* political. As any strong person with his work to do. This is the sense in which I take Pound to mean Culture and Economy: not what's learned in the newspapers everyday and what you remember because it's what you've learned, not what everyone talks about as the latest issue, but what you can't forget when you've forgotten everything else. Memory.

XIII

Moon. Moon. Daylight brighter than print. Moon framed in the green window. Red lobster claw. Newly-fallen snow.

9 A.M. I throw a coat over my pajamas, slip into boots, don't bother to tie the laces, but right out the door my head still ringing into the bright, the steel cold of it. I am still in bed, in the warm coccoon of personal geography, places so large—I stumble down the stairs, thru the high snow into the road, single tire-track of the mail-car, run along the bank one boot kicking the snow behind it into the other, the dream which begins in my feet awakes from it there in the cold puddle of a world. Blue. Steel. Grab the letters and stumble back into bed.

Nothing has happened—one new poetry magazine. Moon. Moon. Daylight brighter than print. Red lobster claw on the window ledge, outward the green window, the blue window, the sun on the glass.

It is becoming flat, certain, definite. The escapes are fewer, more desperate, younger in an older life. It need be no more than that. A geography inclusive of all other places.

"Why do your study here?" asks the woman from the Ellsworth newspaper, coming for coffee in the afternoon. But myth is the motion of the imagination toward world history. What the history of the world would be if we started at Mount Desert Island and took concentric circles outward, if we started at this house and opened our eyes in the center. It is not accidental that you have come here to do your interview. This is where all history begins.

She asks to take a picture of us. We stand in the front-yard by the fence, Lindy holding Robin, my arm around Lindy. This is the center of the world.

Imagination supersedes anthropology, seizes the time of

287

the account and makes it the time of itself; it needs no imaginary history to back it up.

"What is the strange writing you do that I see in your journal? Is it stream of consciousness?"

No. Stream of consciousness assumes that there is an event in which consciousness must be imbedded to happen. Stream of consciousness is the character's thoughts about the action. Here there is no event but the writing. The writing requires no prior existence, is in fact the experience about which nothing else has to be said. Stream of consciousness leads to neurosis and traumatic origins of the plot. Here there is no plot. Consciousness itself is the geography of the brain, not a stream thru it but the events on its axis, its reception of the time of its being, like baseball, the geology of the island, the brewing of the coffee we are drinking, the questions you are asking me, my answers to them: all become part of the text.

*   *   *

Now Wendell is quite angry about my earlier interview with him, not the thing itself, but that I seem to take issue with him in its published form on the matter of subduing naure. "You sit down by a typewriter in a nice warm room, and sure it's easy to write about how nature is so good and man is the evil one who's destroying all this beauty. But things don't look quite the same once you get right down there with her. Nature's not quite so good and friendly. It's cold and storms and winds, and a man has to do everything in his power to keep from being destroyed by nature. If man didn't subdue nature, nature'd subdue man. I know, you and all your friends think that nature is good, and we're the evil lobstermen just killing and taking selfishly for our own interests. You come very easy to say that it's nature as the work of God and the Devil working in man to destroy it. Well, I'm not so sure it's nature and God against man and the Devil. It's man who was made in God's image, and how do you know that nature's not the work of the Devil trying to destroy man."

And one's own nature: how to get inside or outside, how

not to be at war with despite the fact that God and the Devil work together, are indistinguishable in the creation and hisory of, in the interaction between that there is no nature outside of man, but he himself a node thru which the energy thus transformed, as vision, passes. Man wet like the mosses, chlorella, grows in his house; cannot distinguish the moon in his chart in his glands from the moon in his sky, cannot distinguish the shadow he casts from the shadow he is—environment of a creature who enters himself. My fear is not for the lobster or protection across the hard line of kingdom between us. My fear is for the softness of the lobster in ourselves, our exposure not just to wind and snow and freezing temperatures of the North, but the shadow world itself, the psyche, the race, the Northern climate into which we build our fences and lawns and territories and wait in the nation of ourselves for the City of Earth. I am afraid that the current passing thru the whole is what we are allergic to, whether we make ourselves hard and insensitive or become soft and weep.

Sun dims thru the window, Friday, Friday. In the nature of. The richness of, I am not a magician, the weeks pass.

You are a snake. Your body is your many mouths you suck me, dry. I am wet again. Such a sudden change comes over us, a change in winds passing thru the nature, at the nodes of. Neither cold and distant nor weeping for joy, but the current of ecstasy, throbbing and known.

*   *   *

History. Where is history in this chatter, the handliners spreading their hooks, cod in 1915, cod in 1917, the same fish, a different coin, 32¢ a pound. The sea is brilliant and empty; history lies in the records, the files, ox-tongues and cod-tongues, coin in the primary state. Where are the trawlers the bid-lines, fiery imago mundi in Enoch Stanley's head, kept in the cells but not over Cranberry Waters, in Cranberry no longer, the ganglions 700 hooks per, and a bed of haddock torn into, six thousand pounds of hake, the daylight morning to the Manset marketplace? Where are the old men in the ship, the crew of five, the deeds, the cutting of the tongues, splitting shares and salting them aboard? Where is the War of 1892, the invasion of the West Indies by Nova Scotia, flooding of the economy with saltfish when halibut was worth your old shoe (2¢ in Cranberry, reaches 10¢ by the time the middleman gets it to Manset; the peddler takes his nickel inland)? If it were as simple as lobster-fishing, and the current yankee motorboat independence, we could pack up and leave tomorrow, the Ellsworth newspaper might as well know. The imagery behind these islands holds, and is reborn. The dead trashfish thrown thru the hole in the floor, overboard, no name, tangled in the nets of the economy, comes into the halls of men to be knighted and marketed as well. All the unplanted seeds of the ecosphere lie with their greater body against time.

*   *   *

Moving over me like a snake, a cold wind sucks me, dry, I am the nature of you in the nature of coming to me in the mirror of. Devil of. And purse seiner stops in the middle, sets its nets, pulls from there in a circle, moebius, twists them around the pocket of fish, 125 hogsheads of dripping wet born in the net, 1970, Stinson herring cannery. Held at the end of a rope. Time. Hung, hanged, swung aboard. Time. On the fathometer meteors and mackerel, summer and winter fish who move in schols. Earth which is threatened from above, within, below, aboard, is as a node to which who is neither inside outside nor onto calls his survival economy, his vision landscape, and is the transformer of all celestial material, grey sole and gold, coal and the incomplete galactic combusion of the city's factories. The sun gives off the moon gives off, the blue sky, behind the cabala of which sit the stars in their fiery historic path, the gold which backs the system, spreading their hooks into the web of life, feeding in a knot the compartments of space where conscious of the properties it has it lives.

We know that the ball-game can be rained out, and the field turned back into the mud, the scrub, the uninhabitable and Northern vandal forests, that the market can fall out of itself into an old shoe, and the entrepreneurial function is when the cod rots in bilgewater while halibut is turned into bread, shrimp into gold.

In the first days a giant man walks toward the center of the town. He would be the town itself, whose motion supported by the cane is history, whose proper speed is slower because he is 73 years old, but faster too for the same reasons, because he has been alive longer, more direct. He comes from a certain spot by the wharves, takes the same path, we who intercept him and are invited to his home, "come talk with me if you want," at the beginning mind you, before all the rest happened, a bottle of whiskey, some chocolate cookies from Labrador, and pipe tobacco smelling of salt and seaweed, whose landlady's name is Trundy, the big swinging sign sign over his environs, and the small one on his hut: "Enoch's Teepee."

Is the body of Great Cranberry, washed ashore, its genes and fish-buyers, with time and tide, the bottom scoured with draggers, no fish, no business for five miles offshore. Not the sense that history has ended or that Great Cranberry is swallowed in the district of Trundy, but that the hulk of it, the archetype as best we know it, has washed ashore, the last of the old-timers, the beautiful giant cod. In his billfold. The storm-center has changed, but the storm persists, the mark of our time.

* * *

"But man is made in the image of God, not fish," Wendell says. "And Christ came down on this earth to save the souls of men not cows."

Christ came down as the perfect businessman, cod in his right hand, halibut in his left, to chase the money-changers out of the temple, down from Heaven with the balance, as the economist, not to save the souls of cows or the grey soles I agree, but to save the pecuniary itself, the power of the tongue which, when cut out, always precedes the Word, as it precedes World. He came to see that once the tongues had been cut the system could not be changed back to, Great Cranberry could not be returned. We all do the business of our bodies, your share and mine preserved in the Market, the beal or boil, the hill by the brook where the dealer lives and the myth emerges from like whirlwind spreading cash over the waters as in the dream of minting value itself, the entrepreneur who can change a nation from cod to lobsters to shrimp, who rests on, the tail in his mouth, the basic uninflationary value of the wharf, the beal, and etymology, kindred.

Came down into the temple to make change, into the Cranberry Islands to return the tongues, the speech of the elders, so that the name of cod is not separate of the value of cod, who speaks somatically body-speaks of the older world, the world before us, the cold winds which blow it which are nature in Priapus, papoose, magnetic currents that surround, stars that feed pendant on a chain, wingboards that open a hundred, a hundred and fifty feet apart, doors of the atmosphere, and swallow the dragon, galactic fire, influence of, environment is born as well as into, body embodying its production of body, world as thick as wheat, as cod, as 1915, 17, 6,000 pounds.

The newspaper in Ellsworth asks me whether I am an anthropologist or a historian. Anthropology is irrevocably opposed to history as stasis is to motion, as everything is changing all the time, the game rained out rescheduled in the Northern forest-belt the next Giant Year, is called the game of bears, is called the vandalism of bowling green, of handlining. History turns too quickly into visions and fish and coastal rivers, the twine of myth. Newsprint glows, but gold is brighter, and in this world-age the radioactive metals, the urania, are brighter yet, are the Aquarian Water-Carriers, the double helices, precious metals hung on the changes of the zodiac, are worn around the necks of Saint John's matrons in an intermediate time, in cloth coats and Miramichi salmon, glitter unknown, not yet, in Black Harbor; broken tongue speaking of a Fishport, an Oilport, opening into the galaxy into the Bay of Fundy into the New World, and the boat circles in its own weir, stopping up a cove, guarding it, trapping itself for the spring; sowcircle of the open moon in Passamaquoddy Bay.

*   *   *

Daylight brighter than print. Red lobster claw. 3 P.M. Robin holds a coin of an orange ring in his hand so long his hand becomes the grip and he forgets he is holding it. I collect the trash from all the garbage cans inside the house, kleenex and grease-covered towels, first drafts and unfinished letters, and colleges and newspapers, scores of games, diaper liners filled with shit, milk cartons, the whole week up in a blaze, a nice hot burst for a second, leisure of fire to be an art, as we measure our pounds, collect our papers and bags ad infinitum, waiting till the time that something absolutely has to be done, so that we will do it.

The smoke blows over the snow, lovely wet ash. Not all smokes are polluting, this a deep wood smell, an age sticking to my skin anyway, it is not the youth of the world anymore, and that is true either on the outside of the world or the inside of it. Youth is not its nature anymore, its speed, even though I am young. I am old before my time. As the world is as we are all old smoky men.

The fire is out, the garbage can is smouldering on the bottom near the ice. The ashes are blacker. Frodo the grey cat sits on the roof watching their streaming shadows over the snow.

Now I remember. In a dream last night—it was neither nature nor the cold wind, nor in fact any place I know—I am drawn up from the icy Northern sea. I want to fly. I have the magnetic power of the all, to be drawn on its reins into the sun. Another man writes the poem of the wings I fly on, a magician, a beal or bialy.

Superstition! Wendell says. But I say—it is still part of the nature.

It is not fantasy. It is in the deck of seven and twenty winds, seven and twenty powers. And here, now, it is the latter years of wisdom, all images, natural phenomena in our grasp. Sun brighter than newsprint. Red claw brighter than night or day. I no longer fight nature. I cannot subdue it, but the strings are there. I am pulled into sun, into metabolic, into dynamo, into the furnace, hotter than ashes, colder than metal or sea, the fish are molecules, into the nature of the law of itself, where, unavoidably, I am.

XIV

Anciently the monadnocks above the New England peneplain, central granitic mass tearing thru the older rocks,
melting them, transforming them into a horneblende-biotite
stone.

Now small rivers work on this, cutting into weak rock, the
older schists and shales, steered by them around it, worn into
the sea, into: Bartletts Island, Schooner Head, Bar Harbor,
the Cranberries.

The history of matter is uncertain, the weaving of consciousness in the brain, a world we cannot abandon once we
are in it: sedimentation, uplift, followed by the slow settling
of the peneplain, and again, the geography balances out.
History of rock-making comes from we do not know where,
did Freud call it the unconscious?, who has ever seen the
unconscious mind?, the non-body in the body, material that
is sheerly that? Unless it be the just-born cells entering
flayed of everything but what they are, the molten mass, the
batholith, born into sudden and unending erosion. Mount
Desert Range stands above the rough rough waters, barely
conscious, worn by the South, become Devonian, and its
fate: is the streams will wear down their barriers and fill
the basins, carry away the loose topsoil. Monadnocks do not
stand forever, Monads that they are, are so only in our history, and all this, if uninterrupted, and nothing but comet
can interrupt it, and man can only speed it, or unless the
sea-waves come in first to sweep away Island itself.

It is morning. It is now, on this precipice where thought
is a mead and a maple sap and a movement of birds and
waves and the breathing of clams. It is neither present history, nor past event. It is happening now, as the lobstermen
know, as the economy cannot change, as the economy itself

294

is made out of gold. The center of the Earth is yet hot, supplies the material, from the Bay of Fundy to the Connecticut Valley. Quartz and Feldspar. Rock-making is initial craft. The mountains are built for the snows and pounding surf to consume them, and so supply the material for our world age. "Gutta cavat lapidem, consumitur annulus usu." Not Aesop, but though each droplet takes only a stone, the process itself takes everything.

The Pleistocene interrupts. Tongues of ice carry rocks, teeth to grind out their paths. They cut troughs, using up as stone that they themselves would be stone on a colder planet, pass out into Atlantic until world-origin recalls them, as from one appointed task to another. So the end of an age. And yet we are still in the Pleistocene, we are still men.

The Cronian gods give their water to rivers, leave their bones as teeth. The rivers whirl these epidote pebbles against their cracks, rounding out potholes. Where ice sat in the saddle, the waters fill Saddle Pond. And the cirques, leading down into Upper Hadlock Pond from Sargent Mountain. Giant boulders are left everywhere, erratics, stones of a Northernmore origin, one of twenty feet diameter on Professor Liquer's summer estate. Roches moutonnées.

The material of the glacier is no longer rock. Thought has changed it into debris. The beavers come and dam a great volume of water around Duck Brook, a beaver lake. Homo Sapiens works to stop up Round Pond and Ripple Pond, Little Round Pond and Somes Pond. The glaciers have left sand and silt, clay and pebbles, material for the shape of land. The water takes them into bayhead beaches and bars, spits where the sand falls short of the next headland in open waters. Here is matter for a coastal geography in a time of history, a new language of tombolos, tumbles, land which is underwater at high tide; at low tide it joins a bar to the mainland, as Bar Island to Bar Harbor, man and animals can walk across, those hours when the mystery occurs.

The condition is subtle and slight, and happens where it is riding out all else. If the ocean were higher, Mount Desert would be a cluster of small islands, will be, is; even as, if the water were lower, it would be a peninsula, is, with the bridge across Thompson Island and Mount Desert Narrows

(1836 A.D., the Mount Desert Bridge Corporation). Coves become rivers, or part of the continental shelf. Richardsons Brook steals Aunt Bettys Pond and carries it down the water table into Somes Sound. So the Southern shore of Bakers Island, filled with granite boulders, slopes gently seaward, slides under the tide. The ocean rides in on this platform, which breaks it, hiding from saltwater the string of bogs behind.

So Darius Forbes of Paris brings a great bull if there ever was one to the 1840 State Fair at Bangor, Young Silver, a direct descendant of Toby Pigeon. And this will go on as long and far as we have radio signals, these are the purebreds, this is history, and there is no other status.

There is nothing spiritual about this nation; it will return to matter and fishbones, not Brahma, and does not want to return to Brahma. It is consigned to time for an economic moment, is at sea dragging fish with sun and sum, into darkness. They will not be conscribed to the spirit; they will go on stubbornly as what they are, as what the rock is, the conditions of tide. What we will find in time is the glacier. And the energy not used or stored there will melt and fill the rivers, and build up steam in another vat, pouring clear thru the looking glass of inland industrial U.S.A.

Island as national park, as scenic wonder, warm zone which holds birds to the semi-arctic North. Audubon's land and Charles Tracy's land, Mrs. Tracy with her children and a piano, summering not wintering, and a party thrown by them at Somes Tavern in the fall of 1855. Land of Thomas Cole and the Hudson River School of American Painters, not Champlain or Penobscot geography, but an easy sort of beauty, passing with piano lessons and etiquette. Land passed in the Treaty of Utrecht, Cadillac lost the island, half of it was given back to his son. Gulls and Englishmen settle on the outer Ducks and Cranberries, Somes to the center to cut a load of barrel staves, finds his homeland and stays.

It is cove-land, heap-land I speak of, the material cause which has left us with bodies, farm-country. Today I saw Champlain's ship pass and I saw the sailors name the Mountains *Déserts*, Barren. I saw the ships come to Baker. I saw them allowing that world to happen, milking their cows in its dawn, fucking their wives in its stars. I saw the icefields leaving a shore of rock, felt the tilting in my head, that material is also a map of forces, powers in syncline and drift. And I am beginning to hear the waves, that the islands have been connected, that land floats to its own level, that animals swim across.

*　　*　　*

Earthquakes seem to come in geologic time, BUT WE LIVE IN GEOLOGIC TIME—a recognition that is essential, momentary. Time is not vast and library; planets are being created in the galaxy at this very moment, including this planet; sea beasts are emerging to a terrestrium; continents are being molded out of fire. There is no such thing as geologic time. Or if there is, it is now, changed as we change it, as we are changed by what we do to it; as in geologic time Western commerce went out upon the seas and jets crossed the Earth. This is a Carboniferous, the Cambrian, and an age much like the Solar Age, when our planet still lay in the sun. We don't have to examine the conditions for events in some other time; the events are. There is no statistical reality. We don't have to take the outside in or put the inside out. The body is another part of the landscape, a matter, moraine left by forces that precede us or are us, the same, is what is conscious in us and what we are conscious in, what pretends to be history, and is.

We can see the torsion, the stress; we can see that the granite has become separate blocks. The genetic never ceases supplying, the ships must come here in any age, with their goods, and take what is local, what tension there is in exchange, as life returns to, valuables return to, conch shells and coppers; and fish appear in the archaeological lakes; wild animals reach the archaeo-forests. Penobscot Indians come to the mythological world, i.e., Indian Point and Indian Carrying Beach, clam-eaters living in the eternal family of sunlight.

Our possibilities are historic. We are known in the most utter revelation of starlight in the hills. Our possibilities precede the glacier, are the material on which the glacier works as, guided by the valleys, it ascends the mountain, at their top regains its own climatic motion and hones to the Southeast. The mark of the glacier and the structure that preceded it are the same sign, checkerboard, ice-transverse-rock, continuously imposed.

And Freud named the unconscious as if some backroom of the brain. We know now that it is the arms and legs also. The brain is not isolate; there is no id. The unconscious, as any place, is a way of being, a motion including flow of all the cells, all the arteries and nerves, as structural and glacial trends coincide, glacier or heart attack, not a region but a joining of regions. The Indians lived there for centuries. This is not typology; this is nothing that a causal psychology can change. We inhabit our own myth, not the land. Appearing suddenly in the economy of a world: extend that world into, following the anti-cyclone snows, the Atlantic Coast. Mount Monadnock still stands, monad, named Green Mountain, or Cadillac, from physiographic to topographic chart. One structure fights another until both possess the material. We possess only what we can use, then lose our grip on stone, flow to an intrinsic direction. The weak rocks before us make no stress, and these are fields we have always left to other ages to work. We cannot abandon consciousness or purpose; to the point of forgetfulness, when we have forgotten a previous creature to become another, whose purposes are one with purpose.

We cannot know everything. Yet we do. The wish to be encyclopedic, to go to the Moon, is something else, for ice leaves behind construction of stone, retreats into the climate; certain material is lost forever to knowing.

They are blown onto Bakers Island. They live in geologic time. They are forced to name it. They receive goods from England. They fish until they have entered the age of themselves as famous fishermen and great builders of ships. They return with fish to the Newfoundland source, the climate that makes this world possible, thermostat of migratory fish and fowl. They build an empire of the Cranberries, intermarry, wed island to island, large to small to small to large, round to rubble, ocean to debris. All thru the Cranberries and in Cranberry Harbor, their orientation, their domestic scattered with spits, bars, tombolos, thrumcaps, crow islands, rubble. No existence separate of where we are. It is position, and it is not arbitrary, for we cannot know everything, and even if we were able to stand outside the Earth or away from it all, remarkably it would be the same, and this utter condition would impinge on us. It is a knowledge that an ocean which was frozen once is now open. We know everything which could possibly be relevant, and that is our size.